Business Statistics

Business Statistics

A Complete One-Semester Course

Sonia Taylor

First published 2001 by
PALGRAVE MACMILLAN
Houndmills, Basingstoke, Hampshire RG21 6XS and
175 Fifth Avenue, New York, N.Y. 10010
Companies and representatives throughout the world

PALGRAVE MACMILLAN is the global academic imprint of the Palgrave
Macmillan division of St. Martin's Press, LLC and of Palgrave Macmillan Ltd.
Macmillan is a registered trademark in the United States, United Kingdom
and other countries. Palgrave is a registered trademark in the European
Union and other countries.

ISBN 0-333-79445-1

This book is printed on paper suitable for recycling and
made from fully managed and sustained forest sources.

A catalogue record for this book is available
from the British Library.

10   9   8   7   6   5   4   3
10 09 08 07 06 05 04

Copy-edited and typeset by Povey–Edmondson
Tavistock and Rochdale, England

Printed in Great Britain by
J.W. Arrowsmith Ltd, Bristol

CONTENTS

PREFACE

Students:

- Are you a first year student on a course which includes a Statistics module?
- If not, are you planning to do such a course in the near future?
- Do you lack confidence in Mathematics or are you 'rusty'?
- Are you nervous about Statistics?
- Are you looking for a user-friendly textbook?
- Do you want a textbook that keeps statistical theory, long formulae and mathematical calculations to a minimum?

If you answer 'yes' to most of these questions then this is definitely the textbook for you.

Lecturers:

- Are you feeling overworked?

Do not despair – here is a publication that will cut down your preparation considerably. *Business Statistics* is accompanied by lecturer's materials which use the core topics from each chapter of the textbook and provides masters for *all the paperwork* needed by the lecturer on a weekly basis. Revision questions, multi-choice questions suitable for in-class tests and examination-type questions are provided in addition to questions supplied to the students for revision purposes (see Appendix E).

Business Statistics – A Complete One Semester Course has been written as a practical response to the needs of the present-day first-year student on a Business Studies, or related, course who needs to obtain a reasonable grasp of basic statistics in limited time available. It addresses the limitations imposed by a semesterised modular course for large teaching groups of students with uncertain mathematical ability. It is organised as a practicable weekly based course rather than a comprehensive theoretical textbook but it is still suitable for all students studying statistics for the first time. Many students do experience problems initially, so the emphasis throughout is on understanding through practice, interpretation of results and their application to the world of business rather than on depth of knowledge. Statistical theory, unhelpful jargon, the use of formulae and long mathematical manipulations are deliberately kept to a minimum. This encourages students who lack confidence in their own mathematical ability.

The main themes of this book are:

- Chapter 1 introduces the topic of **statistics** generally, defines certain concepts with which you may or may not already be familiar, and concludes with a self-check of the basic arithmetic required for this course.
- **Graphical and numerical description** of different types of data sets are covered in Chapters 2 and 3 with the emphasis being on data **summarisation** as a means of communicating the information they contain to others.
- **Uncertainty** is a concept which is often first encountered in statistics. It is introduced in Chapter 4 as **probability** and enlarged upon in Chapter 5. This chapter describes and uses the normal distribution which fits much business data.

- **Inferential statistics** are introduced in Chapter 6 with the use of **estimation** in the form of **confidence intervals**. This subject is further developed with the **hypothesis testing of various parameters**. Chapter 7 is mainly concerned with a variety of *t*-tests and Chapter 8 with **analysis of variance**.
- Bivariate relationships between variables are analysed in the form of **correlation** and **regression** in Chapter 9 and **chi-squared tests** in Chapter 10.
- **Index numbers** are studied in Chapter 11 to monitor and compare any changes over time. Various **time series** are modelled in Chapter 12 and are then extended into the future to produce **forecasts** in Chapter 13.
- Chapter 14 is included as an introduction to **operational research**. It does not form part of the course – it is here just to give the student a flavour of further applications of statistics in the workplace.
- Chapter 15 deals with **computer analysis** of data in **SPSS**, **Minitab** and, to a limited degree, **Excel** using all the methods covered in the previous chapters.
- **Revision materials** – A short summary of each topic and over 100 questions, including multichoice, are provided with answers in Chapter16.

Each chapter includes the necessary theory but stresses the reasons for, and methods of, carrying out the various techniques and analyses. Plenty of practice is provided with tutorial exercises and supplementary questions. Computer analysis by all methods using both SPSS and Minitab and some Excel is described separately in Chapter 15.

A Complete Set of Lecturer's Materials

For the lecturer there is provided on the Internet (www.palgrave.com) or on hard copy by application from the publisher, a comprehensive set of all the materials necessary to run the course.

Assuming that *Business Statistics* is the set textbook for your course, each student will already have all the subject material; tutorial sheets and supplementary questions with answers for each topic; computer worksheets (both SPSS and Minitab for most topics, Excel for some) with numerical answers for most topics; revision materials for multichoice tests and examinations as well as an initial numeracy check.

The extra materials provided for the lecturer are:

- Handouts for each lecture with gaps left for student participation
- Completed versions of these handouts
- Masters for matching overhead transparencies for each lecture
- Worked solutions to at least one tutorial question for each topic
- SPSS/Minitab/Excel worksheets for all topics covered in lectures
- Annotated computer output for all computer worksheet questions
- Revision materials in addition to those in the textbook
- Examination type questions in addition to those in the textbook
- Multichoice questions in addition to those in the textbook

These materials are listed in full in Appendix E of this book. It is intended that lecture preparation time should be reduced to a minimum so that as much time as possible can be spent on communicating the subject matter to the students rather than on the increasing burden of administration.

This course was originally written for business, accountancy and computing students at the start of modularisation. It has been refined to allow for the increasing size of student groups and a lower standard of numeracy. The course has always been well received by the students who now number about two thousand. The module has been run with the inclusion of Minitab or SPSS or neither.

It can be seen, therefore, that this book is intended as a practical approach to the problem of the restricted time available for both the student and the lecturer. Both the range and the depth of topics taught in a single semester are limited. This book is an honest attempt to solve the very real problem created by increasing student numbers, increasing demands on lecturers' time and students' decreasing mathematical capability. From this point of view I freely admit that the basic approach is quite different from that of most textbooks!

I am indebted to many colleagues, particularly Linda Pryce, with whom I developed the initial course, Jenny Kromer, Jon Blacktop and Jane Parkin who gave generously of valuable time for proof-reading. Others have contributed to this book both willingly and, possibly, inadvertently as the origin of a few of the examples is lost in history!

I also thank my husband, Geoff, for his tolerance during the writing of this book!

(Formerly of the University of Huddersfield)   SONIA ANN TAYLOR

NOTATION AND FORMULAE

Greek alphabet

α	A	alpha	ι	I	iota	ρ	P	rho
β	B	beta	κ	K	kappa	σ	Σ	sigma
γ	Γ	gamma	λ	Λ	lambda	τ	T	tau
δ	Δ	delta	μ	M	mu	υ	U	upsilon
ε	E	epsilon	ν	N	nu	ϕ	Φ	phi
ζ	Z	zeta	ξ	Ξ	xi	χ	X	chi
η	H	eta	o	O	omicron	ψ	Ψ	psi
θ	Θ	theta	π	Π	pi	ω	Ω	omega

Notation

Parameter	Population	Sample
Mean	μ	$\bar{x}$
Standard deviation	σ	s
Variance	σ^2	s^2
Proportion	Π	p
Size	N	n
Correlation coefficient	ρ	r
Rank correlation coefficient	ρ_s	r_s
Regression coefficients	α, β for y-intercept and slope respectively	a, b for y-intercept and slope respectively

x is the independent variable and y the dependent variable in regression

O and E are the observed and expected frequencies, respectively in chi-squared testing

$\hat{\mu}$ and $\hat{\sigma}$ are estimates for μ and σ respectively

d represents differences between the paired values when working with paired data

Σ (Sigma) indicates 'the sum of'

f represents the number of items in a group of frequency data

z is shorthand for the standardised value

t is shorthand for the t value

Formulae

Summary statistics

Mean

$$\bar{x} = \frac{\sum x}{n} \text{ for single numbers} \qquad \bar{x} = \frac{\sum fx}{n} \text{ for frequency data}$$

Population standard deviation

$$s = \sqrt{\frac{\sum(x-\bar{x})^2}{n}} \quad \text{or} \quad \sqrt{\frac{\sum f(x-\bar{x})^2}{n}} \text{ for frequency data}$$

An equivalent formula which is often used is:

$$s = \sqrt{\frac{\sum x^2}{n} - \left(\frac{\sum x}{n}\right)^2} \quad \text{or} \quad s = \sqrt{\frac{\sum fx^2}{n} - \left(\frac{\sum fx}{n}\right)^2} \text{ for frequency data}$$

Sample standard deviation

$$s = \sqrt{\frac{\sum(x-\bar{x})^2}{n-1}} \quad \text{or} \quad \sqrt{\frac{\sum f(x-\bar{x})^2}{n-1}} \text{ for frequency data}$$

An equivalent formula which is often used is:

$$s = \sqrt{\frac{\sum x^2}{n-1} - \left(\frac{\sum x}{n-1}\right)^2} \quad \text{or} \quad s = \sqrt{\frac{\sum fx^2}{n-1} - \left(\frac{\sum fx}{n-1}\right)^2} \text{ for frequency data}$$

Probability

Binomial: For n trials with the probability of success in any one trial being p, the probability of getting r successes is:

$$\frac{n!}{r!(n-r)!} \times p^r(1-p)^{(n-r)}$$

where $n!$ stands for factorial n, i.e. $n \times (n-1) \times (n-2) \ldots 2 \times 1$

Poisson: The probability of a particular number, x, occurring is given by

$$P(x) = \mu^x \frac{e^{-\mu}}{x!}$$

where μ is the mean and $e \cong 2.718$. ($\cong$ means 'approximately equal to')

Exponential: The probability of an event occurring x times is given by:

$$P(x) = \lambda e^{-\lambda x}$$

where λ (lambda) is the mean time between successive events.

Normal distribution

Standardised value

$$z = \frac{x-\mu}{\sigma}$$

Confidence intervals

Percentage or a proportion, π, is given by:

$$\pi = p \pm z\sqrt{\frac{p(100-p)}{n}} \text{ for a percentage or } \pi = p \pm z\sqrt{\frac{p(1-p)}{n}} \text{ for a proportion}$$

Mean from large sample and/or from sample with known standard deviation

$$\mu = \bar{x} \pm z \frac{\sigma}{\sqrt{n}}$$

Mean from small sample with unknown standard deviation

$$\mu = \bar{x} \pm t \frac{s}{\sqrt{n}}$$

Difference of means of paired data

$$\mu_d = \bar{x}_d \pm t \frac{s_d}{\sqrt{n_d}}$$

where $\bar{x}_d$, s_d and n_d refer to the calculated differences.

Hypothesis testing – test statistics

Proportion:

$$\frac{|p - \pi|}{\sqrt{\dfrac{\pi(1 - \pi)}{n}}}$$

Percentage:

$$\frac{|p - \pi|}{\sqrt{\dfrac{\pi(100 - \pi)}{n}}}$$

Mean:

$$\sigma \text{ known, } z = \frac{|\bar{x} - \mu|}{\sigma/\sqrt{n}} \quad \text{or} \quad \sigma \text{ unknown so } s \text{ needed} \quad t = \frac{|\bar{x} - \mu|}{s/\sqrt{n}}$$

Difference of two means with known population standard deviations

$$z = \frac{|\bar{x}_1 - \bar{x}_2|}{\sqrt{\dfrac{\sigma_1^2}{n_1} + \dfrac{\sigma_2^2}{n_2}}}$$

$\bar{x}_1$, $\bar{x}_2$ are the sample means, σ_1, σ_2 are the known standard deviations, n_1, n_2 are the sample sizes.

Difference of two means with unknown population standard deviations

F test:

$$F = \frac{s_1^2}{s_2^2}$$

where s_1 refers to the larger standard deviation so that F is always > 1
  The formula used for 'pooling' the standard deviations is:

$$s_p = \sqrt{\frac{(n_1 - 1)s_1^2 + (n_2 - 1)s_2^2}{n_1 + n_2 - 2}}$$

where s_1 and s_2 are the standard deviations of samples 1 and 2 respectively.

Test statistic:

$$t = \frac{|\bar{x}_1 - \bar{x}_2|}{s_p \sqrt{\dfrac{1}{n_1} + \dfrac{1}{n_2}}} \quad \text{or} \quad t = \frac{||\bar{x}_1 - \bar{x}_2| - c|}{s_p \sqrt{\dfrac{1}{n_1} + \dfrac{1}{n_2}}} \quad \text{for a hypothesised value } c$$

Mann–Whitney non-parametric test:

$$U = R - \frac{n_1(n_1 + 1)}{2}$$

where R is the smaller sum of ranks and n_1 the size of the same sample.

Analysis of variance

The least critical difference

$$CD = t\sqrt{MSE\left(\frac{1}{n_1} + \frac{1}{n_2}\right)}$$

t has the MSE degrees of freedom and one tail.

Correlation and regression

Pearson's product moment correlation coefficient, r (least squares method)

$$r = \frac{S_{xy}}{\sqrt{S_{xx}S_{yy}}} \qquad (-1 \leq r \leq +1)$$

where

$$S_{xx} = \sum x^2 - \frac{\sum x \sum x}{n}$$

$$S_{yy} = \sum y^2 - \frac{\sum y \sum y}{n}$$

$$S_{xy} = \sum xy - \frac{\sum x \sum y}{n}$$

The **regression line** is described, in general, as the straight line with the equation:

$$y = a + bx$$

The **gradient**, b, is calculated from:

$$b = \frac{S_{xy}}{S_{xx}} \quad \text{where } S_{xy} = \sum xy - \frac{\sum x \sum y}{n} \text{ and } S_{xx} = \sum x^2 - \frac{\sum x \sum x}{n}$$

Since the regression line passes through the centroid, both means, its equation can be used to find the *value of a*, the **intercept** on the y-axis:

$$a = \bar{y} - b\bar{x}$$

Spearman's rank correlation coefficient, r_s,

$$r_s = \frac{6 \sum d^2}{n(n^2 - 1)}$$

where d is the difference in rankings and n the sample size.

Chi-squared testing

For any cell the expected frequency is calculated by:

$$\frac{\text{Row total} \times \text{Column total}}{\text{Overall total}}$$

Test statistic for larger than 2×2 table:

$$\sum \frac{(O - E)^2}{E}$$

Test statistic for 2×2 table (Yate's correction):

$$\sum \frac{(|O - E| - 0.5)^2}{E}$$

Index numbers

Index for any time period n: $\quad \dfrac{\text{value in period } n}{\text{value in base period}}$

Time series

Regression models:

Linear model: $\quad y = a + bx$,

Quadratic model: $\quad y = a + bx + cx^2$

Cubic model: $\quad y = a + bx + cx^2 + dx^3$

Exponential smoothing models

Steady model:

New forecast = old forecast + alpha × error in previous forecast

where alpha (α) is the first smoothing constant.

Growth model:

New forecast = previous forecast + alpha × error in previous forecast

$\qquad\qquad\qquad$ + previous trend + beta × error in previous forecast trend

New trend = previous trend + beta × error in previous trend

where beta, β, is the second smoothing constant.

Seasonal decomposition – Additive model

All the formulae in this section are repeated in Appendix C.

1 Introduction to Statistics

1.1 The objectives of this chapter

In this introductory chapter no assumptions are made about any prior statistical knowledge. The main aim is to introduce you gently to the subject of statistics and its use of various types of data. Having studied this chapter you should be aware, in general, of different types of data, methods of data collection and reasons for displaying, summarising and analysing data.

Throughout the book, terms printed in **bold** are either occurring for the first time or are of particular importance. They are described in the glossary in Appendix B.

1.2 What do we mean by statistics?

Statistics are numerical facts or figures. Therefore statistics as a science essentially deals with numbers. It is generally taken to include the systematic collection, classification and analysis of data in order to get a better understanding of some situation. This may mean summarising the data in either tabulated or graphical form. A statistical study might be a simple exploration enabling us to gain an insight into a virtually unknown situation or it might be a sophisticated analysis designed to produce numerical confirmation, or rejection, of some widely-held belief.

1.3 Why do we need statistics?

In business, we may be interested in a set of data in its own right. In this case we could describe it both numerically and graphically in the most appropriate manner – **descriptive statistics**. Alternatively, the set of data may be a sample drawn from a larger population. This population would be the target of our interest. In this case we need to use the information held by the sample to tell us something about its parent population – **inferential statistics**. In another instance we may be interested in the future and so use the data we have up to the present time to estimate the value of a quantity in the future – **forecasting**.

Statistics play a wide role in most aspects of the competitive business world where they provide an essential tool in decision making. During this course you will learn to:

- Describe data, such as profits, in order to assist decision makers
- Estimate some property of a large population of data from a comparatively small sample
- Seek out relationships between pairs of variables such as advertising and sales
- Use known data to forecast a quantity, such as future demand.

First we shall look at some basic considerations which we must always take into account when collecting or handling data. These considerations do not fit into any specific topic area but are applicable throughout this course.

1.4 Types of data and scales of measurement

Any data can take a variety of values or belong to various **categories**, either numerical or non-numerical. The 'thing' being described by the data is known as a **variable**. The values or descriptions you use to qualify or categorise the variable are the **measurements**. These are of different types, each with its own appropriate **scale of measurement** which has to be considered when deciding on suitable methods of graphical display or numerical analysis.

A variable is, therefore, simply something whose 'value' can vary. A car could be red, blue, green, etc. It could be classed as small, medium or large. Its petrol consumption in mpg could be 30, 40, 50, etc. Its year of manufacture could be 1991, 1995, 1999, etc. It would have a particular length. These values all describe the same car but are measured on different 'scales'.

1.4.1 Categorical data

These are generally non-numerical data which are placed into **exclusive categories** and then counted rather than measured. People are often categorised by sex or occupation. A car can be categorised by its make or colour.

1.4.1.1 Nominal data

The scale of measurement for a variable is **nominal** if the data describing it are simple names or labels which cannot be ordered. This is the lowest level of measurement. Numbers may represent nominal data, such as 'codes' for computer analysis, but these can only be used as labels. Vest numbers identify athletes but make no value statements about them. A car registration number only serves to identify the vehicle.

Numbers representing nominal data cannot be used in any arithmetic. Your PIN number allows you access to your bank account, as does your friend's to his, but the sum of them does not allow either of you, never mind both, access to either account. All the data are placed in a limited number of exhaustive categories and any analysis is carried out on the **frequencies** within these categories.

1.4.1.2 Ordinal data

If the **categories** of data can be placed in a meaningful order without making any measurements, then the data are classed as **ordinal**. This is one level up from nominal. We know that the members of one category are more or less than the members of another but we cannot say by how much. For example, the results of a race are decided by the finishing order of the athletes without any reference to their times. The vests they wear might be ordered as 'small', 'medium', 'large' without the aid of a tape measure.

Degree classifications are only ordinal because the difference between first and second class degrees is not the same as the difference between a 'second' and a 'third'.

Questionnaires are often used to collect opinions using the categories: 'Strongly agree', 'Agree', 'No opinion', 'Disagree' or 'Strongly disagree'. The responses may be coded as 1, 2, 3, 4 and 5 for the computer but the differences between these numbers are not claimed to be equal.

In order to analyse ordinal data, all individuals are placed in their relevant categories, the categories are ordered and calculations are performed on their frequencies

1.4.2 Interval and ratio data

In interval and ratio scales of measurement all numbers are defined by standard units, such as metres or grams, so equal difference between numbers means equal distance between measurements. If there is also a meaningful zero, then the fact that one number is twice as big as another means that the measurements are also in that ratio. This data is known as **ratio data**. If the value of zero has no mathematical meaning the data is **interval** only.

1.4.2.1 Interval data

There are very few examples of genuine interval scales. Temperature in degrees Celsius provides one example with the 'zero' on this scale being arbitrary. The difference between 30°C and 50°C is the same as the difference between 40°C and 60°C but we cannot claim that 60°C is twice as hot as 30°C. They are therefore **interval data** but not ratio data. Dates are measured on an interval scale because the zero is arbitrary and not mathematically meaningful.

1.4.2.2 Ratio data

Ratio data must have a meaningful zero as their lowest possible value. For example, the time taken for athletes to complete a race would be measured on this scale. If we consider ages, a child at 12 years old is twice as old as his 6-year-old brother, and the age difference between them is the same as that between his sisters who are 15 years old and 9 years old. Their ages are ratio data but their dates of birth are interval data.

Suppose Bill earns £20 000, Ben earns £15 000 and Bob earns £10 000. The intervals of £5000 between Bill and Ben and also between Ben and Bob represent equal amounts of money. Also the ratio of Bob's earnings to Bill's earnings is in the same ratio as the numbers which represent them (1:2). The value of £0 represents 'no money'. This data set is therefore **ratio** as well as interval.

The distinction between interval and ratio data is more theoretical than practical as the same numerical and graphical methods are appropriate for both. They are usually referred to as **at least interval** data. Much of the data, such as money, that you will study on this course will be measured on this scale.

We have identified three measurement scales – nominal, ordinal and at least interval. The data measured on these scales are classified in the same way and this classification determines which methods of analysis are appropriate.

Any type of data may be analysed using methods appropriate to *lower levels*. For example: interval data may be analysed as ordinal but useful information is lost. If we know that Bill earns £20 000 and Ben earns £15 000 we are throwing information away by only recording that Bill earns 'more than' Ben.

Data cannot be analysed using methods that are only appropriate for *higher level* data as the results will be either invalid or meaningless. For example it makes no sense to code the sex of students as 'male = 1, female = 2' and then report 'the mean value is 1.7'. It is however quite appropriate to report that '70% of the students are female'.

1.4.3 Qualitative and quantitative data

Various definitions exist for the distinction between qualitative and quantitative data. Non-numerical (nominal) data are always described as being **qualitative** (non-metric) data as they describe some qualities without measuring them. **Quantitative** (metric) data which describe some measurement (or quantity) are always numerical. All definitions agree that interval or ratio data are quantitative. Some textbooks, however, use the term 'qualitative' to refer to words only, whilst others also include nominal or ordinal numbers. Problems of definition can arise with numbers, such as house numbers, which identify or rank rather than measure. You do not need to worry about the 'grey areas'.

In the next two chapters we shall study graphical and numerical methods appropriate to each type of data. Statistical techniques are often divided into **parametric statistics** which require data to be interval or ratio and **non-parametric statistics** which are appropriate for use at the lower levels.

1.4.4 Discrete and continuous data

Quantitative data may be **discrete** or **continuous**. If the values that can be taken by a variable change in steps the data is **discrete**. These discrete values are often, but not always, whole numbers. If the variable can take any value within a range it is **continuous**. The number of people shopping in a supermarket is discrete but the amount they spend is continuous. The number of children in a family is discrete but a baby's birth weight is continuous.

1.5 Populations and samples

The **population** is the **entire group** of interest. This definition is not confined to people, as is usual in the non-statistical sense. A statistical population may include objects such as all the houses in a local authority area rather than the people living in them.

It is usually neither possible nor practical to examine every member of a **population** so we use a **sample** – a smaller selection taken from that population – to **estimate** some value or characteristic of the whole population. Care must be taken when selecting the sample as it must be representative of the whole population under consideration in order to tell us anything relevant to that particular population.

Occasionally the whole population is investigated by a **census**, such as the one carried out every ten years in the United Kingdom. The data are gathered from everyone in the population. A more usual method of collecting information is by a **survey** in which a sample is selected from the population of interest and its data examined. Examples of this are the Gallup polls produced from a sample of the electorate to forecast the result of a general election.

Analysing a sample instead of the whole population has many advantages such as the obvious saving of both time and money. It is often the only possible method as the collection of data may destroy the article of interest, e.g. the quality control of rolls of film.

The ideal method of sampling is **random sampling** by which every member of the population has an equal chance of being selected and every selection is independent of all the others. This ideal might not be achieved for a variety of reasons and many other methods can be used (Groebner and Shannon, 1993, Chapter 5).

1.6 Descriptive statistics

Descriptive statistics covers the analysis of the whole population of interest. The facts and figures usually referred to as 'statistics' by the media are very often a numerical and graphical summary of data from a specific group, e.g. unemployment figures. Much of the data generated by a business will be descriptive in nature, as will be the majority of sporting statistics.

1.7 Inferential statistics

If the information we have available is from a sample of the whole population of interest we analyse it to produce the **sample statistics** from which we can infer values for the parent population. This branch of statistics is usually referred to as **inferential statistics**. For example, we use the proportion of faulty items in a sample taken from a production line to estimate the proportion of defective items from the whole line. Pharmaceutical research is an example of the use of inferential statistics. Tests are necessarily limited to a small sample of patients but inferences are applied to the whole relevant patient population.

A descriptive measure from the sample is usually referred to as a **sample statistic** and the corresponding measure estimated for the population is referred to as a **population parameter**. The problem with using samples is that each sample produces a different sample statistic giving us a different estimate for the population parameter. They cannot all be correct so a margin of error is generally quoted with any sample estimations.

1.8 Summary

In this short chapter you have been introduced to the different types of data which we will be using throughout this course. We shall be mainly dealing with interval data, such as money, which we will learn to display, summarise and analyse. It is, however, important to be able to distinguish between the different types of data as this determines which methods of display and analysis are the most appropriate.

Table 1.1

Scale of measurement	Non-numeric data	Numeric data
Nominal	Name or label only	Numbers only identify groups which cannot be ordered
Ordinal	Names or labels can be ranked	These numbers allow ranking but no arithmetic
Interval	Always numeric	Intervals between numbers are meaningful
Ratio	Always numeric	Intervals between numbers are meaningful and also their ratios as the lowest value is a meaningful zero.

You have also been introduced briefly to the two main branches of statistics: descriptive and inferential statistics. Descriptive statistics result from gathering data about a whole group, or population, and reaching conclusions about that group only. Inferential statistics result from gathering data about a sample of a population and then reaching conclusions about the whole population from an analysis of the sample data.

1.9 Check your course prerequisites

There is no exercise connected to the material in this introductory chapter. You should check, or revise, the mathematics that will be assumed during the course. This knowledge is fairly basic. In addition to a sound working knowledge of simple arithmetic you should be able to:

- Work with fractions, decimals and percentages
- Handle large and small numbers
- Carry out simple algebraic manipulations
- Solve fairly simple equations.

The following tutorial should enable you to check these prerequisites. If you find any question particularly difficult you should get some practice from any quantitative analysis or basic mathematics textbook.

1.10 Tutorial 1 – Basic mathematics revision

1 Evaluate

(a) $\dfrac{3}{7} - \dfrac{4}{21} + \dfrac{5}{3}$ (b) $1\dfrac{2}{3} + 2\dfrac{4}{5} - 3\dfrac{1}{2}$ (c) $\dfrac{2}{7} \times \dfrac{14}{25} \times \dfrac{15}{24}$

(d) $\dfrac{16}{21} \div \dfrac{4}{7}$ (e) $\dfrac{4}{9} \times \dfrac{3}{16} \div \dfrac{7}{12}$ (f) $4\dfrac{2}{5} \div \dfrac{11}{12} \times 1\dfrac{7}{8}$

2 (a) Give 489 267 to 3 significant figures

(b) Give 489 267 to 2 significant figures

(c) Give 0.002 615 to 2 significant figures

(d) Give 0.002 615 to 1 significant figure

(e) Give 0.002 615 to 5 decimal places

(f) Give 0.002 615 to 3 decimal places

3 Retail outlets in a town were classified as small, medium and large and their numbers were in the ratio 6 : 11 : 1. If there were 126 retail outlets altogether, how many were there of each type?

4 Convert

(a) 28% to a fraction in its lowest terms

(b) 28% to a decimal

(c) $\dfrac{3}{8}$ to a decimal

(d) $\dfrac{3}{8}$ to a percentage

(e) 0.625 to a fraction in its lowest terms

(f) 0.625 to a percentage

5 Express the following in standard form.
   (a) 296 000   (b) 0.000296   (c) 0.4590   (d) 459.0

   (e) $\dfrac{1}{25000}$ (f) $\dfrac{1}{0.00025}$

6 Reduce the following expressions to their simplest form expanding brackets if appropriate.
   (a) $3a + b + 2a - 4b$ (b) $2a + 4ab + 3a^2 + ab$ (c) $a^2(3a + 4b + 2a)$

   (d) $(x + 2)(x + 4)$ (e) $(x + 2)^2$ (f) $(x + 1)(x - 1)$

7 Make x the subject of the formula

   (a) $y = 5x - 4$ (b) $y = x^2 - 7$ (c) $y = 2(3 + 6x)$ (d) $y = \dfrac{3}{x}$

8 Find the value of x, as a decimal, in the formulae in question 7 when $y = -3$
9 Evaluate the following when $x = -2$, $y = 5$ and $z = 4$
   (a) xy (b) $(xy)^2$ (c) $(xy + z)^2$ (d) $zy - x^2$

   (e) $(x + z)(2y - x)$ (f) $x^2 + y^2 + z^2$

10 Solve for x:

   (a) $3x - 1 = 4 - 2x$ (b) $2(x - 3) = 3(1 - 2x)$ (c) $\dfrac{3}{x - 1} = \dfrac{1}{2}$

Answers

1 (a) $1\dfrac{19}{21}$ (b) $\dfrac{29}{30}$ (c) $\dfrac{1}{10}$ (d) $1\dfrac{1}{3}$ (e) $\dfrac{1}{7}$ (f) 9

2 (a) 489 000   (b) 490 000   (c) 0.0026   (d) 0.003
   (e) 0.002 62   (f) 0.003

3 42 small, 77 medium, 7 large

4 (a) $\dfrac{7}{25}$ (b) 0.28   (c) 0.375   (d) 37.5%   (e) $\dfrac{5}{8}$ (f) 62.5%

5 (a) 2.96×10^5 (b) 2.96×10^{-4} (c) 4.59×10^{-1} (d) 4.59×10^2
   (e) 4.0×10^{-5} (f) 4.0×10^3

6 (a) $5a - 3b$ (b) $3a^2 + 5ab + 2a$ (c) $5a^3 + 4a^2b$ (d) $x^2 + 6x + 8$
   (e) $x^2 + 4x + 4$ (f) $x^2 - 1$

7 (a) $x = \dfrac{1}{5}(y + 4)$ (b) $x = \sqrt{y + 7}$ (c) $x = \dfrac{y - 6}{12}$ (d) $x = \dfrac{3}{y}$

8 (a) 0.2   (b) $+2$ or -2 (c) -0.75 (d) -1

9 (a) -10 (b) 100   (c) 36   (d) 16   (e) 24   (f) 45

10 (a) 1   (b) $1\dfrac{1}{8}$ (c) 7

2 Graphical Representation of Data

2.1 The objectives of this chapter

So far you have considered four different types of data: nominal, ordinal, interval and ratio. In this chapter we will investigate the different ways of presenting this data graphically in a meaningful manner. You are probably already familiar with **bar charts** and **pie charts** so they will be considered fairly briefly. The emphasis will be on **histograms** and **cumulative frequency diagrams** plus an introduction to **stem-and-leaf plots** and **box plots**. Graphs are potentially very good tools for communication, but they must be kept as simple as possible and never be presented so as to mislead the reader. If they cannot be easily understood they are neither use nor ornament!

After studying this chapter you should be able to draw appropriate graphs of given data, interpret different types of graph and also understand those presented in the media.

2.2 Introduction: why do we represent data by graphs?

What is your reaction if you are presented with a table full of figures? I'm sure that you are not filled with delight and an immediate understanding of the situation described by them! On the other hand, a fairly simple graph, if well presented, can quickly convey a general summary of a set of data to its reader. Further examination can then reveal more detail and produce a deeper understanding. If you always keep in mind that the purpose of drawing a graph is to convey information to its reader as easily and quickly as possible you will not go far wrong. Simple graphs make for easy comparisons so never put too much information in any one picture.

2.3 Tabulation

Immediately after collection all new data, **raw data**, are in the form of individual figures. There may be pages of these, often far too many to convey any useful information as they stand. These individual data are ungrouped so the first step in organising them is to produce **grouped data**, i.e. collect like with like in order to reduce the total volume. This grouping can take a variety of forms – some students like to use tally charts – which all result in a **frequency distribution**. Various statistics can be calculated from the frequency distribution and suitable graphs produced.

First determine the range of the data, i.e. largest value – smallest value. Then decide on suitable **class intervals** to give a reasonable number of classes or groups. Somewhere between 5 and 15 classes is generally acceptable – too few will result in loss of detail but too many may obscure the overall picture. In order to keep the work simple it is advisable to group in fives or tens and, in the first grouping, use equal intervals. Data values must not fall into more than one class so the class interval is usually described as, for example, '20 and under 30' so that 30 would go in the next class. Now group the data by constructing a tally chart. For Example 2.1 record the first number, 55, next to the relevant interval, '55 and under 60', with a ' | '. Then allocate the second, 64, to the '60 and under 65' interval, and so on until all the numbers have been recorded. After four strokes it is conventional to draw a diagonal through them for the fifth so that the number of 'fives' can be easily totalled. Total each 'tally' for the frequency in each interval.

EXAMPLE 2.1

The following figures represent the examination marks (%) for 60 students on a business studies course. We shall first find the range, then decide the number of intervals to use, define the class intervals and finally draw up a frequency table.

Table 2.1

55	64	74	53	66	40	52	39	70	59	53	57
62	60	40	45	54	72	47	42	38	60	43	37
61	65	41	54	69	47	80	66	52	78	43	72
44	84	61	67	74	57	60	61	60	56	66	49
54	59	59	60	57	70	61	54	67	54	65	56

Range: $84 - 37 = 47$ These figures would give us either 6 class intervals of 10 or 10 class intervals of 5. Either would be acceptable so we shall first group in classes of 5 and then combine into intervals of 10 and compare the results.

Frequency distribution table

Class Interval	Tally	Frequency
35 and under 40	|||	3
40 and under 45	⭢ ||	7
45 and under 50	||||	4
50 and under 55	⭢ ||||	9
55 and under 60	⭢ ||||	9
60 and under 65	⭢ ⭢		11
65 and under 70	⭢ |||	8
70 and under 75	⭢		6
75 and under 80			1
80 and under 85	||	2

This gives us an overall idea of the 'shape' of the distribution. Does it look better if grouped in tens?

Class interval	Tally	Frequency
30 and under 40	|||	3
40 and under 50	⭢ ⭢		11
50 and under 60	⭢ ⭢ ⭢ |||	18
60 and under 70	⭢ ⭢ ⭢ ||||	19
70 and under 80	⭢ |||	7
80 and under 90	||	2

It is probably easier to interpret this second distribution, i.e. that 'most' of the students pass but get less than 70%. Have we lost any detail of interest? Probably not, in this case. There is no set rule about the number of classes, so just use a 'reasonable' number.

A frequency distribution already gives a good indication of the 'shape' of the data but a well drawn graph, such as a bar chart or histogram, communicates it better.

2.4 Graphs of non-metric data

2.4.1 Bar charts

Bar charts are drawn as a pictorial summary of categorical data. Each bar, which is separated from its neighbours, represents one category and the length of the bar represents the frequency in that category. Alternatively the length of the bar is proportional to the size of the items being considered, for example, sales in Example 2.2. For nominal data the bars may be arranged in any order but with ordinal data the categories are usually presented in ascending order. For comparative purposes the bars may be grouped, the frequencies stacked, or 'percentage charts' drawn, as in Example 2.2.

EXAMPLE 2.2

A shop had sales from four departments for the last four quarters (£000):

Table 2.2

Department	Spring	Summer	Autumn	Winter	Total
Food	160	180	180	200	720
Clothing	280	300	200	300	1080
Furniture	860	560	500	240	2160
Electrical	60	60	100	140	360
Total	1360	1100	980	880	4320

Figure 2.1 Bar charts for comparing the total and departmental quarterly sales
(Diagrams from Microsoft Graph 97 Chart)

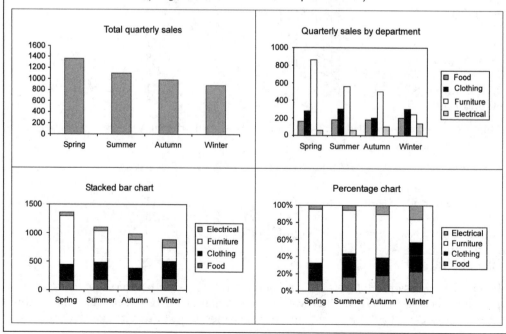

2.4.2   Pie charts

Pie charts are also drawn as a summary of categorical data. The total count of all the data represented is, of course, equivalent to 360° on the 'pie', and the relative frequency within each category is represented by the size of the angle of its sector, i.e. its 'slice'. If pie charts are to be used for comparing relative frequencies between variables then the area of the 'pie' describing each can be drawn so that it represents the total frequency of that variable.

Calculating the sector angles (refer to Table 2.2 for total sales)

$$\text{Food: } \frac{720}{4320} \times 360° = 60° \qquad \text{Clothing: } \frac{1080}{4320} \times 360° = 90° \quad \text{and so on}$$

Figure 2.2

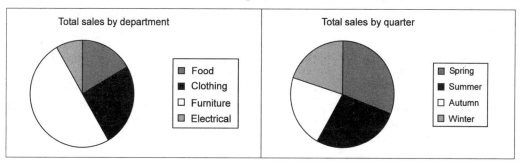

By hand this information can all be put onto one 'pie' by placing a second ring around, say, the departmental pie shown in the first diagram and then subdividing each departmental sector radially between the different quarters.

2.4.3   Pictograms

You are not expected to draw pictograms but it is useful to know how to interpret those shown by the media. You are probably familiar with the type of graph produced by the motor industry in which each little car drawn represents, for example, 1000 cars actually produced. Ten tiny cars might represent 10 000 real cars from one factory, and 20 000 real cars from another factory might be represented by twenty tiny cars. That method of pictorial comparison is fine as its meaning is clear. Other methods can be misleading.

Figure 2.3

If the first car in Figure 2.3 represents 1000 real cars, how many does the second car represent? Its length is twice, its area four times and its volume eight times that of the first car. Does it represent 2000, 4000 or 8000 real cars? Diagrams of this type are open to misinterpretation and should be avoided. Diagrams published in the press need very careful scrutiny if they are not explained numerically.

2.5 Graphs of metric data

2.5.1 *Histograms*

In Section 2.3 we grouped the raw data to form a frequency distribution table. This gave a much clearer picture than did the individual data values. The most usual presentation of metric data is in the form of a **histogram**.

A **histogram** is a pictorial method of presenting frequency data. It appears similar to a bar chart but has two fundamental differences:

- The data must be measurable on a **continuous** scale; for example, lengths rather than colours.
- The **area** of a rectangle rather than its height is proportional to the frequency, so if one column is twice the width of another its height must be halved for the same frequency.

Histograms are produced by all statistical software packages but these often do not give you as much choice in presentation as is available when you draw them by hand.

Using the data in Example 2.1, we can look at the output from Minitab, one of the most commonly used educational packages (Figure 2.4). Figure 2.4(b) has been grouped in 'tens' and the labelling has been moved to the class boundaries, which is always preferable. SPSS produces similar diagrams, but does not allow the labelling to be moved.

Figure 2.4 Examination marks from Example 2.1

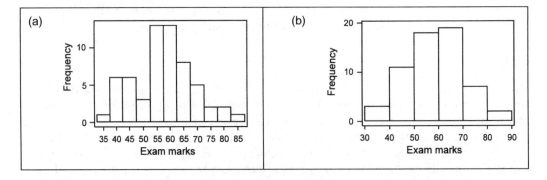

The histograms in Figure 2.4 both show equal class intervals which is the default format in all packages. Neither Minitab nor SPSS will allow for the use of unequal intervals, so this will be described below in the method for hand-drawing histograms.

The construction of a frequency distribution table and histogram are shown in Example 2.3. The data are first grouped in a frequency distribution table:

- Decide on sensible limits if the first or last class interval is left open, for example, 'less than 20', and also decide how many classes you intend to group your data into. Too few classes may hide information about the data, too many classes may hide its overall shape.
- Construct a frequency distribution table, grouping the data into a reasonable number of classes (somewhere in the order of 10). Intervals are usually of the same width for the first summary.

EXAMPLE 2.3

You are working for the transport manager of a large chain of supermarkets which hires cars for its staff. She is interested in the weekly distances covered by these cars. Mileages recorded for a sample of hired vehicles during a given week yielded the following data (Fleet 1):

Table 2.3

138	164	150	132	144	125	149	157	161	150
146	158	140	109	136	148	152	144	145	145
168	126	138	186	163	109	154	165	135	156
146	183	105	108	135	153	140	135	142	128

Decide on sensible class limits and group the data:

Minimum = 105   Maximum = 186   Range = 186 − 105 = 81

Nine intervals of 10 miles width seems reasonable, but the first and last intervals may be wider if data proves to be scarce at the extremes.

Frequency distribution table

Class interval		Frequency
100 and less than 110	||||	4
110 and less than 120		
120 and less than 130	|||	3
130 and less than 140	⊬⊬⊣ ||	7
140 and less than 150	⊬⊬⊣ ⊬⊬⊣ |	11
150 and less than 160	⊬⊬⊣ |||	8
160 and less than 170	⊬⊬⊣	5
170 and less than 180		
180 and less than 190	||	2
	Total	40

It might be preferable to combine the two intervals at each end of the table.

Class interval		Frequency	Frequency/10 miles
100 and less than 120	||||	4	2.0
120 and less than 130	|||	3	3.0
130 and less than 140	⊬⊬⊣ ||	7	7.0
140 and less than 150	⊬⊬⊣ ⊬⊬⊣ |	11	11.0
150 and less than 160	⊬⊬⊣ |||	8	8.0
160 and less than 170	⊬⊬⊣	5	5.0
170 and less than 190	||	2	1.0
	Total	40	

The histogram is then constructed:

- Frequencies are plotted in proportion to the area of each rectangle, so if the intervals (the rectangle bases) are not all the same width their heights need to be calculated. These heights are known as the **frequency densities**, i.e. frequency per constant interval. The most commonly occurring interval is often used.

● Construct the histogram, labelling each axis carefully. Hand-drawn histograms usually show the frequency vertically. (Computer output may be horizontal because it is more convenient for line printers.)

EXAMPLE 2.3 *continued*

Now plot the histogram. If some intervals are wider than others care must be taken that the **areas** of the blocks are proportional to the **frequencies**, so heights are proportional to frequency densities. Figures 2.5(a) and (b) illustrate the difference; (a) has the frequency plotted on the vertical axis and (b) has the **frequency density** with the two outside intervals combined at both of the extremes. It looks more aesthetically pleasing.

Figure 2.5 Histogram of mileages

(a)
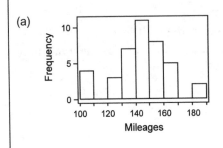

(b)
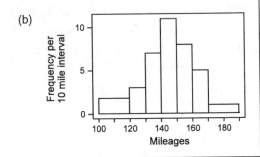

2.5.2 *Frequency polygons*

A **frequency polygon** is constructed by joining the midpoints at the top of each column of the histogram. The area under the polygon is the same as that under the histogram. Polygons can also be drawn without using a histogram. It is often easier to compare two frequency polygons than to interpret a pair of histograms which tend to obscure each other. The polygons are drawn without the histograms, giving a clearer comparison.

For example, if we wished to compare another fleet of forty cars, Fleet 2, with the one in Example 2.3, Fleet 1, the diagram might look like Figure 2.6(b).

Figure 2.6

(a) Histogram of Fleet 1 with frequency polygon
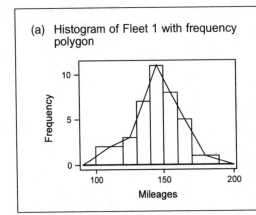

(b) Frequency polygons for comparing Fleet 2 with Fleet 1
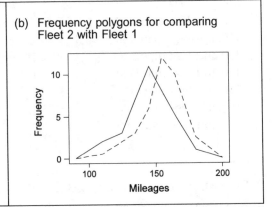

If we wish to compare two fleets of different sizes, frequencies would not give a clear picture. It would be advisable to compare **relative frequencies**. These measure the percentage of the total fleet which lies within each class interval. (See Example 2.4.)

EXAMPLE 2.4

If we wished to compare our Fleet 2 with a much larger fleet, Fleet 3, we would calculate the relative frequencies for each fleet and plot those values instead of the frequencies. This makes the small and large fleets easier to compare because the areas under the graphs are equal.

Table 2.4

| | Fleet 2 | | Fleet 3 | |
Class interval	Frequency	Relative frequency (%)	Frequency	Relative frequency (%)
less than 100	0	0.0	0	0.0
100 and less than 110	0	0.0	9	4.5
110 and less than 120	1	2.5	9	4.5
120 and less than 130	2	5.0	35	17.5
130 and less than 140	4	10.0	70	35.0
140 and less than 150	6	15.0	40	20.0
150 and less than 160	12	30.0	23	11.5
160 and less than 170	10	25.0	12	6.0
170 and less than 180	4	10.0	2	1.0
180 and less than 190	1	2.5	0	0.0
Total	40	100.0	200	100.0

Figure 2.7

(a) Frequency polygons for Fleet 2 (—) and
     Fleet 3 (– –)

(b) Relative frequency polygons for Fleet 2
     and Fleet 3

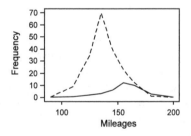
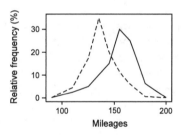

Shape of a distribution

We can also see whether the data distributions are symmetrical or not. If the 'peak' is towards the left and the longer tail towards the right, the data is referred to as 'positively, or right, skewed' and, conversely, if the 'peak' is towards the right and the tail towards the left, it is 'negatively, or left, skewed' and if neither it is 'symmetrical'. The distribution of the Fleet 2 data set is seen to be negatively skewed and Fleet 3 slightly positive but nearly symmetrical. You will meet this concept again later in the course.

Figure 2.8

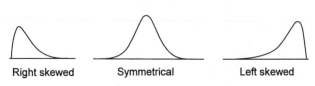

Right skewed   Symmetrical   Left skewed

2.5.3 Stem-and-leaf plots

The **stem-and-leaf plot** displays the data in the same 'shape' as the histogram, although it tends to be shown horizontally. The main difference is that it retains all the original information. The values themselves are included in the diagram so no information is 'lost'.

The stem-and-leaf plot in Figure 2.9 represents the Fleet 1 vehicles. The 'stem', on the left, indicates the first two digits (hundreds and tens) and the 'leaf' shows the units. The 'stem' contains the most significant digits. These may all be different or grouped depending on the spread of the data. The 'leaves', on the right of the vertical line, display the less significant digits. For small numbers these may be units (as in mileages) but for larger numbers they may represent tens or hundreds. For small data sets a leaf will represent a single number but may, for larger sets, represent many.

The first row in Figure 2.9 represents the values 105, 108, 109 and 109. We can see that the mileages travelled range from 105 to 186. Notice that the 'leaves' are arranged in numerical order so that it is easy to find the value of the middle mileage or the third largest, etc. If drawing stem-and-leaf plots by hand, it is necessary to group the values in tens and also to arrange carefully the order of the leaves. Fortunately Minitab and SPSS do this for us!

Figure 2.9

MILEAGES Stem-and-Leaf Plot (From SPSS)

Frequency	Stem	&	Leaf
4	10	.	5899
0	11	.	
3	12	.	568
7	13	.	2555688
11	14	.	00244556689
8	15	.	00234678
5	16	.	13458
0	17	.	
2	18	.	36

Stem width: 10
Each leaf: 1 case(s)

In the larger data set in Figure 2.10, describing the salaries earned by a firm's workers, each stem has been split into 'fives' rather than 'tens'. If the values are high the stem represents thousands rather than the tens above, as indicated by 'stem width' below. The leaves will be one number less significant, in this case measured to the nearest hundred, so the first value is £3600 to 2 s.f. Extreme values may often be grouped together – in this case we have 23 salaries which are greater than or equal to £10 200. For larger data sets the leaves may represent more than one case, but we are informed in Figure 2.10 that each leaf in this stem-and-leaf plot represents just one case.

Figure 2.10

Salary Stem-and-Leaf Plot

Frequency	Stem	&	Leaf
3	3	.	699
12	4	.	000023333344
17	4	.	55556666688888889
17	5	.	01111122224444444
13	5	.	5557777777788
37	6	.	0000000000000000333333333333333333333
15	6	.	666666666666999
4	7	.	2222
6	7	.	558889
2	8	.	14
5	8	.	57777
1	9	.	3
1	9	.	9
23	Extremes		(>=10200)

Stem width: 1000
Each leaf: 1 case(s)

2.5.4 Dot plots

A useful quick picture of the data can be formed by keeping a running total of the situation by means of a **dot plot**. This would be suitable for the 'straw polls' which are invariably taken from voters entering polling stations on election days. All the candidates' names would be displayed on the horizontal axis and a 'dot' plotted against the appropriate name for each voter who favours them. After about the first hour of opening at one particular polling station the picture might look something like Figure 2.11.

Figure 2.11

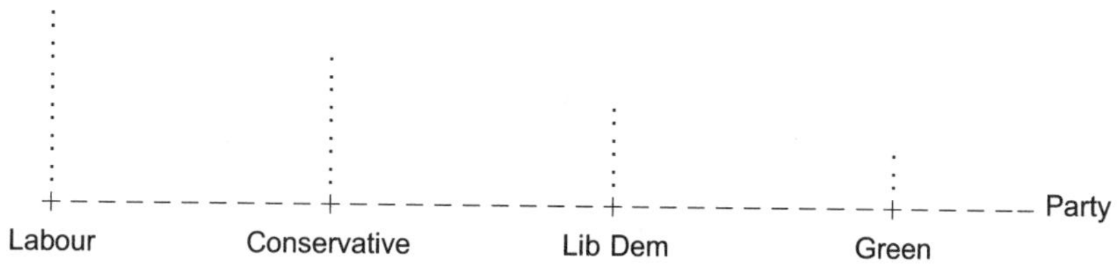

The advantage of this method, as opposed to using a bar chart or a pie chart, is that the picture is built up gradually and there is no need to wait for all the data to be collected before it can be drawn.

2.5.5 Cumulative frequency polygons (ogives)

A **cumulative frequency polygon** is a graphical method of representing the accumulated frequencies up to and including a particular value. Think of it as a running total less than a stated value; for example, the proportion of a workforce earning less than £15 000. These cumulative frequencies are often calculated as percentages of the total frequency. This method is used for estimating median and quartile values and hence the interquartile or semi-interquartile range of the data (see Chapter 3). It can also be used to estimate the percentage of the data above or below a certain value. We shall construct the diagrams in this chapter and use them for estimating statistics in the next.

Method

- Construct a Frequency Table as in 2.5.1
- Use it to construct a Cumulative Frequency Table noting that the **end** of the interval is the relevant value
- Calculate a column of cumulative percentages
- Plot the cumulative percentage against the end of the interval and join the points with straight lines. Cumulative frequencies and percentages are plotted on the vertical axis.

EXAMPLE 2.5

Using again the data from Example 2.3 we shall work through the method for drawing a cumulative frequency polygon. We shall then draw two polygons on the same graph for comparison. In Chapter 3 we shall use these graphs to estimate the **median** mileage, the **interquartile range** and the **semi-interquartile** range of the data.

continued

EXAMPLE 2.5 *continued*

Table 2.5

Mileages less than	Frequency	Cumulative frequency
100	0	0
110	4	4
120	0	4
130	3	7
140	7	14
150	11	25
160	8	33
170	5	38
180	0	38
190	2	40

Figure 2.12   Cumulative frequency polygon for Fleet 1

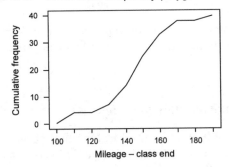

As a picture in its own right, Figure 2.12 is not particularly informative. For example, we can read from it the number of vehicles which did less than 155 miles in the week. This could be estimated from a hand drawn version on graph paper to be 29.

If, however, we use the same technique to compare Fleet 2 and Fleet 3, as we did with frequency polygons, it becomes more meaningful. As with frequency polygons you can see that comparing percentages is 'fairer' than comparing totals.

Table 2.6

Mileages less than	Frequency	Fleet 2 Cumulative frequency	% Cumulative frequency	Frequency	Fleet 3 Cumulative frequency	% Cumulative frequency
100	0	0	0.0	0	0	0.0
110	0	0	0.0	9	9	4.5
120	1	1	2.5	9	18	9.0
130	2	3	7.5	35	53	26.5
140	4	7	17.5	70	123	61.5
150	6	13	32.5	40	163	81.5
160	12	25	62.5	23	186	93.0
170	10	35	87.5	12	198	99.0
180	4	39	97.5	2	200	100.0
190	1	40	100.0	0	200	100.0

continued

EXAMPLE 2.5 *continued*

Figure 2.13

(a) Cumulative frequency polygons for Fleet 2 (—) and Fleet 3 (--)   (b) Percentage cumulative frequency polygons for Fleet 2 (—) and Fleet 3 (--)

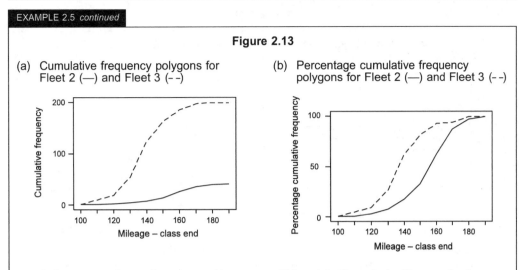

All these cumulative frequency diagrams will be visited again in Chapter 3 when we will use them for various estimations. From Figure 2.13(b) we can see, however, that Fleet 3 had many more low mileage vehicles than Fleet 2 as its steepest rise occurred sooner than that of Fleet 2.

2.5.6   Box plots

Box plots can be constructed for ordinal, interval or ratio data. A box plot is a very useful diagram which summarises information about the location and spread of a set of data in one diagram. It is also referred to as a 'box and whisker plot':

Figure 2.14

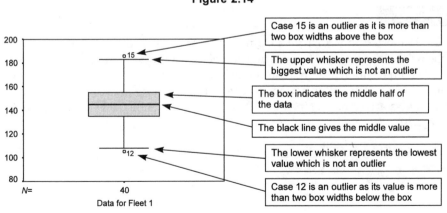

From Figure 2.14 we can see that the middle half of the data ranges from about 135 to about 155 miles, that the highest value is an outlier at about 185 with the lowest, an outlier, at about 105. The middle value is about 145.

This is a useful style of diagram for making comparisons. In Figure 2.15(a) we compare Fleet 1 with Fleet 2 and in Figure 2.15(b) we compare again the sales from the four different quarters from Example 2.2.

Figure 2.15

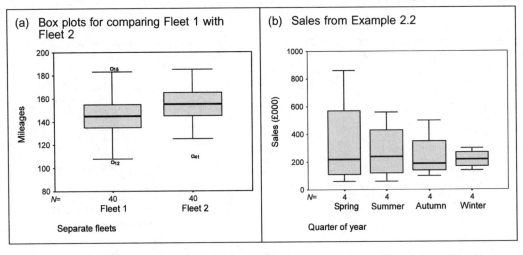

(a) Box plots for comparing Fleet 1 with Fleet 2 — Separate fleets

(b) Sales from Example 2.2 — Quarter of year

From Figure 2.15(a) we can see that the highest values for each of the two plots are similar but that the middle half of the data, the box, is higher for Fleet 2 than for Fleet 1. The spreads, as shown by the boxes, are apparently the same.

For the sales of the combined departments for the separate quarters from Example 2.2 (Figure 2.15(b)) we can see that the lowest values are similar, especially for Spring and Summer, but the highest ones are not. From the boxes it is evident that the spreads are different. The sales cover a wide range of values in Spring but are relatively constant in Winter.

We shall interpret this type of diagram more fully in Chapter 3 when we again consider the black line and the box limits as measures of centrality and spread.

2.6 A complete worked example

EXAMPLE 2.6

You are interested in your firm's claim to promote equal opportunities for male and female workers. You therefore decide to select a random sample of the workforce, send each a questionnaire and use the information to compare graphically male and female salaries. The information received has been tabulated in Table 2.7. The individual salaries, to the nearest £000, can be seen in the stem-and-leaf plots (Figure 2.10).

Table 2.7

| Salary (£000) | Frequency | |
Class interval	Male	Female
less than 10	4	21
10 and less than 15	12	48
15 and less than 20	36	58
20 and less than 25	64	42
25 and less than 30	77	21
30 and less than 40	35	8
40 and less than 60	18	2
over 60	4	0

continued

EXAMPLE 2.6 *continued*

We shall:

- Close the open-ended intervals
- Calculate frequency densities, i.e. frequency per £5000 interval
- Draw histograms
- Calculate relative frequencies (%) to compare the samples of different sizes
- Draw relative frequency polygons
- Draw stem-and leaf plots
- Draw box plots
- Calculate cumulative percentages
- Draw cumulative percentage polygons

Close open intervals: An employee is unlikely to work for less than £5000 p.a., even part-time. The top salary is more debatable, but £100 000 seems reasonable.

Calculate frequency densities

Table 2.8

Salary (£000) Class interval	Male employees		Female employees	
	Frequency	Frequency density (per £5000)	Frequency	Frequency density (per £5000)
5 and less than 10	4	4.0	21	21.0
10 and less than 15	12	12.0	48	48.0
15 and less than 20	36	36.0	58	58.0
20 and less than 25	64	64.0	42	42.0
25 and less than 30	77	77.0	21	21.0
30 and less than 40	35	17.5	8	4.0
40 and less than 60	18	4.5	2	0.5
60 and less than 100	4	0.5	0	0.0
Total	250		200	

Histograms

(The graphics below are from Minitab with the exception of the box plots (SPSS).)

Figure 2.16

(a) Salaries of male employees (£000)   (b) Salaries of female employees (£000)

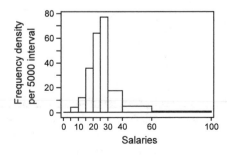

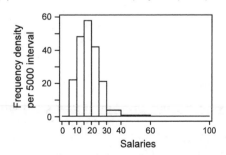

continued

EXAMPLE 2.6 *continued*

Both distributions are positively skewed as might be expected for salaries. The peak for the men occurs between £25 000 and £30 000 which is £10 000 more than that for the women. The top female salary is under £60 000 which is £40 000 less than that of the top male even though, at the other extreme, the minimum values are the same.

Relative frequency polygons

Table 2.9

Salary (£000)		Male employees	Relative frequency (%)	Female employees	Relative frequency (%)
Class interval	Mid-interval	Frequency	(%)	Frequency	(%)
5 and less than 10	7.5	4	1.6	21	10.5
10 and less than 15	12.5	12	4.8	48	24.0
15 and less than 20	17.5	36	14.4	58	29.0
20 and less than 25	22.5	64	25.6	42	21.0
25 and less than 30	27.5	77	30.8	21	10.5
30 and less than 40	35.0	35	14.0	8	4.0
40 and less than 60	50.0	18	7.2	2	1.0
60 and less than 100	80.0	4	1.6	0	0.0
Total		250	100%	200	100%

As would be expected, the frequency polygons lead to exactly the same interpretation as the histograms. The polygons show both sets of data to be positively distributed with the peak for males higher than that for females. The comparison is easier to make with polygons, than with histograms, as the position of the peak is clearer.

Figure 2.17 Relative frequency polygons for male (—) and female (- -) salaries

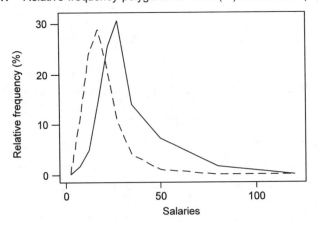

Stem-and-leaf plots

There is more data in this example than is usually illustrated by stem-and-leaf plots. The first plot in Figure 2.18 is for the male salaries (Sex = 1). There are 250 cases, each represented by one leaf. The units we are working with are £1000, so the first leaf represents £7000 and the last £85 000. The longest column, between £25 000 and

continued

EXAMPLE 2.6 *continued*

£30 000, contains 77 cases but you can see by the '+' that it has been cut off as being too long for the graph, so the 'shape' of the plot is a bit misleading.

The second plot for the females (Sex = 2) shows the salaries to range from £5000 to £55 000 with those most common between £15 000 and £20 000.

In this display format, the Minitab version, the left column displays the cumulative frequency starting at each extreme.

Stem-and-leaf plots can be more informative if drawn 'back to back' with a common 'stem' but neither Minitab or SPSS offer this format.

Figure 2.18 Stem-and-leaf displays

```
Stem-and-leaf of Salary    Sex = 1    N = 250
Leaf Unit = 1.0

    4   0   7788
   16   1   001122333444
   52   1   55555556666666777777788888889999999
  116   2   0000001111111111122222222222223333333333334444444444444444444444
 (77)   2   5555555555555555555555555555566666666666666677777777777777788888888888+
   57   3   00000111112234
   43   3   66666777778888899999
   22   4   1234
   18   4   56789
   13   5   234
   10   5   667889
    4   6   0
    3   6
    3   7   1
    2   7
    2   8   2
    1   8   5

Stem-and-leaf of Salary    Sex = 2    N = 200
Leaf Unit = 1.0

   21   0   555555555666667777788
   69   1   000000001111111222222222222222333333333344444444444
  (58)   1   5555555566666666666666667777777777777778888888888888889999999
   73   2   000000001111111122222222233333333334444444444
   31   2   66666677777788888889999
   10   3   3
    9   3   5555668
    2   4
    2   4   7
    1   5
    1   5   5
```

Box plots

The box plots in Figure 2.19 illustrate both the centres of the data and also the spreads.

The lowest values are similar for both sexes. The centre for the females is lower than that for the males. The total spread for the males is greater than that for females but the width of the 'box' is wider for the females. We are mainly interested in the spread of the 'box' and this will be interpreted further in Chapter 3.

There are many more male outliers than female. The case numbers for these are given but, as in this instance the data was input in order of increasing salary magnitude, they are all in numerical order! This numbering of cases can be useful for identification purposes.

continued

EXAMPLE 2.6 *continued*

Figure 2.19 Box plots for comparing male and female salaries

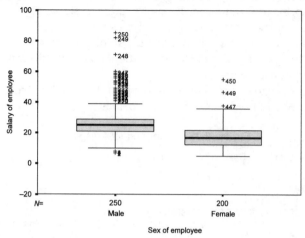

Cumulative percentage diagrams

Cumulative frequencies and cumulative percentages are first calculated.

Table 2.10

Salary (£000)	Male employees			Female employees		
		Cumulative	Cumulative		Cumulative	Cumulative
Interval	Frequency	frequency	%	Frequency	frequency	%
5 and less than 10	4	4	1.6	21	21	10.5
10 and less than 15	12	16	6.4	48	69	34.5
15 and less than 20	36	52	20.8	58	127	63.5
20 and less than 25	64	116	46.4	42	169	84.5
25 and less than 30	77	193	77.2	21	190	95.0
30 and less than 40	35	228	91.2	8	198	99.0
40 and less than 60	18	246	98.4	2	200	100.0
60 and less than 100	4	250	100.0	0	200	100.0
Total	250			200		

In order to compare male and female salaries the cumulative percentages are plotted on the same graph.

Figure 2.20 Cumulative percentages for male (—) and female (- -) salaries

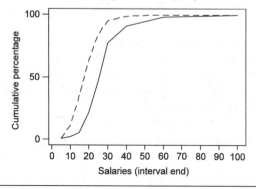

continued

EXAMPLE 2.6 *continued*

We can see that the female salaries rise first, showing that they peak at a lower salary than do the males. In Chapter 3 we shall produce much more information for comparing the salaries from these graphs.

This graphical exploration of data has enabled us to see that males and females do not, in general, earn similar salaries. Do note that it does not, however, tell us anything about their opportunities for advancement so should not be employed in this context.

We have only used graphical comparisons in this chapter. In the next, numerical summaries will enable us to quantify any differences we have identified here.

2.7 Interpretation of published graphs

This section is included mainly as a warning. Take the greatest care when reading published graphs as the author may have a vested interest in their interpretation.

As stated previously for pictograms, you need to be clear how many dimensions are being used in any comparisons. If Box A is twice as long as Box B does it indicate the ratio between them to be 2:1 for length, 4:1 for area or 8:1 for volume?

If comparing histograms, is zero frequency on the vertical axis or are just the column tops being shown? 110 might appear to be double 105 if the base line is at 100. In line graphs the lack of an origin can lead to misinterpretation making the gradient appear excessive.

The list is endless. Books which have been written on the misuse of statistics always devote quite a large section to graphs (Reichman, 1964; Huff, 1991).

2.8 Further methods of graphical description

This chapter has actually included most of the simple graphical presentations. These can be combined in various clever ways to include more information but do be sure, before selecting one for use, that it also conveys this extra information to the recipient. Histograms and stem-and-leaf diagrams can be drawn 'back to back' very usefully for comparing, say, male and female earnings.

In this chapter we have considered only one variable at a time. In Chapter 9 you will meet scatter diagrams which look for associations between two variables. With suitable software this can be extended to three variables, although the resulting graph is not easy to interpret.

More sophisticated forms of statistical analysis, such as factor analysis, have their own graphical output but these will not concern you at this stage.

2.9 Summary

In this chapter we have looked at various ways of presenting data in graphical form. The choice of presentation depends mainly on the scale of measurement of the data (see Table 2.11).

Computer graphical description is included in Worksheets 15.2.1, 15.5.1 and 15.8.1.

Table 2.11

Scale of measurement	Suitable graphical presentation
Nominal	Bar chart, dot plot, pie chart
Ordinal	Bar chart, dot plot, pie chart, box and whisker plot
Interval or ratio	Box and whisker plot, stem-and-leaf plot, histogram, frequency polygon, cumulative frequency polygon

2.10 Tutorial 2 – Graphical presentation

Answers in Appendix A1.

Note: The diagrams drawn in this tutorial will be used in the next to estimate various summary statistics for the same sets of data.

2.1 The following information refers to the number of defective components in 350 boxes.

No. of defective components:	0	1	2	3	4	5	6
No. of boxes:		25	85	99	70	51	14	6

(a) Draw a histogram to represent this data.

(b) Draw a cumulative frequency diagram to represent this data.

2.2 The following figures represent the ages of a sample of 60 male employees:

```
35  44  54  33  46  20  32  19  50  39  33  37
42  40  20  25  34  52  27  22  18  40  23  17
41  45  21  34  49  27  60  46  32  58  23  52
24  64  41  47  54  37  40  41  40  36  46  29
34  39  39  40  37  50  41  34  47  34  45  36
```

(a) Form a grouped frequency distribution, using 10 year intervals.

(b) Construct a histogram to illustrate the distribution of the data.

(c) Add a frequency polygon to your histogram.

(d) Construct a stem-and-leaf diagram with this data.

(e) Draw a percentage cumulative frequency diagram of the data.

2.3 The following table refers to the height of 50 students in a class:

Height (inches)	Frequency
60 and less than 64	2
64 and less than 66	6
66 and less than 68	11
68 and less than 69	9
69 and less than 70	10
70 and less than 72	8
72 and less than 74	2
74 and less than 80	2

(a) Form a frequency density distribution.

(b) Draw a histogram to represent the data.

(c) Draw a percentage cumulative frequency polygon of the data.

2.11 Supplementary exercise 2

Note: Keep your graphs for use in Chapter 3 for the estimation of summary statistics.

2.4 The table shows the salaries (£000) for a sample of 300 employees.

Salary (£000)	Number of employees
0 and less than 10	35
10 and less than 20	75
20 and less than 30	96
30 and less than 40	42
40 and less than 50	52

(a) Draw a histogram to represent this data.

(b) Add a frequency polygon to the histogram.

(c) Form a cumulative frequency table and use it to construct a cumulative frequency polygon.

2.5 In a work study exercise for a hotel group a manager observed the following times, in seconds, being taken to compile customer bills.

155	246	255	196	366	270	172	262	262	206
263	296	325	142	202	322	250	456	330	224
186	112	115	127	266	266	415	316	325	292
217	235	72	177	281	210	192	202	49	316
261	352	256	311	346	78	441	364	211	231

(a) Draw up a frequency distribution table using classes widths of 50 and from it draw a histogram of the data.

(b) Draw a cumulative frequency diagram of the data.

2.6 The profits of a sample taken from a group of hotels in a consortium were organised into the following table:

Range of profits	Number of hotels
less than £20 000	3
£20 000 and less than £30 000	5
£30 000 and less than £40 000	10
£40 000 and less than £50 000	21
£50 000 and less than £60 000	12

(a) Draw up a frequency density table for this data and draw a histogram.

(b) Form a cumulative frequency distribution and draw a cumulative frequency ogive.

2.7 The take-home pay (£) of 40 manual workers from a company for a particular week was:

482	392	499	412	440	444	420	418
446	540	394	365	412	458	428	484
482	394	450	444	440	494	436	420
460	425	500	390	414	354	554	475
390	460	422	500	470	428	380	463

(a) Construct a grouped frequency distribution.

(b) Draw a histogram.

(c) Draw a frequency polygon.

(d) Draw a percentage cumulative frequency ogive.

2.8 The two frequency distributions below represent the examination scores of a sample taken from each of two consecutive year groups of Business Studies students. Compare them graphically.

Examination scores	Frequency Year 1	Frequency Year 2
less than 30	5	2
30 and less than 40	14	8
40 and less than 50	29	20
50 and less than 60	20	35
60 and less than 70	8	15
70 and over	4	10

(a) Construct frequency density tables for both groups.

(b) Draw histograms for each group on the same diagram.

(c) Draw frequency polygons for each group on the same diagram.

(d) Construct cumulative percentage tables for each group.

(e) Draw cumulative percentage ogives for both groups on the same diagram.

3 Numerical Summary of Data

3.1 The objectives of this chapter

In Chapter 2 you learned how to represent a set of data by a single graph. In this chapter you will learn how to summarise the many values in a data set by just one or two. This summary usually describes the centre of the data and how far the individual values are spread each side of that centre. The measures of centrality we shall study will be mode, median and mean, and the measures of spread will be range, interquartile range, semi-interquartile range and standard deviation. We shall concentrate on the mean and standard deviation. You will learn to estimate these figures from graphs and calculate them from raw data. You will also learn to use a statistical calculator.

After studying this chapter you should know which measures of centrality and spread are appropriate for any given data set, how to calculate them by hand and on your calculator, and how to interpret the values produced.

3.2 Introduction: why summarise data numerically?

We repeat the question asked in Chapter 2: how do you react when faced with a large table full of figures? The graphs in the last chapter should have helped your understanding of given data sets. The problem is that a graph cannot be communicated very simply to another person either verbally or in writing. If, however, we make a statement such as the average mark obtained in an examination is 65 and the marks ranged from 40 to 75 the recipient gains a reasonable understanding of the situation. In this example the figure of 65 gives an idea of the general **location** of the data and the range of 40 to 75 a measure of its **dispersion** about its centre.

3.3 Measures of centrality (location)

In this section we look for a single figure to represent the whole data set. This is often called the **average** but in statistics different averages are calculated for different types of data so we need to be more specific as to which 'average' we intend.

3.3.1 Mode

The **mode** is the most commonly occurring value. (Think of the old-fashioned term 'mode' meaning fashion or that which is most commonly worn.) This measure of average is suitable for all different types of data from nominal to ratio (see Section 1.4).

We can count males and females and report the higher frequency; we can see from the charts which pop song is most popular; historically we know the most common degree classification awarded. Each of these results is a **modal** value, usually referred to simply as the mode. To find the mode of a set of numbers we just find which number has the highest frequency.

The numbers 1, 1, 1, 2, 2, 3, 4, 4, 6 would have a modal value of 1 as that number occurs more often than any other.

In a histogram the modal value occurs within the highest peak (see Section 3.5).

3.3.2   Median

Since the **median** is the middle member of a data set we must be able to place the data in some meaningful order. This measure is therefore, not suitable for nominal data. The most popular, or modal, pop song is meaningful but the middle, or **medial**, pop song is not. If a data set can be ordered then we can pick the middle member as being typical of it. We can find the degree classification of the middle member of a class; we can identify the athlete who finished the race in the middle of the field; we can find the middle child in a class placed in height order. To find the median of a set of numbers we just place them in order and find the middle one for an odd number of values, or the average of the middle two for an even number of values.

The numbers 1, 1, 1, 2, 2, 3, 4, 4, 6 would have a median of 2 as that is the middle value when they are placed on order.

In a histogram the median would split the area of the histogram into two equal halves. In a cumulative frequency polygon it is the 50th percentile (see Section 3.5).

3.3.3   Mean

The **mean** is the value usually referred to as the 'average'. It is found by adding all the values and dividing their sum by the number of values contributing to it:

$$\bar{x} = \frac{\Sigma x}{n} \tag{3.1}$$

where $\bar{x}$ is the mean, x is a data value, Σ (sigma) is the shorthand symbol for 'the sum of' and n is the number of values. The values must be measurable on an interval or ratio scale for the addition to be valid. The mean is not suitable for nominal or ordinal data. For example it makes no sense to calculate the mean sex of the members of a class even if numerical codes are used to identify males and females separately. We can calculate a mode and median for degree classifications in a year group but a mean value is not valid.

In business matters, the mean is the usual measure of the financial average. It is the only average given by a statistical calculator although mode and median may be produced by a computer package. The mean is the measure of centrality that will be used throughout this course although you should familiarise yourself with the median and the mode also.

The numbers 1, 1, 1, 2, 2, 3, 4, 4, 6 would have a mean value of $24/9 = 2.67$ as the sum of the 9 values is 24.

EXAMPLE 3.1   A small set of individual numbers

The following values represent the number of faulty garments returned to a store per day during a certain period:

13, 9, 10, 6, 7, 12, 4, 13, 14, 6, 9, 4, 8, 3, 10

The store manager needs to find some useful measure of centrality, an average, in order to summarise them.

A useful step is to rewrite them in ascending order, giving:

3, 4, 4, 6, 6, 7, 8, 9, 9, 10, 10, 12, 13, 13, 14

This data has five **modes** as the numbers 4, 6, 9, 10 and 13 all appear twice.

There are an odd number of values (15), so the **median** is the middle number that is, the 8th, giving 9. The easiest way to find the middle is to add one to the number of values and then divide the result by two, that is, $(15 + 1)/2 = 8$. (Had there been 14 values (an even number), the **median** would have been half way between the middle two, that is, the mean the 7th and the 8th.)

The **mean** is found by adding all the returns together and dividing by the number of days during which they were returned.

$$\frac{3+4+4+6+6+7+8+9+9+10+10+12+13+13+14}{15} = \frac{128}{15} = 8.53$$

Which of these measures is most useful to the store manager?

The mode is no use because there are five modes in this data. The median is a reasonable measure because it is fairly central, but the mean is a better representation of all the daily returns because all the data have been used to calculate it.

EXAMPLE 3.2   Discrete grouped data

If the number of returns were recorded for a whole year, the data would be summarised in a frequency table (see Section 2.3) rather than as individual values:

Table 3.1

Number of returns (x)	0	3	4	5	6	7	8	9	10	11	12	13	14
Number of days (f)	2	7	9	12	24	40	75	98	56	25	14	2	1

The **mode** of this data is the most common number of returns made per day. We can see that 9 garments were returned on 98 occasions, so 9 is the modal number of returns.

The **median** is the number of returns on the middle day. We have 365 days in total so the middle day will be $(365 + 1)/2 = 183$. A running total of days will show that 8 returns or less occur on 169 days and 9 returns or less on 267 days, so 9 garments would be returned on the 183rd day.

In order to find the **mean** number of returns per day we need the total number of returns to be divided by 365 days.

In symbolic form $\bar{x} = \dfrac{\Sigma fx}{n}$ (3.2)

where $\bar{x}$ is the mean and Σfx is the product of each data value and its frequency. This is an extension of equation (3.1).

continued

EXAMPLE 3.2 *continued*

Table 3.2

Number of returns (x)	0	3	4	5	6	7	8	9	10	11	12	13	14
Number of days (f)	2	7	9	12	24	40	75	98	56	25	14	2	1
fx	0	21	36	60	144	280	600	882	560	275	168	26	14

$$\bar{x} = \frac{\Sigma fx}{n} = \frac{21 + 36 + 60 + 144 + 280 + 600 + 882 + 560 + 275 + 168 + 26 + 14}{365} = \frac{3066}{365} = 8.4$$

Fortunately we do not always need to find the mean by this type of calculation once the method is fully understood. It is preferable to use a statistical calculator in standard deviation mode. The processes of inputting the data values, x, and outputting the value for the mean, $\bar{x}$, will vary from one make of calculator to another, especially when dealing with frequency data, so make sure that you read the instruction booklet for your particular calculator.

First work through Example 3.1 inputting the separate values, x, and outputting their mean value, $\bar{x}$ (its exact value is 8.53 recurring). Next work through Example 3.2, frequency data, making sure that you input the pairs of numbers in the order specified by your calculator instructions, and check that you get the same value, 8.40, for the mean.

EXAMPLE 3.3   Continuous grouped data

Suppose the previous store belonged to a country-wide chain and the distribution describing the value of returned garments for the year was:

Table 3.3

Value of returns (£00)	Number of days
less than 20	6
20 and less than 30	17
30 and less than 40	38
40 and less than 50	53
50 and less than 60	79
60 and less than 70	94
70 and less than 80	53
80 and less than 100	25
100 or more	0

The **modal class** is the class interval within which we find the highest number of days, that is, '60 and less than 70' returns. We shall see in Section 3.5 how to estimate a more precise value within this interval.

The **medial class** is the one within which we find the middle number of days: $(365 + 1)/2 = 183$. By calculating a running total of the number of days, we find that the 183rd day occurs in the interval '50 and less than 60' (£00). This median will be estimated more precisely in Section 3.5.

continued

EXAMPLE 3.3 *continued*

The **mean** requires the total value of garments returned to be divided by the total number of days. As in Example 3.2 the frequency is the number of days on which a certain value of garments was returned. But what should we use for the value of x? We cannot input a range into a calculator so we use the mid-point of the interval to represent all the values within it. The total value of returns in any range can be calculated to be fx as before. As previously $\Sigma fx/n$ gives the mean. A sensible lower limit for the lowest interval is zero and that for the highest interval is irrelevant as its frequency is zero.

Table 3.4

Number of returns	Number of days	Midpoint (x)	fx
less than 20	6	10	60
20 and less than 30	17	25	425
30 and less than 40	38	35	1 330
40 and less than 50	53	45	2 385
50 and less than 60	79	55	4 345
60 and less than 70	94	65	6 110
70 and less than 80	53	75	3 975
80 and less than 100	25	90	2 250
100 or more	0		0
Total	365		20 880

The mean value is therefore $\dfrac{\Sigma fx}{n} = \dfrac{20880}{365} = 57.2$ (£00).

Once the mathematical method has been understood, it is preferable, to use a statistical calculator in standard deviation mode. These vary considerably in their methods of dealing with frequency data so be sure to consult your calculator booklet and input the interval mid-point and frequency as a pair of values in the correct order. Check that you get the correct answer which is 57.205 5 before rounding off to a more appropriate number of significant figures.

Further complete worked examples of each type follow in Section 3.4.

3.4 Measures of spread

A measure of centrality alone is not sufficient to describe a set of measurements. We also need to say how their values are dispersed about that centre. For example, the two sets of numbers 21, 22, 23, and 6, 22, 38 both have mean and median values of 22 but, clearly, describe sets of data which vary considerably in spread. In order to find any measure of spread, the data must be measurable on the ordinal scale at least. Nominal data cannot be meaningfully ordered so it is impossible to identify a spread. In this chapter we shall consider range, interquartile range and standard deviation as the main measures of dispersion.

3.4.1 Range

The **range** of a set of data is simply the total width of its spread, that is, the largest value less the smallest value. The range is however a poor measure of spread as it only takes into account the two extreme data values. The two sets of data 21, 22, 23 and 6, 22, 38 have ranges of $23 - 21 = 2$ and $38 - 6 = 32$, respectively. The second has a much larger spread than the first.

3.4.2 Interquartile range

The **interquartile range** avoids using only the extremes as it describes the spread of just the middle half of the ordered data. The ordered data is split into quarters with the same number of values in each. The quartiles are the values which divide the distribution into these four equal parts: the first quartile, Q_1, is the value below which 25% of the observations lie; the second quartile, Q_2, is the median or middle value and Q_3 has 75% of the observations below and 25% above it. The interquartile range is therefore the difference between the third and first quartile, $= Q_3 - Q_1$. Some books also quote the **semi-interquartile range** which, as its name suggests, is $(Q_3 - Q_1)/2$.

As a simple illustration; consider for the eleven ordered numbers 2, 2, 3, 5, 5, 5, 6, 6, 7, 7, 7. The first quartile, Q_1, is the $[(11 + 1)/4] = $ 3rd number (3); the median, Q_2, is the $[(11 + 1)/2] = $ 6th value (5); the third quartile, Q_3, is the $[(11 + 1)3/4] = $ 9th value (7). The interquartile range is therefore $7 - 3 = 4$. The semi-interquartile range would be $4/2 = 2$. This idea has been demonstrated with a very small data set; a larger data set is needed to make these measures more meaningful as they are less influenced by individual values.

Graphically an interquartile range is estimated from a cumulative frequency diagram, as we shall see in Section 3.5.

3.4.3 Population standard deviation

The **standard deviation** is, as the name implies, the standard measure of spread used in statistics. The population standard deviation is the figure calculated when we have all the data, that is, the whole population of interest, in the analysis. It is most conveniently produced with the aid of a statistical calculator, using the $x\sigma_n$ button. We will generally use a calculator in this course to calculate standard deviation but we shall work through a few examples by hand in order to aid understanding.

The standard deviation is also known as 'root mean square deviation' and is calculated by squaring and then adding the deviations from the mean, finding the mean of the squared deviations, and then square-rooting the result.

$$s = \sqrt{\frac{\Sigma(x - \bar{x})^2}{n}} \quad \text{or} \quad s = \sqrt{\frac{\Sigma f(x - \bar{x})^2}{n}} \text{ for frequency data} \tag{3.3}$$

x	represents the value of the data
f	is the frequency of that particular value
$\bar{x}$	is the shorthand way of writing 'mean'
s	is the shorthand way of writing 'standard deviation'
Σ	is the shorthand way of writing 'the sum of'.
$\sqrt{}$	means 'take the positive square root'. The negative root has no meaning when describing spread.

The standard deviation is therefore a measure of how closely the data is grouped about the mean: the larger the standard deviation wider the spread of data. It is a measure of how well the mean represents the whole data set.

An equivalent formula which is often used is:

$$s = \sqrt{\frac{\Sigma x^2}{n} - \left(\frac{\Sigma x}{n}\right)^2} \quad \text{or} \quad s = \sqrt{\frac{\Sigma fx^2}{n} - \left(\frac{\Sigma fx}{n}\right)^2} \text{ for frequency data} \qquad (3.4)$$

We shall now find measures of spread for the data sets in Examples 3.1 to 3.3.

EXAMPLE 3.1 *continued*   A small set of individual numbers

The small set of individual data for faulty garments returned is:

3, 4, 4, 6, 6, 7, 8, 9, 9, 10, 10, 12, 13, 13, 14

The **range** is the largest value minus the smallest value $= 14 - 3 = 11$ garments
For the interquartile range we must first establish which are the quartiles.

There are 15 numbers so the quartiles, Q_1, Q_2, and Q_3 are the values of the $\frac{15+1}{4}$th,

the $\frac{2(15+1)}{4}$th, and the $\frac{3(15+1)}{4}$th observations, that is, the 4th, the 8th, and the 12th

observations respectively. These have the values 6, 9 and 12, respectively, giving $Q_1 = 6$, $Q_2 = 9$ and $Q_3 = 12$ garments.

The interquartile range is therefore $Q_3 - Q_1 = 12 - 6 = 6$ garments
The **standard deviation** is a measure of dispersion about the mean, $\bar{x}$, which we have already found to be 8.53 garments.

Table 3.5

x	$x - \bar{x}$	$(x - \bar{x})^2$
3	−5.53	30.58
4	−4.53	20.52
4	−4.53	20.52
6	−2.53	6.40
6	−2.53	6.40
7	−1.53	2.34
8	−0.53	0.28
9	+0.47	0.22
9	+0.47	0.22
10	+1.47	2.16
11	+2.47	6.10
12	+3.47	12.04
13	+4.47	19.98
13	+4.47	19.98
14	+5.47	29.92
	Total	177.66

continued

EXAMPLE 3.1 *continued*

The standard deviation $\sqrt{\dfrac{\sum(x-\bar{x})^2}{n}}$ is therefore $\dfrac{\sqrt{177.66}}{15} = \sqrt{11.844} = 3.44$ garments

Using your calculator in SD mode and following your instruction booklet carefully, input this individual data and output the **population standard deviation**, $x\sigma_n$. You should find that you get 3.40. This is the correct figure; the difference is due to rounding errors in the hand calculation of the mean.

EXAMPLE 3.2 *continued* Discrete grouped data

Table 3.1 has been repeated. The mean value is 8.40 returns.

Table 3.1

Number of returns	0	3	4	5	6	7	8	9	10	11	12	13	14
Number of days	2	7	9	12	24	40	75	98	56	25	14	2	1

The standard deviation is calculated using the formula for frequency data.

Table 3.6

Number of returns (x)	Number of days (f)	$x - \bar{x}$	$(x - \bar{x})^2$	$f(x - \bar{x})^2$
0	2	−8.40	70.56	141.12
3	7	−5.40	29.16	204.12
4	9	−4.40	19.36	174.24
5	12	−3.40	11.56	138.72
6	24	−2.40	5.76	138.24
7	40	−1.40	1.96	78.40
8	75	−0.40	0.16	12.00
9	98	+0.60	0.36	35.28
10	56	+1.60	2.56	143.36
11	25	+2.60	6.76	169.00
12	14	+3.60	12.96	181.44
13	2	+4.60	21.16	42.32
14	1	+5.60	31.36	31.36
	Total 365			Total 1489.60

The standard deviation $\sqrt{\dfrac{\sum f(x-\bar{x})^2}{n}}$ is therefore $\sqrt{\dfrac{1489.60}{365}} = \sqrt{4.0811} = 2.020$ returns

Check this figure using your calculator. The correct figure is 2.020 17 giving 2.02 (3 s.f.)

EXAMPLE 3.3 continued   Continuous grouped data

As for the calculation for the mean, the midpoint of each interval is first identified as its typical value, x. The mean value of returns is 57.2 garments.

Table 3.7

Value of returns	Number of days	Midpoint (x)	$x - \bar{x}$	$(x - \bar{x})^2$	$f(x - \bar{x})^2$
less than 20	6	10	−47.2	2227.84	13 367.04
20 and less than 30	17	25	−32.2	1036.84	17 626.28
30 and less than 40	38	35	−22.2	492.84	18 727.92
40 and less than 50	53	45	−12.2	148.84	7 888.52
50 and less than 60	79	55	−2.2	4.84	382.36
60 and less than 70	94	65	+7.8	60.84	5 718.96
70 and less than 80	53	75	+17.8	316.84	16 792.52
80 and less than 100	25	90	+32.8	1075.84	26 896.00
100 or more	0				0.00
Totals	365				107 399.60

The standard deviation $\sqrt{\dfrac{\sum f(x - \bar{x})^2}{n}}$ is therefore $\sqrt{\dfrac{107.3996}{365}} = \sqrt{294.25} = 17.15$ (£00)

Check on your calculator. The exact figure should be 17.1536.

In practice the mean and standard deviation are found together using a calculator rather than separately, in the next examples we will calculate both parameters together.

EXAMPLE 3.4   Grouped discrete data

The frequency distribution in Table 3.8 shows the time during which costly machines in a computing laboratory were idle.

Find the mode, median and mean and standard deviation for the following set of data:

Table 3.8

Number of idle days (x)	Number of machines (f)	fx	$x - \bar{x}$	$(x - \bar{x})^2$	$f(x - \bar{x})^2$
0	5	0	−2.29	5.244	26.22
1	24	24	−1.29	1.664	39.94
2	30	60	−0.29	0.084	2.52
3	19	57	+0.71	0.504	9.58
4	10	40	+1.71	2.924	29.24
5	5	25	+2.71	7.344	36.72
6	2	12	+3.71	13.764	27.53
Total	95	218			171.75

continued

EXAMPLE 3.4 *continued*

Mode	= Most common number of idle days = 2 days
Median	= Middle (48th) number of idle days = 2 days

$$\textbf{Mean} \quad = \frac{\text{Total number of idle days}}{\text{Total number of machines}} = \frac{218}{95} = 2.29 \text{ days}$$

or, by calculator, $\bar{x} = 2.29474$, rounded to 2.29 days (3 s.f.)

The standard deviation $\sqrt{\dfrac{\sum f(x - \bar{x})^2}{n}}$ is therefore $\sqrt{\dfrac{171.75}{95}} = \sqrt{1.8079} = 1.34$ days (3 s.f.)

or, by calculator, standard deviation $= 1.34457$, rounded to 1.34 days (3 s.f.)

EXAMPLE 3.5   Grouped continuous data

A class of students were asked to keep a record of the time they spent at a computer in a particular week. Find the modal interval, the medial interval and the mean of these times.

Table 3.9

Time (minutes)	Number of students
less than 20	2
20 and less than 40	5
40 and less than 60	4
60 and less than 90	6
90 and less than 120	5
120 and less than 180	7
180 and less than 240	3
240 and less than 360	2
more than 360	1

First it is necessary to close the top interval so that its midpoint can be found. A reasonable value might be set at any time over 480 minutes which would make its width at least the same as that of the previous interval. We shall go for that value giving a midpoint of 420 minutes.

Table 3.10

Time (minutes)	Midpoint (x)	Number of students (f)	fx	$x - \bar{x}$	$(x - \bar{x})^2$	$f(x - \bar{x})^2$
less than 20	10	2	20	−106	11 236	22 472
20 and less than 40	30	5	150	−86	7396	36 980
40 and less than 60	50	4	200	−66	4356	17 424
60 and less than 90	75	6	450	−41	1681	10 086
90 and less than 120	105	5	525	−11	121	605
120 and less than 180	150	7	1050	+34	1156	8092
180 and less than 240	210	3	630	+94	8836	26 508
240 and less than 360	300	2	600	+184	33 856	67 712
more than 360	420	1	420	+304	92 416	92 416
Totals		35	4045			282 295

continued

EXAMPLE 3.5 *continued*

Modal interval	= Most common interval	= 120 to 180 minutes
Medial interval	= Interval including middle (18th) student	= 90 to 120 minutes
Mean	$= \dfrac{\text{total time}}{\text{total number of students}} = \dfrac{4045}{35} = 115.6$	= 116 minutes (3 s.f.)

or, by calculator, $\bar{x} = 115.571$, rounded to 116 minutes (3 s.f.)

The standard deviation $\sqrt{\dfrac{\Sigma f(x - \bar{x})^2}{n}}$ is therefore $\sqrt{\dfrac{282295}{35}} = \sqrt{8065.6} = 89.8$ minutes

or, by calculator, s = 89.8075, rounded to 89.8 minutes (3 s.f.)

3.4.4 Sample standard deviation

Most applied statistical work is based on the analysis of a sample because the data from the whole population of interest is rarely available. It is necessary to calculate the sample standard deviation as an estimate of the population standard deviation. It has been found that doing the calculation exactly as in the examples above results in a biased result. An unbiased – and more accurate – result is obtained from a slightly different formula with $n - 1$ as the denominator instead of n.

The unbiased formulae are:

$$s = \sqrt{\frac{\Sigma(x - \bar{x})^2}{n - 1}} \quad \text{or} \quad s = \sqrt{\frac{\Sigma f(x - \bar{x})^2}{n - 1}} \text{ for frequency data} \tag{3.5}$$

On the calculator we use the $x\sigma_{n-1}$ button. If the sample size is large there is very little difference between n and $n - 1$, but for a small sample it can make a considerable difference.

EXAMPLE 3.6   Sample standard deviations for Examples 3.1 to 3.5

Example 3.1

Population standard deviation = 3.44 (3.40 from calculator)
Sample standard deviation

$$s = \sqrt{\frac{\Sigma(x - x)^2}{n - 1}} = \sqrt{\frac{177.66}{14}} = \sqrt{12.69} = 3.56 \text{ (rounding errors)}$$

The calculator gives 3.5227 giving 3.52 (3 s.f.)

Example 3.2

Population standard deviation = 2.02 (2.02 from calculator)
Sample standard deviation

$$s = \sqrt{\frac{\Sigma f(x - \bar{x})^2}{n - 1}} = \sqrt{\frac{1489.6}{364}} = \sqrt{4.0923} = 2.02$$

The calculator gives 2.0229 giving 2.02 (3 s.f.)

continued

EXAMPLE 3.6 *continued*

Example 3.3

Population standard deviation = 17.2
Sample standard deviation

$$s = \sqrt{\frac{\Sigma f(x - \bar{x})^2}{n - 1}} = \sqrt{\frac{107399.6}{364}} = \sqrt{295.05} = 17.2$$

The calculator gives 17.177 giving 17.2 (3 s.f.)

Example 3.4

Population standard deviation = 1.34
Sample standard deviation

$$s = \sqrt{\frac{\Sigma f(x - \bar{x})^2}{n - 1}} = \sqrt{\frac{171.75}{94}} = \sqrt{1.827} = 1.35$$

The calculator gives 1.3517 giving 1.35 (3 s.f.)

Example 3.5

Population standard deviation = 89.81
Sample standard deviation

$$s = \sqrt{\frac{\Sigma f(x - \bar{x})^2}{n - 1}} = \sqrt{\frac{282295}{34}} = \sqrt{8302.8} = 91.1$$

The calculator gives 91.12 giving 91.1 (3 s.f.)

Notice that the sample standard deviations are each slightly larger than the corresponding population standard deviation. If you are not certain which of the two standard deviation buttons to use on your calculator, select the one that gives the larger value.

When the whole population is not available for analysis, as is usually the case, the sample standard deviation should be used. **We shall use the sample standard deviation** throughout the remainder of this course.

3.5 Estimation of summary statistics from graphs

In this section we shall use the histograms and cumulative frequency diagrams produced in Chapter 2. In practice it is obviously much quicker and more accurate to calculate the summary statistics directly from the raw data. If, however, you only have the graphs it is important to be able to make estimates from them instead.

The mode can be estimated more precisely within the modal interval from a histogram of continuous data and the median, other quartiles and interquartile range can be estimated from a cumulative frequency diagram.

3.5.1 *Estimating the mode from a histogram*

For discrete data the mode is simply the value which has the highest frequency. If the data is continuous and collected into a grouped frequency distribution, the mode must lie somewhere within the modal interval, that is, the interval with the highest frequency. The frequencies of the adjacent columns are used to estimate the mode within this interval on the assumption that it is more likely to lie nearer to the column with the higher frequency. Example 3.7 shows the modal class is now divided in the same ratio as the differences between the modal frequency and the frequency of the adjacent classes by drawing crossed diagonals on the protruding part of the longest column.

EXAMPLE 3.7   Estimating the mode from a histogram

Mileages covered by a fleet of vehicles (Example 2.3)

Figure 3.1   Histogram of mileages

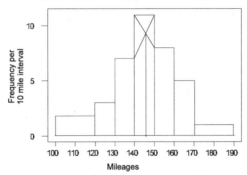

Because the 150 to 160 interval has a higher frequency than the 130 to 140 interval we would expect the mode to lie towards the right of the modal interval, 140 to 150. By drawing the diagonals to the tops of the adjacent columns we can see that they intersect at about 146 miles giving a more precise estimate for the mode. A larger, hand-drawn histogram will produce a better estimate than a small print-out.

Salaries of male and female employees (Example 2.6)

Figure 3.2   **Figure 3.3**

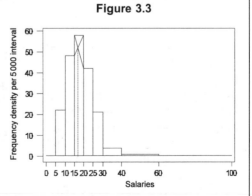

The modes of the male and female salaries are estimated to be £26 000 and £17 000 respectively. As stated previously, a larger diagram would be preferable.

3.5.2 *Estimating the median, quartiles and interquartile range from ogive*

The median divides the ordered data into two equal halves with 50 per cent of the observations above and 50 per cent below it. The median is called the 50th percentile. Similarly the lower quartile, Q_1, is the 25th percentile and the upper quartile, Q_3, is the 75th percentile. From a cumulative frequency diagram these values can be found by drawing horizontal lines from the 25%, 50% and 75%, or their equivalent cumulative frequency, values on the vertical axis to the graph; then drawing vertical lines from the points of contact to the horizontal axis and reading off the values.

EXAMPLE 3.8 Estimating the median, quartiles and interquartile range

Mileages covered by a fleet of vehicles

See Table 2.5 and Figure 2.12 in Example 2.5.

Since there are 40 observations in this data we can take the 10th, 20th and 30th cumulative values to correspond to Q_1, Q_2, and Q_3 respectively. Reading these from the graph gives the 134, 146 and 156, respectively.

The median is therefore 146 miles, the upper quartile 156 miles, the lower quartile 134 miles and the interquartile range $156 - 134 = 22$ miles. The semi-interquartile range is $22/2 = 11$ miles.

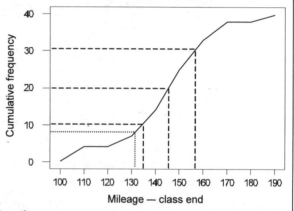

Figure 3.4 Cumulative frequency polygon for Fleet 1

We can also use this method for finding specific percentiles. For example, the number of vehicles travelling less than 131 hours $= 8$, or 20% of the whole fleet.

Salaries of male and female employees

See Figure 2.13 in Example 2.5.

These values are already plotted as percentiles. The estimated median salaries are £25 000 and £18 000 for males and females respectively. For males the upper and lower quartiles are £29 000 and £20 000 giving an interquartile range of £9000. For females the corresponding figures are £22 000 and £12 000, giving £10 000 as the interquartile range and £5000 as the semi-interquartile range. This shows that, although the females' salaries are lower, they have the larger spread.

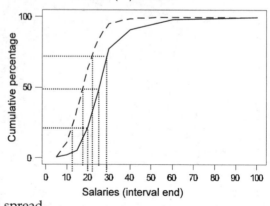

Figure 3.5 Cumulative percentages for male (—) and female (- -) salaries

3.6 Other summary statistics

3.6.1 *Centrality*

We have covered all the usual summary statistics in Sections 3.3 to 3.5. There are, however, a few more that are calculated in specialised circumstances.

In this chapter we have used the term 'mean' for the 'average' which is calculated by adding together all the values and dividing the result by the number of values, instead of the specific term, '**arithmetic mean**'.

The **geometic mean**, which is often used when handling index numbers, is calculated by multiplying the n values together and then finding the nth root. The **harmonic mean**, which is defined as 'the reciprocal of the arithmetic mean of the reciprocals of the data', is sometimes used when analysing ratios. **Weighted means** are calculated when it is desirable for the contribution of some of the data to be greater than that of the rest, perhaps because of size or importance. This is similar to the method for dealing with frequency data when the value is multiplied by the frequency, within each class, totalled and divided by the total number of values.

3.6.2 *Spread*

The most common summaries of spread are **standard deviation** for interval or ratio data and **interquartile range** for ordinal data. Another measure often used is **variance** which is the square of the standard deviation. This has the advantage of being easier to manipulate arithmetically than the standard deviation but is much more difficult to interpret in terms of units. For example, if the standard deviation of a group of salaries is in £000 then the variance is in $(£000)^2$!

The **mean absolute deviation** is the average size of deviation from the means of each value. We cannot use the average deviation as a measure of spread because the positive and negative deviations cancel out but the size of deviation can be used if the signs are ignored. The mean absolute deviation is a sensible measure as it takes all the data into account but absolute values are difficult to manipulate arithmetically so it is not in general usage. One measure which is used, especially in financial circles, is the **coefficient of variation**. This measures relative dispersion as it calculates the standard deviation as a percentage of the mean and so cuts out the effect of factors such as inflation.

3.6.3 *Skewness*

Figure 3.6

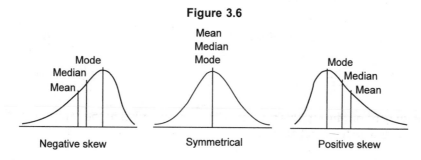

| Negative skew | Symmetrical | Positive skew |

The ordering of the mode, median and mean determines the skewness of any data distribution. In Section 2.5.2 we looked at the skewness of a distribution as illustrated by a histogram or frequency polygon (see Figure 2.8).

The **coefficient of skewness** is calculated from the formula: $\dfrac{3(\text{mean} - \text{median})}{\text{standard deviation}}$

You can see from the formula that the greater the deviation of the median from the mean is the more skewed is the data.

These other summary statistics are described in more detail in many textbooks on statistics (Weimer, 1993, Chapter 3).

3.7 Computer numerical summary of Example 3.1

Minitab output

Descriptive statistics

Variable	N	Mean	Median	TrMean	StDev	SE Mean
Returns	15	8.533	9.000	8.538	3.523	0.910

Variable	Minimum	Maximum	Q1	Q3
Returns	3.000	14.000	6.000	12.000

SPSS output

Descriptives

			Statistic	Std. Error
Number of garments returned	Mean		8.53	.91
	95% Confidence Interval for Mean	Lower Bound	6.58	
		Upper bound	10.48	
	5% Trimmed Mean		8.54	
	Median		9.00	
	Variance		12.410	
	Std. Deviation		3.52	
	Minimum		3	
	Maximum		14	
	Range		11	
	Interquartile Range		6.00	
	Skewness		−.004	.580
	Kurtosis		−1.120	1.121

Instructions for producing this type of output are included in the computer worksheets 15.2.2, 15.5.2 and 15.8.2 in Chapter 15.

3.8 Summary

In this chapter we learned how to replace data sets by typical numbers, averages, representing them as an aid to better understanding. We have seen that statistics such as the mean, mode and median can provide easy-to-calculate, single measures of centrality, but that care must be exercised in selecting the most appropriate one to use for each type of data (see Table 3.11)

Measures of the variability of a data set about its centre are also important but you may have found them more difficult to understand. The most appropriate statistic also depended on the type of data: for ordinal data, it is usually the interquartile range about the median, and for interval or ratio data it is the standard deviation about the mean (see Table 3.11).

We also learned how to estimate summary statistics from graphically presented data although these are not as accurate as those calculated from the original data.

Table 3.11

Scale of measurement	Suitable summary statistics
Nominal	Mode; no measure of spread.
Ordinal	Mode, median; Range, interquartile range, semi-interquartile range.
Interval or ratio	Mode, median, mean (any type); Range, interquartile range, semi-interquartile range, standard deviation, any of the other statistics in Section 3.6

3.9 Calculator practice

Use your calculator in **standard deviation mode**, making reference to your instruction booklet until completely confident with the procedure. These questions are all asking for the calculation of the **mean** and the **sample standard deviation**.

1 The number of new orders received by a company over the last 25 working days were recorded as follows:

    3 0 1 4 4 4 2 5 3 6 4 5 1 4 2 3 0 2 0 5 4 2 3 3 1

Use your calculator to estimate the mean and standard deviation for the number of orders received over all similar working days.

2 The mileages recorded for a sample of company vehicles during a given week were:

138	164	150	132	144	125	149	157
146	158	140	147	136	148	152	144
168	126	138	176	163	119	154	165
146	173	142	147	135	153	140	135
161	145	135	142	150	156	145	128

Estimate the mean and standard deviation of the mileages of all the cars for the week.

3 The number of breakdowns each day on a section of road were recorded for a sample of 250 days as follows:

Number of breakdowns	0	1	2	3	4	5
Number of days	100	70	45	20	10	5

Estimate the mean and standard deviation for breakdowns on all days on that section of road.

4 Determine the means and standard deviations of the whole of Groups A and B from which these two samples have been taken:

Annual salary ($)	Number from Group A	Number from Group B
15 000 but under 20 000	5	0
20 000 but under 25 000	17	19
25 000 but under 30 000	21	25
30 000 but under 35 000	3	4
35 000 but under 40 000	1	0
40 000 but under 50 000	1	0

Answers

1 Mean = 2.84 orders   Standard deviation = 1.70 orders
2 Mean = 146.8 miles   Standard deviation = 13.05 miles
3 Mean = 1.14 breakdowns   Standard deviation = 1.25 breakdowns
4 Mean = (A) £25 600 (3 s.f.)   Standard deviation = (A) £5110
        (B) £25 900   (B) £3120

3.10 Tutorial 3 – Data summary

All tutorial answers are to be found in Appendix A1.

3.1 For the following set of numbers:

210   198   204   199   192   197   201   203   196

State   (a) the range,   (b) the median,
Calculate   (c) the mean,   (d) the population standard deviation

3.2 A rope manufacturer has the choice of two heavy denier continuous filament polyester yarns which are identical apart from yarn strength. He tests 12 bobbins from each type of yarn and obtains the following strengths (g/denier):

Yarn A   4.08 4.82 4.55 4.88 4.06 4.50 4.69 4.27 4.92 4.30 4.65 4.28
Yarn B   4.40 4.30 4.29 4.28 4.40 4.65 4.47 4.48 4.59 4.56 4.20 4.18

Calculate the mean, sample standard deviation and range for each yarn.

3.3 From the following information on the number of defective components in 1000 boxes, calculate the mean and standard deviation for the whole of the production line.

Number of defective components	0	1	2	3	4	5	6
Number of boxes	25	306	402	200	51	10	6

3.4 From the frequency distribution of the monthly viewing times of a sample television audience, calculate:

(a) the mean,

(b) the standard deviation, for the whole viewing audience.

Monthly viewing times (hours)	Number of viewers (hundreds)
50 and less than 54	2
54 and less than 58	7
58 and less than 62	11
62 and less than 66	12
66 and less than 70	9
70 and less than 74	6
74 and less than 78	2
78 and less than 82	1

3.5 The following are the IQ scores for a random sample of 11-year olds. Calculate the mean and standard deviation for all 11-year olds.

IQ (x)	80–84	85–89	90–94	95–99	100–104	105–109	110–114	115–119
Children (f)	8	13	22	24	11	10	7	5

3.6 For the data in Question 2.1 (p. 26), find the mode and median of the number of defective items produced.

3.7 For the graphs drawn for the data in Question 2.2 (p. 26), estimate the mode, median and interquartile range of the number of the ages of the employees. Find also the percentage of workers under 21 years old and the percentage of them who are over 50 years old.

3.8 For the graphs drawn for the data in Question 2.3 (p. 26), estimate the mode, median and interquartile range of the student heights. What percentage of the students are over 6 feet tall?

3.11 Supplementary exercise 3

These data sets are the same as those in Supplementary Exercise 2 so those graphs should be used for the estimations.

3.9 The table shows the salaries (£000) of the employees of a company.

Salary (£000)	Number of employees
0 and less than 10	35
10 and less than 20	75
20 and less than 30	96
30 and less than 40	42
40 and less than 50	52

(a) Estimate the modal salary from the histogram drawn for Question 2.4 (p. 27).

(b) Estimate the median from the cumulative frequency diagram drawn for Question 2.4.

(c) Estimate the quartile values and so calculate the interquartile range of the salaries.

(d) From the frequency data above calculate the mean salary and the standard deviation for the salaries of the whole company.

3.10 In a work study exercise for a hotel group a manager observed that the following times, in seconds, were taken to compile customer bills:

155	246	255	196	366	270	172	262	262	206
263	296	325	142	202	322	250	456	330	224
186	112	115	127	266	266	415	316	325	292
217	235	72	177	281	210	192	202	49	316
261	352	256	311	346	78	441	364	211	231

(a) From the frequency distribution already drawn up for this data in Question 2.5 (p. 27) calculate the mean and standard deviation of the compilation times.

(b) Estimate the modal time from the histogram.

(c) Estimate the median from the cumulative frequency diagram drawn for Question 2.5.

(d) Estimate the quartile values and, hence calculate the interquartile range of the compilation times.

(e) How many of the bills took over six minutes to compile?

3.11 The profits of a group of hotels in a consortium were organised into the following table:

Range of profits	Number of hotels
less than £20 000	3
£20 000 and less than £30 000	5
£30 000 and less than £40 000	10
£40 000 and less than £50 000	21
£50 000 and less than £60 000	12
£60 000 and less than £100 000	9

(a) Estimate the modal profit from the histogram drawn for Question 2.6 (p. 27).

(b) Estimate the median from the cumulative frequency diagram drawn for Question 2.6.

(c) Estimate the quartile values and so calculate the interquartile range of the profits.

(d) From the frequency data above calculate the mean profit and the standard deviation for the profits of the whole hotel group.

(e) Estimate the percentage of hotels that made more than £75 000 profit.

3.12 The take-home pay (£) of 40 manual workers from a company for a particular week was:

482	392	499	412	440	444	420	418
446	540	394	365	412	458	428	484
482	394	450	444	440	494	436	420
460	425	500	390	414	354	554	475
390	460	422	500	470	428	380	463

(a) From the frequency distribution drawn up for this data in Question 2.7 (p. 28) calculate the mean and standard deviation of the take-home pay.

(b) Estimate the modal take-home pay from the histogram.

(c) Estimate the median from the cumulative frequency diagram drawn for Question 2.7.

(d) Estimate the quartile values and so calculate the interquartile range of the take-home pay.

(e) What percentage of the workforce took home less than £400 per week?
What percentage of the workforce took home more than £500 per week?

3.13 The two frequency distributions below represent the examination scores of two consecutive year groups of Business Studies students.

Examination scores	Frequency Year 1	Frequency Year 2
less than 30	5	2
30 and less than 40	14	8
40 and less than 50	29	20
50 and less than 60	20	35
60 and less than 70	8	15
70 and over	4	10

(a) Estimate the modal exam scores for the two groups from the two histograms drawn for Question 2.8 (p. 28).

(b) Estimate the median marks from the cumulative frequency diagrams drawn for Question 2.8 (p. 28).

(c) Estimate the quartile marks and so calculate the interquartile range of the marks for each group.

(d) From the frequency data above calculate the mean and standard deviation of the marks for each group.

(e) What percentage of each of the year groups scored over 50%?

(f) Compare, in a single sentence, the performance of the two groups.

4 Probability

4.1 Objectives of this chapter

Many students find it difficult to make the transition from the **certainty of mathematics** to the **uncertainty of statistics**, so the main aim of this chapter is for you to gain some appreciation of the role played by probability in uncertain situations.

Having studied this chapter you should be able to use **symmetry** and **past frequencies** to calculate **probabilities** and **expected values**, and to use these decision making tools to make choices concerning the uncertain future.

4.2 Introduction: the role of probability in statistics

We all cope with uncertainty in everyday life by making risky decisions. Shall we carry an umbrella as we think it is **likely** to rain or **risk** getting wet? Do we allow 40 minutes for a journey because that will **probably** be long enough, or can we **risk** 30 minutes by assuming no hold-ups? Do we buy a particular share because the **chances** are that the price will rise? We make this subjective type of decision daily without the help of any quantitative evidence. In business it would be preferable to make objective decisions on the basis of numerical evidence in order to minimise risk and uncertainty. If we can replace 'unlikely', 'probably', 'risk' and 'chance' with values, then comparisons can be made and a more logical decision making process employed.

One of the main differences between mathematics and statistics is that mathematics deals with certainty whereas statistics is mainly concerned with uncertainty. In maths you carry out a calculation and state the answer. In statistics calculations are still performed but the answer usually includes some phrase such as 'it is likely that . . .', 'there is a 95% probability that . . .', 'we are 90% certain that . . .', etc. In other words black and white have been replaced by various shades of grey.

We may know the most probable life expectancy of the females in the United Kingdom but we have no idea how long any woman will live. Insurance tables are built up from what happens 'on average' but tell us nothing about individuals. The insurance company may possess a very good record of what has happened in the past, but cannot be certain of what will happen in the future either 'on average' or in any individual case. A firm may know its monthly sales for many years past but it cannot be certain what they will be for the next month; it can only make a reasonable **estimation**.

The role of statistics is to reduce uncertainty to a minimum, to produce the **best estimations possible** and to accompany them with some **measure of their uncertainty**. If the sales of some non-seasonal commodity for the past 24 months are known, what is the most likely value next month and how big a margin of error should be placed on that estimate? How do we choose between two types of machinery which will probably produce different returns at different times during their different lives? What effect is this choice likely to have? Alternatively, would the expected returns be better if money were simply invested?

In most circumstances we cannot analyse a whole population. For example strength testing of textile fibres is done on only a very small proportion as the process results in their destruction. We know the average strength of the yarns that were tested, but what about all the others? Because we rarely have perfect knowledge of an entire population estimations are unlikely to be completely accurate. A statistician will not be completely sure of his results so he will quote conclusions based on a sample and his confidence in them. This is usually quoted in terms of 'probability': there is a high probability (0.95) that the mean strength will be 5.0 g per denier. Alternatively, he might feel more comfortable stating that the mean strength lies somewhere between 4.8 g and 5.2 g per denier.

4.3 Probability as a measure of uncertainty

4.3.1 Measures of uncertainty

Probability **measures** the extent to which an event is likely to occur; it is the **numerical measure** of the **likelihood of its occurrence**.

- It can be measured by the ratio of favourable outcomes to non-favourable outcomes (**odds**)
- It is generally measured by the ratio of favourable outcomes to all possible outcomes (**probability**)

Probability can be **calculated** from various sources:

- simple probability calculated from **symmetry**
- simple probability calculated from **frequencies**
- conditional probability calculated from **contingency tables**
- conditional probability calculated from **tree diagrams**

4.3.2 Value of probability

Probability always has a value between 0 (impossibility) and 1 (certainty).

This can be summarised as $0 \leq P(E) \leq 1$ where $P(E)$ is the probability of an event occurring. An **event** may include more than one **outcome**, for example, for a die the event 'an even number' includes the three outcomes '2', '4', and '6'.

Probability of 0.0	corresponds to 'impossible'
0.1	corresponds to 'extremely unlikely'
0.5	corresponds to 'evens chance'
0.8	corresponds to 'very likely'
1.0	corresponds to 'certainty'

4.3.3 Assessing probability

- From symmetry based on the geometry, or symmetry, of the situation which gives an intuitive expectation – the **a priori approach**
- From past experience using relative frequencies – the **empirical approach**
- From 'gut feeling' – the **subjective approach**.

Let $P(E)$ be the probability of an event happening. By the a priori approach $P(E) = 1$ means that event E must always occur, there is no possible alternative outcome; by the empirical approach it means that it has always occurred up to now but that it is not inevitable; by the subjective approval it means that we feel certain that it will occur.

Let us take a numerical example. If a coin has landed 'heads up' 10 times out of the last 10 tosses, what is the probability of getting a head on the next toss of the same coin? The a priori method suggests 1/2, because 1/2 of the faces are heads; the empirical method gives $10/10 = 1$, because that has been the ratio of heads to all possible outcomes in the past; the subjective gut feeling is to doubt the fairness of the coin and so suggest that only a head is possible, that is, 1. Alternatively, the opposite gut feeling may be that a tail is definitely due, therefore 0!

4.4 Probability from symmetry

The theory of probability was developed in the gaming situation which depends upon the symmetry of dice, cards, roulette wheels, etc.

We can define the probability of an event E taking place as:

$$P(\text{event } E) = \frac{\text{Number of equally likely outcomes in which } E \text{ occurs}}{\text{Total possible number of equally likely outcomes}} \tag{4.1}$$

Invoking symmetry, there is no need to do any experiments. This is the reason for the term 'a priori', which means deductive or without investigation.

If we had a single die with the number 6 on four faces and the number 2 on the other two we would know from the geometry of the situation that the probability of getting an even number is **certainty**, that the probability of getting an odd number is **impossibility**, and that the probability of getting 6 is four chances out of six. The definition in Equation (4.1) therefore seems quite satisfactory in this case.

The shorthand version of this is:

- $P(\text{even number}) = 6/6 = 1$
- $P(\text{odd number}) = 0/6 = 0$
- $P(6) = 4/6$
- $P(2) = 2/6$

Note that for a set of **exhaustive** events – which cover all possibilities between them – the probabilities always **sum to unity,** that is, they always add up to 1.

In general terms: $$P(E) = \frac{r}{N} \tag{4.2}$$

where E is the event, r the number of favourable outcomes and N the number of possible outcomes. We shall look at some further examples from the gaming situation, even though their application is limited in the world of business, because this is the classic approach to probability.

EXAMPLE 4.1   Coins

Tossing 1 coin

Possibilities: head, tail $P(\text{a head}) = 1/2 = 0.5$ $P(\text{a tail}) = 1/2 = 0.5$

Tossing 2 coins

Possibilities: head head, head tail, tail head, tail tail

$P(2 \text{ heads}) = 1/4$ $P(2 \text{ tails}) = 1/4$ $P(1 \text{ head and } 1 \text{ tail}) = 2/4$

continued

EXAMPLE 4.1 *continued*

Tossing 3 coins

Possibilities: head head head,   head head tail, head tail head, head tail tail,
              tail head head,   tail tail head,   tail head tail,   tail tail tail

$P(3 \text{ heads}) = 1/8$ $P(2 \text{ heads}) = 3/8$ $P(1 \text{ head}) = 3/8$ $P(0 \text{ heads}) = 1/8$

$P(3 \text{ tails}) = 1/8$ $P(2 \text{ tails}) = 3/8$ $P(1 \text{ tail}) = 3/8$ $P(0 \text{ tails}) = 1/8$

Note that the sum of all the probabilities is always one. This makes sense. These sets are exhaustive so one of these outcomes **must** occur and $P(\text{certainty}) = 1$.

EXAMPLE 4.2   Dice

Rolling a single die

Possibilities: 1, 2, 3, 4, 5, 6

$P(6)$ $= 1/6$ $P(\text{anything but 6})$ $= 5/6$

$P(\text{an even number}) = 3/6$ $P(\text{an odd number}) = 3/6$

Again each pair of probabilities sums to 1.

Rolling a pair of dice

All possibilities are shown in a possibility space diagram (Figure 4.1). This is useful as the regular pattern makes the answers easy to find in rows, diagonals or columns.
   Make use of the fact that all possibilities sum up to 1, that is,

   $P(\text{no 4s}) = 1 - P(\text{at least one 4})$

Figure 4.1

```
1,1   1,2   1,3   1,4   1,5   1,6
2,1   2,2   2,3   2,4   2,5   2,6
3,1   3,2   3,3   3,4   3,5   3,6
4,1   4,2   4,3   4,4   4,5   4,6
5,1   5,2   5,3   5,4   5,5   5,6
6,1   6,2   6,3   6,4   6,5   6,6
```

$P(\text{any double}) = 6/36$
$P(\text{double 4}) = 1/36$
$P(\text{numbers add up to 4}) = 3/36$
$P(\text{numbers add up to less than 4}) = 3/36$
$P(\text{numbers add up to more than 4}) = 30/36$
$P(\text{at least one 4}) = 11/36$ $P(\text{no 4s}) = 25/36$
$P(\text{an even total}) = 18/36$ $P(\text{an odd total}) = 18/36$

EXAMPLE 4.3

Suppose 100 000 tickets are sold for a state lottery and you buy 50 of them, what is the probability that you will win a prize?

$$P(\text{winning}) = \frac{\text{Number of your tickets}}{\text{Total number of tickets}} = \frac{50}{100\,000} = 0.0005$$

In a more complicated situation, such as the rolling of three or four dice it is more convenient to combine the probabilities from each die than to list all possibilities.

4.4.1 Combining independent probabilities

If events are independent of each other then the probabilities are combined by multiplication. Events are independent if the outcome of one is not affected by the outcome of the others; for example, the result of rolling one die does not influence the result of rolling another die. The probability of throwing one four with one die is 1/6, so think of the probability of throwing a double four with two dice as being 'a sixth of a sixth', that is, $(1/6) \times (1/6) = (1/6)^2$.

EXAMPLE 4.4 Calculate probabilities for multiple dice

One throw

P(any one die scoring six in one throw) $= 1/6$

P(a score is not a six for one throw) $= 5/6$

Two throws

P(two sixes from two dice) $= 1/6 \times 1/6 = (1/6)^2$

P(one six from two dice) $\quad = 1/6 \times 5/6$ (if the first die is six)

$\qquad\qquad\qquad\qquad\quad + 5/6 \times 1/6$ (if the second die is six)

$\qquad\qquad\qquad\qquad = 2 \times (1/6)(5/6)$

P(no sixes from two dice) $\quad = 5/6 \times 5/6 = (5/6)^2$

Three throws

P(three sixes from three dice) $= 1/6 \times 1/6 \times 1/6 = (1/6)^3$

P(two sixes from three dice) $\quad = 1/6 \times 1/6 \times 5/6 + 5/6 \times 1/6 \times 1/6 + 1/6 \times 5/6 \times 1/6$

$\qquad\qquad\qquad\qquad\qquad = 3 \times (1/6)^2 \times (5/6)$

P(one six from three dice) $\qquad = 1/6 \times 5/6 \times 5/6 + 5/6 \times 1/6 \times 5/6 + 5/6 \times 5/6 \times 1/6$

$\qquad\qquad\qquad\qquad\qquad = 3 \times (1/6) \times (5/6)^2$

P(no sixes from three dice) $\quad = 5/6 \times 5/6 \times 5/6 = (5/6)^3$

Can you see the pattern emerging? The probability of one six from 5 dice is:

$$5 \qquad\qquad \times \qquad\qquad (1/6)^1 \qquad\qquad \times \qquad\qquad (5/6)^4$$

number of dice $\qquad$ one dice showing six $\qquad$ four dice not showing six

In general, if the probability of success in any one trial is p, the probability of getting r successes from n trials is:

$$\frac{n!}{r!(n-r)!} \times p^r (1-p)^{(n-r)} \qquad\qquad\qquad\qquad (4.3)$$

where $n!$ stands for factorial n, that is, $n \times (n-1) \times (n-2) \dots 2 \times 1$

For example

$$P(3 \text{ sixes in 5 throws}) = \frac{5!}{3!2!} \times \left(\frac{1}{6}\right)^3 \left(\frac{5}{6}\right)^2 = 10 \times \frac{5^2}{6^5} = 0.0322$$

This makes use of the **binomial distribution** (see Section 5.3.1). The coefficient $\frac{n!}{r!(n-r)!}$ can be found directly from many calculators and also without calculation using Pascal's triangle:

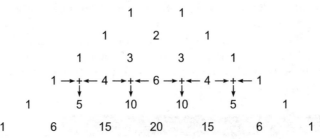

Figure 4.2 Pascal's triangle

Each line starts with the number 1, the next number is the sum of the numbers on either side of it in the previous line, and so on until it ends with another 1. If we threw 6 dice the sixth row of the coefficients would be used in calculating the probability of getting 0, 1, 2, 3, 4, 5 and 6 sixes respectively.

Find the following probabilities using the coefficients from the fourth row of Pascal's triangle

$P(4 \text{ sixes with 4 dice}) = 1 \times (1/6)^4 \times (5/6)^0 = 1/1296 \quad = 0.00077$

$P(3 \text{ sixes with 4 dice}) = 4 \times (1/6)^3 \times (5/6)^1 = 20/1296 \quad = 0.0154$

$P(2 \text{ sixes with 4 dice}) = 6 \times (1/6)^2 \times (5/6)^2 = 150/1296 = 0.1157$

$P(\text{less than 2 sixes with 4 dice}) = P(0 \text{ sixes}) + P(1 \text{ six})$

$$= 1 \times (1/6)^0 \times (5/6)^4 + 4 \times (1/6)^1 \times (5/6)^3$$

$$= 0.4823 + 0.3858 = 0.8681$$

Alternatively $\quad = 1 - (0.0008 + 0.0154 + 0.1157) = 0.8681$

By using equation (4.3) any combinations of independent probabilities can be calculated.

$P(\text{getting 3 sixes with 5 dice}) = \dfrac{5!}{3!2!} \times (1/6)^3 \times (5/6)^2 = 0.0322$

$P(\text{getting 3 sixes with 6 dice}) = \dfrac{6!}{3!3!} \times (1/6)^3 \times (5/6)^3 = 0.0536$

4.5 Probability from relative frequency

An alternative way to look at probability is to carry out an experiment to determine the proportion of favourable outcomes **in the long run**.

$$P(E) = \frac{\text{Number of times } E \text{ has occurred}}{\text{Number of times experiment was run}} \tag{4.4}$$

This is the **frequency definition of probability** and is referred to as the **empirical** approach. There is no way of estimating the probability without doing an experiment or observing past data. (Section 4.5.1 merely illustrates the procedure.)

Relative frequency is the proportion of all the **possible times** an event has **actually occurred**.

4.5.1 Estimating probability from long-term relative frequency

As the number of trials increases the relative frequency demonstrates a **long-term** tendency to settle down to a constant value. This value is the probability of the event. But, how long is this 'long term'?

Table 4.1 Relative cumulative frequencies recorded from tossing a single coin

Total number of throws	Result	Number of heads	Proportion of heads
1	H	1	1.00
2	H	2	1.00
3	T	2	0.67
4	T	2	0.50
5	H	3	0.60
6	T	3	0.50
7	H	4	0.57

We can see that the values of the relative frequency (proportion of heads) are converging. If we carry on in this manner for as many flips of the coin as it takes for the relative frequency to settle down, and then plot the result on graph paper, we might get a picture similar to Figure 4.3.

Figure 4.3 Proportion of heads

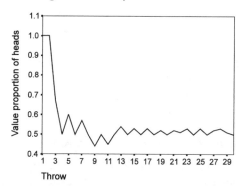

By about the 14th toss the proportion has settled down to about 0.5 which gives the long-term probability for the next outcome being a head.

The outcome of an individual trial is either 1 or 0 heads.

The long-term tendency gives the estimated probability.

More formally: If r trials out of n result in the event E, then the probability of the event E, assuming each outcome is equally likely, is:

$$P(E) = \frac{r}{n} \tag{4.5}$$

Note: n must be a large number because the accuracy of the estimate of probability improves as the sample size increases.

Suppose we produce a new type of ballpoint pen and wish to find the probability of any one pen being defective. The a priori approach is obviously no use as we have no prior knowledge. We therefore have to take the empirical approach of sampling the production and using the proportion of defective pens in the sample to estimate the probability of any one pen being found faulty.

4.5.2   *Estimating probability from frequency tables*

An alternative estimation of probability can be made from **frequency tables** (see Section 2.3)

EXAMPLE 4.5   Estimating probability from frequency

The data in Table 4.2 refer to the annual salaries of a group of workers.
Since the figures are not simple enough for mental arithmetic, it is advisable to calculate relative frequency. Cumulative relative frequency might also be useful.

Table 4.2

Annual salary (£)	Number of employees	Relative frequency	Cumulative relative frequency
5000 to <5500	3	0.03	0.03
5500 to <6000	4	0.04	0.07
6000 to <7000	7	0.07	0.14
7000 to <8000	11	0.11	0.25
8000 to <10 000	18	0.18	0.43
10 000 to <12 000	31	0.31	0.74
12 000 to <15 000	22	0.22	0.96
15 000 to <20 000	4	0.04	1.00
Total	100	1.00	

What is the probability that a worker chosen at random:

Earns over £15 000?	0.04 (from relative frequency)
Earns less than £10 000?	0.43 (from cumulative relative frequency)
Earns between £10 000 and £15 000?	0.96 − 0.43 = 0.53
Earns between £6000 and £12 000?	0.74 − 0.07 = 0.67

4.5.3   *Estimating probability from histograms*

A further alternative is that probability can be estimated from a **histogram** (see Section 2.5) frequency or frequency density. This method is particularly useful if the original data are not available.

EXAMPLE 4.6   Histograms

Figure 4.4 shows the time, to the nearest minute, it had taken an employee to get to work on 50 occasions. From this graph we can estimate the probability that the journey will take between any given lengths of time on the following day.

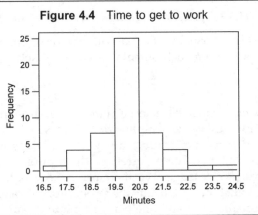

Figure 4.4   Time to get to work

continued

EXAMPLE 4.6 *continued*

From Figure 4.4 the probability of the journey taking between 19.5 and 20.5 minutes can be estimated to be $25/50 = 0.5$

What is the probability of taking:

less than 19.5 min?	$(1 + 4 + 7)/50 = 0.24$
less than 20.5 min?	$(1 + 4 + 7 + 25)/50 = 0.74$
more than 20.5 min?	$1 - 0.74 = 0.26$
between 19.5 and 21.5 min?	$(25 + 7)/50 = 0.64$

4.6 Probabilities from contingency tables

If we have mutually exclusive data on each variable the frequencies can be displayed in a **contingency table**. Mutually exclusive events can have only one outcome; for example, people are either drivers or learners or non-drivers.

Table 4.3

	Driver status		
Gender	Driver	Learner	Non-driver
Male	70	0	10
Female	90	10	20

A contingency table displays all possible combined outcomes and the frequency of each observation. All contingencies, that is, all possibilities, are included in the table. No element can be placed in more than one cell as the categories of each variable are mutually exclusive. Relative frequencies are calculated as estimations of equivalent probabilities.

As before when looking for relative frequencies – how many fulfil the condition required out of how many possibilities? Since we are now combining probabilities we must be sure of the exact requirements:

- 'And' requires both conditions to be satisfied
- 'Or' requires either or both to be satisfied. Be careful not to include 'both' twice
- 'If it is known that' or 'given that' limits the possibilities to just that specific subgroup

EXAMPLE 4.7

A supermarket did a survey to investigate customers' spending on drink in relation to their mode of travel. The results are shown in Table 4.4.

Table 4.4

	Expenditure on drink		
Mode of travel	None	1p and under £20	At least £20
On foot	40	20	10
By bus	30	35	15
By car	25	33	42

continued

EXAMPLE 4.7 *continued*

The table is first completed by calculating all row and column totals.

Table 4.5

Mode of travel	None	1p and <£20	At least £20	Total
		Expenditure on drink		
On foot	40	20	10	70
By bus	30	35	15	80
By car	25	33	42	100
Total	95	88	67	250

What is the probability that a customer selected at random:

(a) will spend at least £20? $\qquad$ $67/250 = 0.268$

(b) will travel by car? $\qquad$ $100/250 = 0.400$

(c) will spend at least £20 and travel by car? $\qquad$ $42/250 = 0.168$

(d) will spend at least £20 or travel by car? $\qquad$ $(67 + 25 + 33)/250 = 0.500$

(e) will spend less than £20? $\qquad$ $1 - 0.268 = 0.732$ from (a)

(f) will not travel by car? $\qquad$ $1 - 0.400 = 0.600$ from (b)

(g) will not travel by car and will spend < £20? $\qquad$ $(40 + 20 + 30 + 35)/250 = 0.500$

(h) will not travel by car or will spend < £20? $\qquad$ $(250 - 42)/250 = 0.832$

It does not matter how you arrive at the subtotals. There are various methods using set notation and formulae, but the simplest way is just to total the cells which meet the required condition.

EXAMPLE 4.8

A magazine subscription service conducted a survey to study the relationship between the number of subscriptions per household and family income. The survey, based on 1000 interviews, produced the results shown in Table 4.6.

Table 4.6

Number of subscriptions per household	Less than £10 000	£10 000 to £14 999	£15 000 to £19 999	At least £20 000	Total
		Family income			
0	28	54	78	23	183
1	29	151	301	73	554
2	15	31	69	57	172
>2	0	19	40	32	91
Total	72	255	488	185	1000

continued

EXAMPLE 4.8 *continued*

Find

(a) P(household had income < £15000) $(255 + 72)/1000 = 0.327$

(b) P(household had 1 subscription) $554/1000 = 0.554$

(c) P(household having an income $\geq$ £15000 had no subscriptions)

$$(78 + 23)/(488 + 185) = 0.150$$

(d) P(household with < £10000 had more than two subscriptions) $0/72 = 0.000$

(e) P(household had at least one subscription) $1 - 183/1000 = 0.817$

(f) P(household had either an income < £15000 or more than one subscription)

$$(327 + 69 + 57 + 40 + 32)/1000 = 0.525$$

Very often you will need to build the contingency table from limited information which may appear to be incomplete but is often sufficient to build up a complete table. As each number is entered in the appropriate cell, it should be possible to infer other values from the total or from a subtotal.

4.7 Conditional probability

If the probability of the outcome of a second event depends upon the outcome of a previous event, the second is **conditional** on the outcome of the first. This concept is easiest to understand when illustrated by a few examples.

EXAMPLE 4.9

Cards

Two cards are selected from a full pack **without replacement**. Any probabilities concerning the second card depend on which card has previously been removed or, more to the point, which cards are still available for selection.

> P(the first card being an ace) $= 4/52$
> P(second card being an ace) $= 3/51$ if the first card was an ace
> but $4/51$ if it was not
> P(first card being a picture) $= 12/52$
> P(second card being a picture given that the first was a picture) $= 11/51$
> P(second card being a picture given that the first was not a picture) $= 12/51$

The word 'given' is represented by |. For example, P(second card being a picture | first card was a picture).

continued

EXAMPLE 4.9 *continued*

Given information about the first card drawn from a pack of playing cards, find the probabilities of the second card being a heart? In each case there are 51 cards remaining but how many of them are hearts?

P(second a heart | first a heart)	12/51
P(second a heart | first not a heart)	13/51
P(second a heart | first a spade)	13/51
P(second a heart | first not a spade)	Here we do not know how many hearts remain after the first withdrawal so we cannot decide whether the answer is 12/51 or 13/51.

EXAMPLE 4.10

200 workers, of whom 80 are male, were questioned about their driving capabilities. Three-quarters of the females were qualified drivers and two-thirds of the 30 non-drivers were female. Ten of the employees were learning to drive.

Table 4.7 Contingency table

		Driver status		
Gender	Qualified	Learner	Non-driver	Total
Male				80
Female	3/4 of females = 90		20	
Total		10	30	200

Complete the contingency table and use it to answer the questions below.

Table 4.8

		Driver status		
Gender	Qualified	Learner	Non-driver	Total
Male	70	0	10	80
Female	90	10	20	120
Total	160	10	30	200

(a) What is the probability of any worker being a qualified driver? 160/200 = 0.800

(b) What is the probability of a male worker being a qualified driver?

$$70/80 = 0.875$$

(c) What is the probability of a qualified driver being male? 70/160 = 0.438

(d) What is the probability of a female being a non-driver? 20/120 = 0.167

(e) What is the probability of a non-driver being female? 20/30 = 0.667

Some examples which can be worked through using contingency tables may be solved more easily by other methods. We shall solve Example 4.11 first using a contingency table then with the aid of a **tree diagram**.

Tree diagrams

Tree diagrams provide a systematic approach to listing all the possible outcomes of combined events. They are also known as **probability trees**.

- Tree diagrams can be drawn for more than two events
- All possible outcomes at each event are shown as branches
- At each branching all the probabilities must sum to one
- Consecutive events follow along the branches
- Combined probability along a series of branches is found by multiplication
- Combined probabilities are added if more than one series of branches is favourable
- For the complete tree all the combined probabilities must sum to one.

EXAMPLE 4.11

Suppose the probability of rainfall tomorrow depends on today's weather. If it rains today, there is a probability of 0.7 that it will rain tomorrow, whilst if today is fine, there is a probability of 0.55 that it will rain tomorrow. Suppose that the probability of rain today is 0.6. What are the probabilities that it will be fine tomorrow?

Let A be the event of rain today, $\bar{A}$ the event of no rain today, and B the event of rain tomorrow.

The word 'given' is represented by |

From the information above:

$$P(A) = 0.6, \quad P(B|A) = 0.7, \quad P(B|\bar{A}) = 0.55$$

Solution using contingency table

Insert these probabilities in a contingency table and calculate the other cell values. Remember that, assuming the events are independent, the probability of two events happening is the product of their individual probabilities, and that, for any row or column the cell probabilities sum to the value under the total probability.

Table 4.9

Today's weather	Rain tomorrow (B)	Tomorrow's weather Fine tomorrow ($\bar{B}$)	Total
Rain (A)	$0.7 \times 0.6 = 0.42$	$0.6 - 0.42 = 0.18$	0.6
Fine ($\bar{A}$)	$0.55 \times 0.4 = 0.22$	$0.4 - 0.22 = 0.18$	$0.4\ (1 - 0.6)$
Total	$0.42 + 0.22 = 0.64$	$0.18 + 0.18 = 0.36$	1.0

Find the corresponding conditional probabilities for no rain tomorrow:

$$P(\bar{B}|A) = 0.18/0.6 = 0.3 \qquad P(\bar{B}|\bar{A}) = 0.18/0.4 = 0.45$$

continued

EXAMPLE 4.11 *continued*

This was not an easy exercise with the information given in this example so we will try another method.

Solution using tree diagram

$$P(A) = 0.6 \qquad P(B|A) = 0.7 \qquad P(B|\bar{A}) = 0.55$$

First we insert the given probabilities into the tree diagram.

Figure 4.5

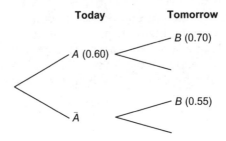

Next, using the fact that at any branching point the probabilities sum to 1 we insert the missing probabilities.

$$P(\bar{A}) = 1 - 0.6 = 0.4; \quad P(A \text{ and } \bar{B}) = 1 - 0.7 = 0.3; \quad P(\bar{B}|\bar{A}) = 1 - 0.55 = 0.45$$

Figure 4.6

Today	Tomorrow	Outcome	Probability
A (0.60)	B (0.70)	AB	$P(AB) = 0.60 \times 0.70 = 0.42$
	$\bar{B}$ (0.30)	$A\bar{B}$	$P(A\bar{B}) = 0.60 \times 0.30 = 0.18$
$\bar{A}$ (0.40)	B (0.55)	$\bar{A}B$	$P(\bar{A}B) = 0.40 \times 0.55 = 0.22$
	$\bar{B}$ (0.45)	$\bar{A}\bar{B}$	$P(\bar{A}\bar{B}) = 0.40 \times 0.45 = 0.18$

Always check that the probabilities sum up to 1.

$$P(A \text{ and } B) = 0.42$$
$$P(A \text{ and } \bar{B}) = 0.18$$
$$P(\bar{A} \text{ and } B) = 0.22$$
$$P(\bar{A} \text{ and } \bar{B}) = 0.18$$

From the diagram we can find other combinations:

$$P(A \text{ or } B) = \text{Probability of at least one rainy day} = 0.42 + 0.18 + 0.22 = 0.82$$
$$P(\bar{A} \text{ or } \bar{B}) = \text{Probability of at least one day being fine} = 1 - 0.42 = 0.58$$

For this example the tree diagram is more straightforward than the contingency table.

EXAMPLE 4.12

A new office computer network has been installed and some of the employees are having difficulty logging on to it. A technician has given them some tuition and the problems encountered during the practice session are recorded. These data result in the following probabilities:

An employee has a 0.9 probability of logging on successfully at her first attempt.

If she is successful at any time, the same probability applies on her next two attempts.

If she is not successful at any time, she loses confidence and the probability of suceeding on any subsequent attempt is only 0.5.

Use a tree diagram to find the probabilities that:

(a) she is successful on all her first three attempts
(b) she fails at the first attempt but succeeds on the next two
(c) she is successful just once in three attempts
(d) she is still not successful after the third attempt.

Figure 4.7

1st attempt	2nd attempt	3rd attempt	Outcome	Probability
		S (0.9)	SSS	$0.9 \times 0.9 \times 0.9 = 0.729$ (a)
	S (0.9)	F (0.1)	SSF	$0.9 \times 0.9 \times 0.1 = 0.081$
S (0.9)		S (0.5)	SFS	$0.9 \times 0.1 \times 0.5 = 0.045$
	F (0.1)	F (0.5)	SFF	$0.9 \times 0.1 \times 0.5 = 0.045$ (c)
		S (0.9)	FSS	$0.1 \times 0.5 \times 0.9 = 0.045$ (b)
	S (0.5)	F (0.1)	FSF	$0.1 \times 0.5 \times 0.1 = 0.005$ (c)
F (0.1)		S (0.5)	FFS	$0.1 \times 0.5 \times 0.5 = 0.025$ (c)
	F (0.5)	F (0.5)	FFF	$0.1 \times 0.5 \times 0.5 = 0.025$ (d)

(a) P(she is successful on all her first three attempts) $= 0.729$
(b) P(she fails at the first attempt but succeeds on the next two) $= 0.045$
(c) P(she is successful just once in three attempts) $= 0.045 + 0.005 + 0.025 = 0.075$
(d) P(she is still not successful after the third attempt) $= 0.025$

4.8 Expected values

A commonly used method in decision-making problems is the consideration of **expected values**. The expected value for each decision is calculated and the option with the maximum or minimum value (dependent upon the situation) is selected.

The expected value of each decision is defined by:

$$E(x) = \Sigma px \tag{4.6}$$

where x is the value associated with each outcome, $E(x)$ is the expected value of the event x and p is the probability of x happening. If you bought 5 out of 100 raffle tickets for a prize of £25 the expected value of your winnings would be $0.05 \times £25 = £1.25$. Clearly this is only a theoretical value because in reality you would win either £25 or £0.

EXAMPLE 4.13

Two independent operations of uncertain duration, A and B, are started simultaneously. The probabilities associated with each duration are given in Table 4.10.

Table 4.10

	Operation A		Operation B	
Duration (days) (x)	Probability (p)		Duration (days) (x)	Probability (p)
1	0.0		1	0.1
2	0.5		2	0.2
3	0.3		3	0.5
4	0.2		4	0.2

Determine whether A or B has the shorter expected completion time.

Operation A

$E(x) = \Sigma px = (1 \times 0.0) + (2 \times 0.5) + (3 \times 0.3) + (4 \times 0.2) = 2.7$ days

Operation B

$E(x) = \Sigma px = (1 \times 0.1) + (2 \times 0.2) + (3 \times 0.5) + (4 \times 0.2) = 2.8$ days

Hence operation A has the shorter expected completion time.

EXAMPLE 4.14

A marketing manager is considering whether to distribute his company's product nation-wide or regionally. Use the data in Table 4.11 to decide on the more profitable method of distribution.

Table 4.11 Distribution

	National distribution		Regional distribution	
Level of demand	Net profit (£m) (x)	Probability that demand is met (p)	(£m) (x)	Probability that demand is met (p)
High	4.0	0.50	2.5	0.50
Medium	2.0	0.25	2.0	0.25
Low	0.5	0.25	1.2	0.25

continued

EXAMPLE 4.14 *continued*

Expected profits:

National distribution $E(x) = \Sigma px = 4.0 \times 0.5 + 2.0 \times 0.25 + 0.5 \times 0.25 = 2.625$ (£m)

Regional distribution $E(x) = \Sigma px = 2.5 \times 0.5 + 2.0 \times 0.25 + 1.2 \times 0.25 = 2.050$ (£m)

The marketing manager should opt for national distribution because it is expected to produce the higher profit.

EXAMPLE 4.15

A company which is considering hiring a computer has two models, A and B, in mind.

The cost of computers A and B are £10 000 and £15 000 per annum, respectively. Estimates of the annual savings produced and their associated probabilities are shown in Table 4.12.

Table 4.12

Computer A	Computer B
£5000 with a probability of 0.3	£5000 with a probability of 0.3
£10 000 with a probability of 0.3	£10 000 with a probability of 0.3
£15 000 with a probability of 0.4	£15 000 with a probability of 0.1
	£20 000 with a probability of 0.1
	£30 000 with a probability of 0.2

Decide which computer the company should hire in order to maximise overall savings.

Expected savings (£000)

Computer A: $0.3 \times 5 + 0.3 \times 10 + 0.4 \times 15 = 10.5$

Computer B: $0.3 \times 5 + 0.3 \times 10 + 0.1 \times 15 + 0.1 \times 20 + 0.2 \times 30 = 14.0$

Expected profits (£000)

Computer A: $10.5 - 10 = 0.5$ An expected profit of £500

Computer B: $14.0 - 15 = -1.0$ An expected loss of £1000

The company should hire Computer A

4.9 Further work with probability

Probability forms the basis of arguably the most important branch of statistics – inferential statistics. You will study three aspects of inference later in this course when we shall consider:

- **Confidence intervals,** by which the most probable range for a population value is estimated from a sample
- **Hypothesis testing,** by which the probability that a hypothesised population value is correct or incorrect is based on the analysis of a sample
- **Forecasting,** by which probable future values are inferred from the analysis of past values.

In addition to possibility-space diagrams, contingency tables and probability trees, Venn diagrams are often used to illustrate combined probabilities. Because probability is such an important topic in statistics much work has been done in this field. There are many standard probability distributions and much can also be inferred about a population of new data if it can be shown to follow one of these distributions. In Chapter 5 we shall study the normal distribution because it is widely applicable in the world of business. In later chapters we shall also use sets of probability tables constructed from other probability distributions. More advanced statistics textbooks can be consulted for information on standard distributions.

4.10 Summary

Our own actions are often subconsciously based on probability when we make choices or take risks. The role of statistics is to quantify the uncertainty so that we can make informed estimations and logical choices, particularly in the world of business.

In this chapter we have only introduced the basic concepts of probability. Probability can be studied in great depth in more advanced courses. Much of the work has been concerned with methods of quantifying uncertainty in the form of numerical probabilities. These have been based on symmetry or on relative frequencies from existing data. We have calculated combined probabilities with the help of contingency tables and tree diagrams and we have calculated expected values as an aid to making choices.

Table 4.13

Number of events	Appropriate methods to use
1 event	Calculation
2 events	Calculation, contingency tables, probability trees, Venn diagrams
> 2 events	Calculation, probability trees, Venn diagrams.

We shall continue to use probability throughout this course and will make regular reference to tables which are based on specific probability distributions.

4.11 Probability tutorial

Answers in Appendix A1.

4.1   If the probability of a successful outcome is 0.2, what is the probability of failure?

4.2   With a single die, what is the probability of scoring:

(a) 6, (b) an even number, (c) a number divisible by 3, (d) 0?

4.3   If one card is taken at random from a normal pack of 52 playing cards, what is the probability of getting:

(a) an ace, (b) a club, (c) the ace of clubs, (d) an ace or a club,
(e) a picture card (J, Q, K), (f) a red card, (g) a red king, (h) a red picture?

4.4   Three coins are tossed. List all the possibilities and use them to find:

(a) the number of possible outcomes, (b) $P(3$ heads$)$, (c) $P(2$ heads$)$, (d) $P(1$ head$)$, (e) $P(0$ heads$)$, (f) the sum of all the probabilities found.

4.5 Draw a space diagram to represent the sample space of the outcomes for throwing a blue and a red dice. Use it to find:

(a) P(a score of 4), (b) P(a score of more than 7), (c) P(a double), (d) P(an even score), (e) P(both dice show even scores), (f) P(the score on the blue die is greater than that on the red).

4.6 A bag contains 6 red discs, 4 blue discs and 2 green discs. If a single disc is withdrawn a random find:

(a) P(blue), (b) P(not red), (c) P(blue or red), (d) P(not blue or red).

4.7 Typing speeds of office workers have been found to vary considerably. In a recent dexterity survey the following typing rates were recorded:

Words per minute (wpm)	Number of workers
20–29	320
30–39	400
40–49	350
50–59	200
60–69	50
70–79	5

Calculate the relative frequencies of each group of workers, and find the probability that a worker selected at ranom:

(a) is expert with a typing speed 60 wpm, or faster

(b) needs practice, being slower than 40 wpm

(c) is in neither of these extreme groups?

4.8 Records were kept of 200 students enrolling for a degree course. The completed records showed the following frequencies:

	Result	
Sex	Graduating	Not graduating
Male	90	20
Female	80	10

Find:

(a) Probability of any student graduating

(b) Probability of a male student graduating

(c) Probability of a female student graduating

(d) Probability of a graduate being female

(e) Probability of a graduate being male.

4.9 Fifty male and fifty female students, were asked whether they agreed with the proposition 'Statistics are often misleading'. Seventy students, thirty of whom were male, agreed. Find using a contingency table:

(a) P(a student agreeing)

(b) P(a student being female)

(c) P(a student being male)

(d) P(a student agreeing given that he is male)

(e) P(a student agreeing given that she is female)

(f) P(a student who agrees is female)

(g) P(a student who agrees is male)

4.10 Consider the table below which shows the number (to the nearest hundred) of various kinds of dwellings found in the suburban area of Bradfield.

	Private dwellings	Council dwellings	Total
One bedroom	600	1000	1 600
Two bedroom	3000	1700	4 700
Three bedroom	4400	1800	6 200
Total	8000	4500	12 500

(a) P(dwelling is private)

(b) P(dwelling has one bedroom)

(c) P(dwelling is private and has two bedrooms)

(d) P(dwelling is council and has three bedrooms)

(e) P(dwelling has least two bedrooms)

(f) P(dwelling is private or has two bedrooms)

(g) P(dwelling has three bedroom | it is private)

(h) P(dwelling has one bedroom | it is private)

(i) P(dwelling is private | it has three bedrooms)

(j) P(dwelling is a council property | it has three bedrooms)

4.12 Supplementary exercise

4.11 If two cards are withdrawn from a standard pack of playing cards, without replacement, use a tree diagram to find the following probabilities for picture cards, (Jack, Queen, King):

(a) P(two pictures)

(b) P(only one picture)

(c) P(no pictures)

4.12 A bag contains seven red discs, three blue discs, and two yellow discs. If three discs are withdrawn without replacement what is the probability that (a) all three are red, (b) the first one is red and the other two are blue, (c) all three are yellow?

(Use a tree diagram or any other method you prefer.)

4.13 Repeat question 4.12 if each disc is replaced before another is withdrawn.

4.14 Whether a student gets up on time depends on whether or not he has remembered to set his alarm the evening before. 90% of the time he remembers, the other 10% he forgets. When the clock is set, he will get up on time 95% of occasions. If it is not set, the chance that he will oversleep is 65%.

Use a tree diagram to find the probability that he will oversleep.

4.15 A two-stage rocket is to be launched on a space mission. The probability that the lift-off will be a failure is 0.1. If the lift-off is successful the probability that the separation of the stages will be a failure is 0.05. If the separation is successul, the probability that the second stage will fail to complete the mission is 0.03.

What is the probability that the whole mission will be:

(a) a success, (b) a failure?

4.16 Suppose that out of a group of people, 30% own both a house and a car, 40% own a house and 70% own a car. What is the probability of any person owning neither a house nor a car?

4.17 On a given day a petrol station serves three times as many men as women.

Two types of petrol are available, grade A and grade B.

Customers pay by cash or cheque.

70% of men and 40% of women buy grade A petrol

Of the men buying grade A petrol, 80% pay by cheque, of the men buying grade B petrol, 60% pay by cheque

Of the women buying grade A petrol, half pay by cheque, of the women buying grade B petrol, 40% pay by cheque.

Find the probability that (a) a customer buys grade A petrol, (b) a customer pays by cheque, (c) a woman customer pays by cheque, (d) a customer who pays by cheque for grade A petrol is a man. (You are advised to use a tree diagram.)

5 Normal Distribution

5.1 Objectives of this chapter

As we have seen in Chapters 2 and 3, data can be distributed symmetrically or it can be skewed. The most commonly occurring distribution is a symmetrical one usually referred to as the **normal distribution**. If your data can be shown to follow this distribution, you can make use of standard statistical probability tables in order to analyse your own data. Other probability distributions will be described briefly, but the main aim of this chapter is to describe the use of the normal distribution in depth.

Having studied this chapter you should be able to analyse completely any data shown to be normally distributed and be aware that similar methods can be applied to other, often skewed, distributions.

5.2 Introduction: importance of the normal distribution

Most naturally-occurring phenomena have been found to follow the normal distribution. It describes many human characteristics but is also applicable in other situations, such as manufacturing, in which a target value is commonly hit but may be missed by small amounts. In this case, the distribution of sample means is found to be normal, even if the underlying distribution is not (more of this in Chapter 6), and so the normal distribution plays a key role in the application of many statistical techniques. The normal distribution describes continuous data but it has been found to approximate to many discrete distributions also. It is, therefore, a useful tool for decision-makers who meet both types of data in the field of business.

5.3 A brief look at other probability distributions

As we shall see in Section 5.4, data which follow the normal distribution are continuous and reasonably symmetrical. Obviously the data you collect cannot be guaranteed to meet these criteria, so we will consider briefly some other distributions which might describe real data, whether they are discrete or continuous, symmetrical or skewed.

You should be able to recognise whether the data are discrete or continuous (Section 1.4) and a brief look at a histogram should give you some idea about its shape (Section 2.5.1). Commonly occurring distributions for modelling data are given in Table 5.1.

Table 5.1

| Type | Observed data | | | |
	Discrete		Continuous	
Shape	Symmetric	Skewed	Symmetric	Skewed
Distribution	Binomial	Poisson	Normal	Exponential

A formula is known for each distribution and standard tables have been produced giving information about the areas under any given section of the curve. Because these are all probability distributions, the area beneath the whole curve is equal to one. Once the appropriate distribution has been identified, the standard tables are used to calculate probabilities about the population from which the observed data has been drawn.

5.3.1 Binomial distribution

You have already met the binomial distribution in Section 4.4 (formula (4.3)).

We showed that for n trials, with the probability of success in any one trial being p, the probability of getting r successes is:

$$\frac{n!}{r!(n-r)!} \times p^r(1-p)^{(n-r)} \tag{4.3}$$

where $n!$ stands for factorial n, that is, $n \times (n-1) \times (n-2) \ldots 3 \times 2 \times 1$

Suppose we know from past experience that 15% of a consignment of items are likely to be defective, $p = 0.15$. The probability of finding 2 defective items in a sample of 7 is:

$$P(2 \text{ defectives in a sample of } 7) = \frac{7!}{2!5!} \times \left(\frac{15}{100}\right)^2 \left(\frac{85}{100}\right)^5 = 21 \times 0.15^2 \times 0.85^5 = 0.210$$

For a medium value of p, such as $p = 0.15$, the distribution will be skewed for small values of n, but will become symmetrical when n is large as for, say, 200.

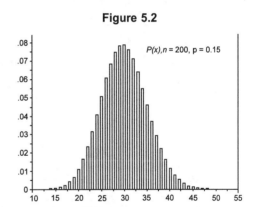

| Figure 5.1 | Figure 5.2 |

If a binomial distribution has a large value for n and a very small value for p, so that the mean, np, is also small, then the binomial distribution approximates to a Poisson distribution with the same mean (see Section 5.3.2).

If a binomial distribution has a large value for n and p is not very small, so that the mean, np, is large, then the binomial distribution approximates to a normal distribution with the same mean and standard deviation (see Section 5.3.4).

5.3.2 Poisson distribution

The Poisson distribution describes random, discrete, rare events, such as the occurrence of an accident on a particular stretch of motorway. The mean number, μ, is the expected number in a given time period.

The probability of a particular number, x, occurring is given by

$$P(x) = \mu^x \frac{e^{-\mu}}{x!} \tag{5.1}$$

where μ is the mean and $e \cong 2.718$ ($\cong$ means 'approximately equal to').

When the value of μ is very small, say $\mu = 0.001$, the distribution is very skewed, even for fairly large samples. For small values of μ the Poisson and the binomial distribution give very similar results but as μ gets larger the Poisson distribution approximates to the normal distribution.

Figure 5.3

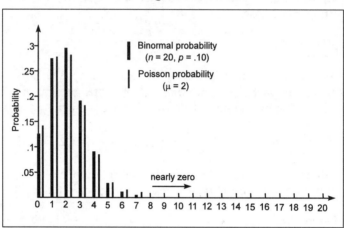

For any Poisson distribution with mean n, variance $= n$, standard deviation $= \sqrt{n}$. Figure 5.4 is a summary of all these approximations for discrete distributions.

Figure 5.4

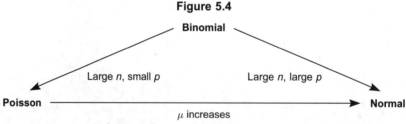

Since random discrete variables follow the Poisson distribution, events are found to follow a Poisson distribution, then the events can be shown to be random.

5.3.3   (Negative) exponential distribution

The probability distribution usually referred to as the exponential distribution is, in fact, the negative exponential distribution with the formula:

$$P(x) = \lambda e^{\lambda x} \tag{5.2}$$

where λ (lambda) is the mean time between successive events.

If the discrete Poisson distribution might describe the number of arrivals joining a queue in a given time, the continuous negative exponential distribution would describe the time between arrivals.

For this distribution the low probabilities predominate. Figure 5.5 shows the probability density function for $\lambda = 2$, 4 and 10. Note that the larger the value of λ the lower the main mass of the values, as is to be expected when the time between events is larger.

When the number of times an event occurs in a time interval has a Poisson distribution, with mean λ, the number of these time intervals between successive occurrences has an exponential distribution with $f(x) = \lambda e^{-\lambda x}$.

Section 5.3 has provided only a very short look at a few standard probability distributions; more can be found in deeper statistics textbooks (Weimer, 1993, Chapters 6 and 7).

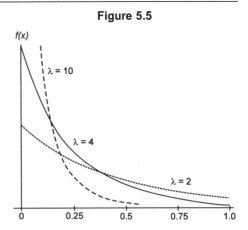

Figure 5.5

5.4 The characteristics of the normal distribution

The normal distribution is a symmetrical distribution centred on the mean of the data with a spread depending on its standard deviation. It is a suitable model for many naturally occurring variables which tend to be symmetrically distributed about a central modal value, the mean. The normal distribution approximately fits the actual observed frequency distributions of many naturally occurring phenomena, for example, human characteristics such as height, weight and IQ, and also the output from many processes, for example, weights, volumes, and so on.

As we saw in Section 5.2 this is a very important widely occurring distribution which is extensively used when analysing business data. In Sections 5.4 to 5.7 we shall look firstly at all normal distributions, then at the standardised normal distribution and finally see how this is used in analysis of observed data. Strictly speaking any observed data should be checked for normality before using this method of analysis. This can be easily done in SPSS or Minitab using the standard tests provided.

The normal distribution is not a single normal curve, but a **family of curves**, each one defined by its mean, μ, and standard deviation, σ. μ and σ are called the parameters of the distribution.

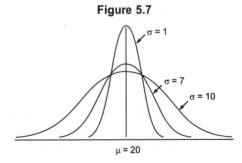

Figure 5.7

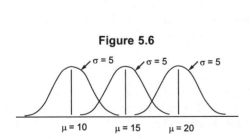

Figure 5.6

Figure 5.6 shows normal curves with the same standard deviation but different means and Figure 5.7 shows curves with the same mean but different standard deviations. The curves have common characteristics:

- The curve is bell-shaped
- It is symmetrical about the mean (μ)
- The mean, mode and median coincide.

The area beneath the normal distribution curve

No matter what the values of μ and σ are for a normal probability distribution, the total area under the curve is equal to **one**. We can therefore consider partial areas under the curve to represent probabilities. The percentage of data between a stated number of standard deviations below and above the mean is the same for all normal distributions, as illustrated in Figure 5.8.

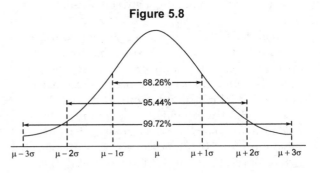

Figure 5.8

Note that the curve neither finishes nor meets the horizontal axis at $\mu \pm 3\sigma$, it only approaches it and actually goes on indefinitely.

Although all normal distributions have much in common, they will all have different numbers on the horizontal axis depending on the values of the mean and standard deviation and the units of measurement involved. We cannot, therefore, make use of the standard normal tables at this stage.

5.5 Standardised normal distribution

No matter what units are used to measure the original data, the first step in any calculation is to transform the data into a **standardised normal variate** following a standard distribution with a **mean of zero** and a **standard deviation of one**. The effect of this transformation is to describe a particular value by the number of standard deviations it is away from the mean. This standardised normal variate is without units as they cancel out in the calculation.

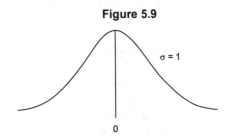

Figure 5.9

The **standardised normal distribution** is symmetrically distributed about zero and approaches the x-axis after three standard deviations from the mean.

The formula for describing x as an exact number of standard deviations (z) away from the mean (μ) is:

$$z = \frac{x - \mu}{\sigma} \tag{5.3}$$

The process of calculating z, the **standardised value**, is known as **standardising**.

In Figure 5.9, any point on the curve is described by the number of standard deviations away from the mean. The curve approaches the x-axis when the absolute value of z exceeds 3.

The value of z enables us to find from the normal tables the area under the curve between the given value, x, and the mean. This is the probability of a value occurring between the given value, x, and the mean, μ, denoted by Q for quantile. (This is easier to understand with numbers!)

For the standardised normal distributions the standard normal tables are used (see Appendix D).

5.6 Finding probabilities under a normal curve

The steps in the procedure are:
- Draw a sketch of the situation
- Standardise the value of interest
- Use the standard tables to find its associated area under the curve
- If necessary, combine the area found with another to give the required area
- Convert this to
    - a probability, using the area as found since total area = 1 or
    - a percentage, multiplying the area by 100 since total area = 100% or
    - a frequency, multiplying the area by the total frequency

    as required by the question.

EXAMPLE 5.1

The manager of a new supermarket wished to estimate the likely expenditure of his customers. A sample of till slips from a similar supermarket describing weekly spending by 500 randomly selected customers was collected and analysed. This expenditure was found to be approximately normally distributed with a mean of £50 and a standard deviation of £15. Knowing this we can find the following information about shoppers at the new supermarket.

The **probability** that any shopper selected at random:
(a) spends more than £80 per week
(b) spends less than £50 per week.

The **percentage** of shoppers who are expected to:
(c) spend between £30 and £80 per week
(d) spend between £55 and £70 per week.

The **expected number** of shoppers who will:
(e) spend less than £70 per week
(f) spend between £37.50 and £57.50 per week.

(a) The probability that any shopper selected at random spends more than £80 per week.

We need $P(x > £80)$, the probability that a customer spends over £80

$\mu = £50$, $\sigma = £15$, $x = £80$

Figure 5.10

First standardise:

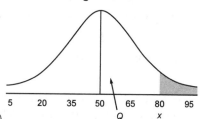

$$z = \frac{x - \mu}{\sigma} = \frac{80 - 50}{15} = \frac{30}{15} = 2.00$$

From Table D1:

$z = 2.00 \Rightarrow Q = 0.4772$

(z in the margin, Q in the body of the tables)

Note: The $\Rightarrow$ symbol stands for 'implies that', that is, if $z = 2.00$ then $Q = 0.4772$.

Therefore: $P(x > £80) = 0.5 - 0.4772 = 0.0228$

continued

EXAMPLE 5.1 *continued*

(b) The probability that any shopper selected at random spends more than £50 per week

No need to do any calculations for this question! The mean is £50 and, because the distribution is normal, the median is also £50. Half the shoppers, 250, are therefore expected to spend more than £50 per week.

Using the frequency definition of probability: $250/500 = 0.5$

(c) The percentage of shoppers who are expected to spend between £30 and £80 per week

We first need $P(£30 < x < £80)$, then we convert the result to a percentage.

Our normal tables provide the area between a particular value and the mean so we need to split the area between £30 and £80 into the partial areas on each side of the mean. Then the partial areas, £30 to £50 and £50 to £80 can be calculated separately and the two parts recombined.

$\mu = £50$, $\sigma = £15$,

$x_1 = £30$, $x_2 = £80$

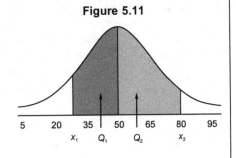

Figure 5.11

$P(£50 < x < £80)$

From (a) $x = 80 \Rightarrow z_2 = 2.00 \Rightarrow Q_2 = 0.4772$

$P(£30 < x < £50)$

$$z_1 = \frac{x - \mu}{\sigma} = \frac{30 - 50}{15} = \frac{-20}{15} = -1.333$$

(The table values are all positive, so when z is negative we invoke the symmetry of the situation and use its absolute value in the table.)

From tables: $z_1 = -1.333 \Rightarrow Q_1 = 0.4088$ (by interpolation)

(Q_1 lies between 0.4082 ($z = 1.33$) and 0.4099 ($z = 1.34$) and is one-third of the distance between them (0.0017), being nearer to 0.4082 so $0.4082 + 0.0006 = 0.4088$)

Therefore:

$$P(£30 < x < £80) = Q_1 + Q_2 = 0.4088 + 0.4772 = 0.8860$$

The whole area is equivalent to 100% so 0.8860 of it $= 88.6\%$

(d) Percentage of shoppers expected to spend between £55 and £70

We first need $P(£55 < x < £70)$, then we convert the result to a percentage.

$\mu = £50$, $\sigma = £15$,

$x_1 = £55$, $x_2 = £70$

We now need to find the area between the mean and £70 (Q_2) and then subtract the area between the mean and £55 (Q_1).

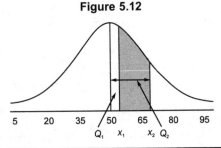

Figure 5.12

continued

EXAMPLE 6.1 *continued*

$P(£50 < x < £70)$

$$z_2 = \frac{x - \mu}{\sigma} = \frac{70 - 50}{15} = \frac{20}{15} = 1.333$$

From tables $Q_2 = 0.4088$ (by interpolation)

$P(£50 < x < £55)$

$$z_1 = \frac{x - \mu}{\sigma} = \frac{55 - 50}{15} = \frac{5}{15} = 0.333$$

From tables $Q_1 = 0.1305$ (by interpolation)

Therefore:

$$P(£55 < x < £70) = Q_2 - Q_1 = 0.4088 - 0.1305 = 0.2783$$

Percentage of shoppers expected to spend between £55 and £70 is
$0.2783 \times 100 = 27.8\%$

(e) The expected number of shoppers who will spend less than £70 per week

$\mu = £50$, $\sigma = £15$, $x = £70$

Figure 5.13

The area we need is that between the
mean and £70 plus the 0.5 which falls
below the mean.

$P(£50 < x < £70)$

First standardise: $z = \dfrac{x - \mu}{\sigma} = \dfrac{70 - 50}{15}$

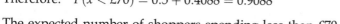

$$= \frac{20}{15} = 1.333$$

From tables: $z = 1.333 \Rightarrow Q = 0.4088$

Therefore: $P(x < £70) = 0.5 + 0.4088 = 0.9088$

The expected number of shoppers spending less than £70 is 0.9088 of the total
$= 0.9088 \times 500 = 454.4$ which is between 454 and 455 shoppers.

(f) The expected number of shoppers who will spend between £37.50 and £57.50 per week

We first need $P(£37.50 < x < £57.50)$. This is then multiplied by the total frequency.

$\mu = £50$, $\sigma = £15$,

$x_1 = £37.50$, $x_2 = £57.50$

Figure 5.14

Our normal tables give the area between a
value and the mean so we need to split the
area between £37.50 and £57.50 into partial
areas each side of the mean; calculate the
partial areas separately and then recombine
them.

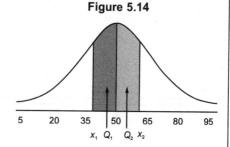

continued

EXAMPLE 5.1 *continued*

$P(\pounds 37.5 < x < \pounds 50)$

$$z_1 = \frac{x - \mu}{\sigma} = \frac{37.5 - 50}{15} = \frac{-12.5}{15} = -0.833$$

When z is negative use its absolute value in the table.

From tables: $z_1 = -0.833 \Rightarrow Q_1 = 0.2976$ (by interpolation)

$P(\pounds 50 < x < \pounds 57.5)$

$$z_2 = \frac{x - \mu}{\sigma} = \frac{57.5 - 50}{15} = \frac{7.5}{15} = 0.500$$

From tables: $z_2 = 0.500 \Rightarrow Q_2 = 0.1915$

Therefore: $P(\pounds 37.50 < x < \pounds 57.50) = Q_1 + Q_2 = 0.2976 + 0.1915 = 0.4891$

Therefore the expected number of shoppers who spend between £37.50 and £57.50 is $0.4891 \times 500 = 244.55$, that is, 244 or 245 shoppers.

5.7 Finding values from given proportions

In Example 5.1 we were given the value of x and had to find the area under the normal curve associated with it. Another type of problem gives the area, even if indirectly, and asks the associated value of x.

EXAMPLE 5.2

Using the data in Example 5.1, calculate values of the shopping basket.

The value below which:
(a) 70% of the customers are expected to spend
(b) 45% of the customers are expected to spend.

The value expected to be exceeded by:
(c) 10% of the till slips
(d) 80% of the till slips.

The value below which:
(e) 350 of the shoppers are expected to spend
(f) 100 of the shoppers are expected to spend.

(a) The value below which 70% of the shoppers are expected to spend

$\mu = \pounds 50$, $\sigma = \pounds 15$, $x = \pounds$?

We first need to find the value of Q.

70% of the total area, 1.00, is below $x \Rightarrow$
20% is between μ and $x \Rightarrow Q = 0.2000$

Figure 5.15

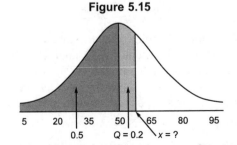

continued

EXAMPLE 5.2 *continued*

From tables:

$Q = 0.2000$ (in the body of the table) $\Rightarrow z = 0.524$ (in the margin of the table, by interpolation as z lies between 0.52 and 0.53 and is a little nearer to 0.52)

We now know the value of z and need to find x.

Using standardising formula:

$$z = \frac{x - \mu}{\sigma}$$

$$0.524 = \frac{x - 50}{15}$$

$$15 \times 0.524 = x - 50$$

$$7.86 = x - 50$$

$$7.86 + 50 = x$$

$$£57.86 = x$$

The value below which 70% of customers spend is £57.86.

Alternatively, rearrange the formula first to give:

$$x = z\sigma + \mu$$

and then substitute the values into it directly. If your algebra is a bit rusty try using the fact that $z = 0.524$ tells us that x is 0.524 standard deviations above the mean. Its value is therefore

$$\mu + 0.524\sigma = 50 + 0.524 \times 15 = £57.86$$

(b) The value below which 45% of the shoppers are expected to spend

$\mu = £50$, $\sigma = £15$, $x = £$?

45% below x is equivalent to 5% between x and μ, so $Q = 0.05$

From tables, if $Q = 0.05 \Rightarrow z = 0.126$ (by interpolation)

We know, however, that x is below the mean so z is negative, $z = -0.126$.

Figure 5.16

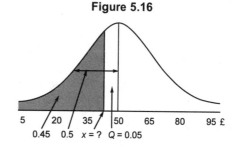

Using the standard formula:

$$z = \frac{x - \mu}{\sigma}$$

$$-0.126 = \frac{x - 50}{15}$$

$$15 \times -0.126 = x - 50$$

$$-1.89 = x - 50$$

$$-1.89 + 50 = x$$

$$£48.11 = x$$

The value below which 45% of customers spend is £48.11

continued

EXAMPLE 5.2 *continued*

Alternatively x is 0.126 standard deviations below the mean

$$x = \mu - 0.126\sigma = 50 - 0.126 \times 15 = £48.11$$

(c)   The value expected to be exceeded by 10% of till slips

$\mu = £50$, $\sigma = £15$, $x = £?$

Figure 5.17

10% above x is equivalent to 40% between x and μ so $Q = 0.40$

From tables if $Q = 0.40 \Rightarrow z = 1.282$ (by interpolation)

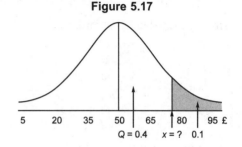

Using the standard formula:

$$z = \frac{x - \mu}{\sigma}$$

$$1.282 = \frac{x - 50}{15}$$

$$15 \times 1.282 = x - 50$$

$$19.23 = x - 50$$

$$19.23 + 50 = x$$

$$£69.23 = x$$

The value exceeded by 10% of the till slips is £69.23

Alternatively: $x = \mu + 1.282\sigma = 50 + 1.282 \times 15 = £69.23$

(d)   The value expected to be exceeded by 80% of the till slips

$\mu = £50$, $\sigma = £15$, $x = £?$

Figure 5.18

80% above $x \Rightarrow 30\%$ between x and μ so $Q = 0.30$

From tables, if $Q = 0.30 \Rightarrow z = 0.842$ (by interpolation)

We know that x is below the mean so z is negative.

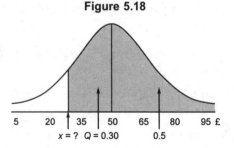

Using the standard formula:

$$z = \frac{x - \mu}{\sigma}$$

$$-0.842 = \frac{x - 50}{15}$$

$$15 \times -0.842 = x - 50$$

$$-12.63 = x - 50$$

$$-12.63 + 50 = x$$

$$£37.37 = x$$

The value exceeded by 80% of the till slips is £37.37

Alternatively: $x = \mu - 0.842\sigma = 50 - 0.842 \times 15 = £37.37$

continued

EXAMPLE 5.2 *continued*

(e)   The value below which 350 of the shoppers are expected to spend

350 shoppers out of 500 is 70%, so once this conversion has been made the calculation is exactly the same as (a), giving an answer of £57.86.

(f)   The value below which 100 of the shoppers are expected to spend

$\mu = £50$, $\sigma = £15$, $x = £$?

100 customers below x is the same as 150 between x and μ so $Q = 150/500 = 0.30$

From tables, if $Q = 0.30 \Rightarrow z = 0.842$ (by interpolation)

We know that x is below the mean so z is negative.

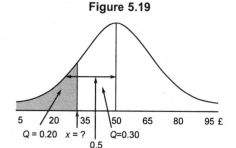

Figure 5.19

Using the standard formula:

$$z = \frac{x - \mu}{\sigma}$$

$$-0.842 = \frac{x - 50}{15}$$

$$15 \times -0.842 = x - 50$$

$$-12.63 = x - 50$$

$$-12.63 + 50 = x$$

$$£37.37 = x$$

The value below which 100 shoppers are expected to spend is £37.37

Alternatively $x = \mu - 0.842\sigma = 50 - 0.842x15 = £37.37$

In Examples 5.1 and 5.2 we have considered all the possible variations in the use of the normal distribution with a large set of data with given mean and standard deviations.
Plenty of extra practice is provided in the Exercises 5.10 and 5.11.

5.8   Further applications of the normal distribution

Any process or procedure which aims at a target but is not precise enough to hit it every time will produce errors which are normally distributed. Analysis of past errors is very important as it offers a reasonable estimate of the size of future errors and the probability of being able to hit the target within any given specification.

Many quality control models are based on the normal distribution as production errors are often found to be normally distributed. What is the probability of being able to produce metal washers to meet the specification 15 ± 1 mm? This is another way of asking the question 'What percentage of the production do you expect to meet this specification?'

Assuming the production is centred on the correct target, the precision of the production depends on the standard deviation of the errors. From Figure 5.8, we can see that, for example, 95% of production will be within two standard deviations of the target.

The normal distribution is similarly employed in stock control. Analysing previous demands on stock enables stores to be managed so that a balance is kept between overstocking goods and running out of supplies.

In modelling or forecasting, predictions (or 'fitted values') are produced but they are unlikely to fit the individual data completely accurately. The difference between the actual and the model's fitted values are called 'residuals' which are very often normally distributed. Their analysis therefore gives an estimate of the accuracy of models or forecasts.

The normal distribution can be put to many other uses by statisticians. On this course we shall meet it again many times – its uses ranging from estimation (Chapter 6) to forecasting (Chapter 13).

5.9 Summary

You should now understand the importance of probability distributions in general and that of the normal distribution in particular. We have concentrated on the normal distribution but other probability distributions can be used if they fit your data better. Standard tables are available for all probability distributions. The most commonly used tables are published in most statistics textbooks and can be found in Appendix D. A full range appears in specialised booklets such as *Elementary Statistics Tables* (Henry R. Neave, 1992, Routledge).

If your data set approximately follows a normal distribution, with known mean and standard deviation, you should now be able to make use of the standardised normal distribution to analyse it. It is essential that you understand the normal distribution before you move on to other topics which make use of it.

5.10 Tutorial 5 – Normal distribution

Answers in Appendix A1.

5.1 The lengths of steel beams made by a particular steel mill are normally distributed with a mean of 8.25 metres and a standard deviation of 0.07 metres.

(a) Find the probability that the length of a steel beam will be over 8.40 metres.

(b) Find the probability that the length of a steel beam will be between 8.20 and 8.40 metres.

(c) For a particular application, any beam less than 8.05 metres must be scrapped. What percentage of beams would the company expect to scrap?

(d) If the company expected to scrap 1% of the production as being too long, what would be the maximum acceptable length?

5.2 The time taken by a student to walk to the university has been shown to be normally distributed with mean of 16 minutes and standard deviation of 2.1 minutes. He walks in once a day during term time, 180 days per year, and leaves home 20 minutes before his first lecture. Find:

(a) The probability that he is late for his first lecture,

(b) The number of days per year he is likely to be late for his first lecture.

(c) If he arrives with 5 minutes to spare he has a cup of coffee. How many cups is he likely to manage during his three year course?

(d) If he has 7½ minutes to spare he also has a bacon sandwich. How many of these is he likely to eat during his course?

5.3 For many years a company has been using a standardised test as a guide for hiring new secretaries. The test scores are normally distributed with mean of 800 and standard deviation of 100. There has been an unusually high number of applicants in recent months and it has been suggested that only the applicants who score in the upper 10% should be considered further. What is the minimum test score an applicant would need for further consideration?

5.4 A commercial grower produces cabbages having masses which are normally distributed with mean of 1 kg and standard deviation 0.15 kg. He sells these as 'small', 'medium' and 'large' when they are weighed and found to be less than 0.75, between 0.75 and 1.20, and over 1.20 kg respectively.

(a) From a plot producing 8000 cabbages estimate how many are likely to be:

   (i)   Small
   (ii) Medium
   (iii) Large?

(b) If the grower wished to label 40% of his production as large, what weight should he set as the lower limit of this group?

5.5 If a set of marks for a statistics examination is approxmately normally distributed with a mean of 74 and a standard deviation of 7.9 find:

(a) The lowest pass mark if 10% of the students are failed

(b) The highest mark graded B if the top 5% get A.

5.6 A soft drinks machine is regulated by its manufacturer so that it discharges an average of 200 ml per cup. If the amount delivered is normally distributed with standard deviation equal to 15 ml:

(a) What percentage of the cups will contain over 225 ml?

(b) What is the probability that a cup contains between 175 ml and 225 ml?

(c) How many of the cups are likely to overflow if 250 ml cups are used for the next 10 000 drinks?

(d) What percentage would fall below a permissible minimum of 150 ml?

5.7 A manufacturer finds that although he promises delivery of a certain item within 20 working days, the time he actually takes to deliver to customers is normally distributed with a mean of 16 and a standard deviation of 2.5 working days.

(a) What proportion of customers receive their deliveries late?

(b) What proportion of customers receive deliveries within 10 to 15 working days?

(c) To how many days should his delivery promise be amended if it is required that only 2% of deliveries should be late?

(d) What proportion of customers will receive deliveries within 20 working days if the manufacturer manages to reduce the standard deviation of delivery time to 1.5 working days?

5.8 The mean life of a keyboard is typically 6 years with a standard deviation of 1.3 years. If the manufacturer wishes to replace no more than 3% of keyboards under guarantee how long should the guarantee be, to the nearest month?

5.9 Items coming off a production line are measured and have been found to have a mean diameter of 1500 mm and a standard deviation of 0.5 mm.

    (a) Quality control requirements are that the items should measure between 1498.5 mm and 1501.5 mm. What percentage of the items will meet these requirements?

    (b) Another part of the process produces items with holes which are normally distributed with a mean diameter of 1501 mm and a standard deviation of 1 mm. What percentage of the holes will have diameters between 1498.5 and 1501.5 mm?

    (c) What percentage of holes will need to be enlarged because they have diameters less than 1498.5 mm?

5.10 A fertiliser is produced in 25 kg plastic sacks. The filling process has been shown to have a mean weight of 26 kg with a standard deviation of 1.2 kg.

    (a) What is the probability of any sack being under the nominal weight?

    (b) What is the probability of a sack being more that 1 kg underweight?

    (c) Assuming the standard deviation remains unchanged, to what mean weight should the process be set if only 1% of the sacks are to be underweight?

5.11 Supplementary Exercise 5

5.11 Invoices at a particular store have amounts which follow a normal distribution with a mean of £84.65 and a standard deviation of £6.26.

    (a) What percentage of invoices will be over £100?

    (b) What percentage of invoices will be below £50?

    (c) What percentage of invoices will be between £50 and £70?

    (d) What percentage of invoices will be between £70 and £90?

    (e) Above what amount will 95% of the invoices lie?

    (f) Below what amount will 10% of the invoices lie?

    (g) What value will be exceeded by 20% of the invoices?

5.12 The weights of 500 students are normally distributed with a mean of 66.5 kg and a standard deviation of 2.8 kg.

    (a) How many students have weights:

        (i) Greater than 70 kg?

        (ii) Less than 60 kg?

        (iii) Between 65 and 70 kg?

        (iv) Between 60 and 65 kg?

    (b) What weight is exceeded by the heaviest 25 students?

5.13 The mean time taken by 500 office workers at a large mail-order company to log on to their computer network is 72.5 seconds, with a standard deviation of 5.5 seconds. Assuming these times to be normally distributed:

(a) How many would have logged on in less than a minute?

(b) How many would take more than one and a half minutes to log on?

(c) If the slowest 15% were sent for retraining, what time did they fail to beat?

(d) If the top 25 workers got a rise, what time did they beat?

5.14 The height of adult males is normally distributed with a mean of 172 cm and a standard deviation of 8 cm. What height is exceeded by 99% of males?

5.15 Packages from a packing machine have a mass which is normally distributed with mean 200 g and standard deviation 2 g. Find the probability that a package from the machine weighs:

(a) Less than 197 g

(b) More than 200.5 g

(c) Between 198.5 g and 199.5 g.

5.16 Bags of flour packed by a particular machine have masses which are normally distributed with mean 500 g and standard deviation 20 g. Two per cent of bags are rejected for being underweight and 1 per cent of bags are rejected for being overweight. Between what range of values should the mass of a bag of flour lie if it is to be accepted?

5.17 Eggs may be classified as standard, if they weigh less than 46.0 g, medium if they weigh between 46.0 g and 56.0 g, or large weighing over 56.0 g. Suppose the eggs laid by a particular breed of hen have a mean weight of 50.0 g, and that the weights are normally distributed with standard deviation 5.0 g. Find what percentage of the eggs laid by these hens fall into each class.

5.18 A company has a large sales staff. The amount of monthly expenses claimed by each salesman follows a normal distribution with mean of £230 and a standard deviation of £45.

Find the proportion of salesmen whose monthly claim:

(a) Lies between £230 and £250

(b) Is more than £250

(c) Lies between £200 and £230

(d) Is less than £200

(e) Is more than £150

(f) Lies between £180 and £220

(g) Lies between £210 and £290.

5.19 Petrol consumption for all types of small car is normally distributed with a mean of 30.5 mpg and standard deviation of 4.5 mpg. A manufacturer wants to make a car which will be more economical than 95% of small cars. What must be its consumption in mpg?

5.20 In the horticultural industry the wages of a certain grade of part-time worker are normally distributed with a standard deviation of £4.00. If 20% of the staff earn less than £30 per week, what is the mean wage? What percentage of the staff, if any, earn over £50 per week?

6 Estimation

6.1 Objectives of this chapter

The subject of statistics is often more concerned with the grey area of what is **the most likely solution** than the ability to produce **an exact answer**. Frequently we do not have sufficient information to enable us to calculate an exact value of a parameter for a whole population of data; instead we have to make the best estimate we can of this value. This is generally done by taking a sample from the same population, calculating the required statistic from this and then using the result as an estimate of the true value for the whole population (see Section 1.5).

If many different samples are taken, they will inevitably produce many different results. All these results cannot be correct so one figure is usually quoted as being the most likely value. A margin of error surrounding this figure is also quoted. This margin of error is used to produce **a confidence interval**, centred on the sample value, which is considered to be the best we can manage with the limited data at our disposal.

After studying this chapter you should be able to calculate point estimates and confidence intervals for such population parameters as means and proportions and also interpret confidence intervals correctly. You should also appreciate the need for estimation and its use in preference to making rigid claims, which may be unjustified, about population parameters.

6.2 Why estimate?

In order to find a true answer about any population with absolute accuracy we need to have all possible relevant information about every member of that population. This is rarely available as, for example, in the ten-year **census** which enumerates the whole population of the United Kingdom and Northern Ireland.

More often, when we wish to know something about a **population**, we cannot possibly analyse all the cases belonging to it as they are either not available or the task of data collection is too costly in time and/or money. The larger the sample, the better the estimations will be, so a balance has to be struck between cost and accuracy. In industry the collection of data for analysis from a production line is often destructive and so large samples could reduce the profitability of the company. The science of quality control makes use of the techniques we shall study in this chapter.

By taking a representative **sample** from the population of interest and analysing it, we can find out all about the sample and also make **inferences** about the parent population. This is the best we can do in the light of limited knowledge. We cannot infer an exact result but a likely range of values together with a probability that this interval includes the 'true' population value. We generally wish, in the world of business, to be 95% confident that the interval calculated will include the true value, but this admits a 5% probability of being wrong! Sampling inevitably introduces error, **sampling error**, because each sample taken will produce a different estimate of the population value.

6.3 Sampling

Sampling theory is a whole subject in its own right! It is absolutely essential that a sample is as representative as possible of the population because any result produced from the sample is used to estimate a corresponding result for the population. Commonsense rightly suggests that larger samples will be more representative but more expensive to take and analyse. A random sample is ideal for statistical analysis but other methods have also been devised for when random sampling is not feasible. Some sampling methods are described very briefly below.

6.3.1 Simple random sampling

Simple random sampling assumes every member of the population has an equal chance of being independently selected. All members of the population are labelled with a number and random numbers should be used to select the sample. This is the best method of sampling, as independence of sample members is assumed by many statistical tests. Unfortunately all members of the population have to be available for selection and this is rarely the case.

6.3.2 Systematic sampling

Systematic sampling is useful when the whole sampling frame is not available. The population is listed and every nth member is included in the sample after the first has been selected randomly. Sampling from a production line may make use of this method.

6.3.3 Stratified random sampling

Stratified random sampling is useful when the population consists of a number of distinct subpopulations and there is more difference between the subpopulations than within each of them. The population is split into these differing groups – strata. A random subsample is then drawn from each, in proportion to the strata size. The human population might be split by age groups before each age group is sampled separately and the subsamples reunited for analysis.

6.3.4 Multistage sampling

Multistage sampling is useful when random sampling is virtually impossible because the population is very widely spread. The whole population is considered to be split into a number of primary units, each of which is composed of secondary units. Random samples are taken from each level of unit. The result of a general election might be forecast by this method.

6.3.5 Cluster sampling

Cluster sampling is useful when the population consists of a very large number of similar clusters which are geographically distant. In this case there is more difference within the clusters than between them. This is a form of multistage sampling in which the population is split into a series of small similar clusters. The clusters can then be split into smaller clusters or analysed as a whole.

6.3.6 *Quota sampling*

The sample is broken down according to certain controls, for example, age groups of men and women separately in the same proportion as their age groups in the population. Interviewers will then seek interviewees in these ratios to ensure that the sample is non-random. Market research often makes use of this method.

6.4 Point and interval estimates

There are two types of **estimate** for a **population parameter**:

A **point estimate** – one particular value;
An **interval estimate** – an interval centred on the point estimate.

6.4.1 *Point estimate*

Assuming the sample has been taken correctly, a point estimate for a population parameter is a single relevant statistic calculated from the sample which serves as the best estimate for the population parameter of interest. Gallup polls before a general election survey a sample of the electorate and use the results from the sample to estimate the proportion of the total electorate that is expected to vote for each political party. We shall concentrate on the point estimates, $\bar{x}$ for mean (μ), and, p for proportion (π) (see Chapter 3). A shorthand way of indicating that a value is only an estimate is $\hat{\mu}$ (μ hat) or $\hat{\pi}$ (π hat).

6.4.2 *Interval estimate (confidence interval)*

Sometimes it is more useful to quote two limits between which the population parameter is expected to lie, together with the probability of it lying in that range. For example, 'There is a 95% probability that between 65% and 69% of the electorate will vote for Labour.'

The limits are called the **confidence limits** and the interval between them is the **confidence interval (CI)**.

The **confidence interval** is, therefore, an interval centred on the point estimate within which we expect a population parameter to lie. The size of the sample and the standard deviation are used to calculate the **standard error of the mean**, $s/\sqrt{n}$, which is also called the standard deviation of the mean. The number of standard errors included in the interval is found from statistical probability tables: **normal tables** if we know the population standard deviation, **t-tables** if we do not.

The width of the confidence interval for a mean depends on three factors:

- The degree of confidence we wish to have in the result – the probability of it including the 'truth', for example, 95%
- The size of the sample, n
- The amount of variation among the members of the sample, that is, its standard deviation, s.

The effect of sample size and confidence level are explored in Examples 6.2 and 6.3. Most of this chapter concentrates on the estimation of means but we shall first look briefly at the estimation of proportions or percentages.

6.5 Confidence intervals for a percentage or proportion

The only difference between calculating confidence intervals for percentages or proportions is that percentages add up to 100 and proportions add up to 1. The methods are identical although the formulae differ. Percentage is more commonly used so Examples 6.1 to 6.3 will estimate population percentages.

The confidence interval for a population percentage or a proportion, π, is given by:

$$\pi = p \pm z\sqrt{\frac{p(100 - p)}{n}} \quad \text{for a percentage}$$

or   (6.1)

$$\pi = p \pm z\sqrt{\frac{p(1 - p)}{n}} \quad \text{for a proportion}$$

where: π is the unknown population percentage or proportion
p is the sample percentage or proportion, that is, the point estimate for π
z is the appropriate value from the normal tables
n is the sample size.

The standard errors are $\sqrt{\frac{p(100 - p)}{n}}$ for a percentage and $\sqrt{\frac{p(1 - p)}{n}}$ for a proportion.

The samples must be large (> 30) so that the normal tables may be applied to the formula.

We therefore estimate the confidence limits as being at z standard errors on either side of the sample percentage or proportion. The value of z from the normal tables depends upon the degree of confidence required. If the degree of confidence is 95% we are prepared to be incorrect in our estimate 5% of the time and we look for α to be 5% in the standard table. Confidence intervals are always symmetrical so we use the two-tail row for confidence intervals.

EXAMPLE 6.1

In order to investigate shopping preferences at a supermarket, a random sample of 175 shoppers were asked whether they preferred the bread baked in-store to that from the large national bakeries. 112 of those questioned stated that they preferred the bread baked in-store. Find the 95% confidence interval for the percentage of all the store's customers who prefer bread baked in-store.

The point estimate for the population percentage, π, is $p = \frac{112}{175} \times 100 = 64\%$

Use the formula: $\pi = p \pm z\sqrt{\frac{p(100 - p)}{n}}$ where $p = 64$ and $n = 175$

From Table D3 (Appendix D):

For 95% confidence, $\alpha = 5\%$, two tails gives $z = 1.96$

$$p \pm z\sqrt{\frac{p(100 - p)}{n}} \Rightarrow 64 \pm 1.96 \times \sqrt{\frac{64 \times 36}{175}} = 64 \pm 7.1$$

The confidence limits for the population percentage, π, are 56.9% and 71.1% or $56.9\% < \pi < 71.1\%$

The percentage of customers preferring bread baked in-store is between 57% and 71%.

Confidence intervals do not have to be produced at the 95% level of confidence. Let us see the effect of different levels of confidence.

EXAMPLE 6.2

Use the data in Example 6.1: $p = 64\%$ and $n = 175$ customers.

From the normal tables

For 90% confidence $z = 1.64$, and for 99% confidence $z = 2.58$

$$90\% \text{ CI} \quad 64 \pm 1.64 \times \sqrt{\frac{64 \times 36}{175}} = 64 \pm 6.0 \Rightarrow 58.0\% < \pi < 70.0\%$$

$$95\% \text{ CI} \quad \text{(from Example 6.1)} \qquad\qquad \Rightarrow 56.9\% < \pi < 71.1\%$$

$$99\% \text{ CI} \quad 64 \pm 2.58 \times \sqrt{\frac{64 \times 36}{175}} = 64 \pm 9.4 \Rightarrow 54.6\% < \pi < 73.4\%$$

We can see that our confidence that an interval includes the true population percentage increases as the width of the interval increases. If 100 samples of size 175 were taken we would expect 90 to include the true population percentage at the 90% level, and so on.

What happens as we vary the sample size?

EXAMPLE 6.3

Substitute different sample sizes in Example 6.1 with $p = 64\%$ and keep the confidence level at 95%. z will be 1.96 whatever the value of n.

$$n = 75 \quad 64 \pm 1.96 \times \sqrt{\frac{64 \times 36}{75}} = 64 \pm 10.9 \Rightarrow 53.1\% < \pi < 74.9\%$$

$$n = 175 \quad \text{(from Example 6.1)} \qquad\qquad \Rightarrow 56.9\% < \pi < 71.1\%$$

$$n = 275 \quad 64 \pm 1.96 \times \sqrt{\frac{64 \times 36}{275}} = 64 \pm 5.7 \Rightarrow 58.3\% < \pi < 69.7\%$$

Comparing the width of the three confidence intervals we can see that our estimations become more precise as the sample size increases. If we know the precision required, the appropriate **sample size** can be calculated from the same formula.

Clearly the larger the sample size the better from the statistical point of view but the more expensive will be the sampling exercise. Statistical sampling generally becomes a balancing act between precision and expense!

The effect of sample size and confidence level is the same whether we are investigating confidence levels for percentages or means.

6.6 Confidence intervals for one mean

The method for calculating the confidence interval for a mean is basically the same as the method for percentages. We first find the point estimate and then produce an interval around it with confidence limits equal to an appropriate number of standard errors. This number comes from either normal tables or *t*-tables depending on the answers to two questions:

- Do we know the population standard deviation?
- Is the sample a large one, that is, over 30?

If we know the population standard deviation the normal tables are satisfactory. If we need to estimate the population standard deviation from the sample there may be errors in its estimation so a wider confidence interval is needed. This is provided by the *t*-tables.

If we do not know the population standard deviation but the sample is large, generally taken to be over 30, the estimation error will be small, so, again, the normal table is appropriate. Both tables give similar results for large samples.

If we know the population standard deviation, σ, we make use of it in the calculation; if we do not know it then we use its point estimate, the sample standard deviation, s, instead.

The choice of statistical table is summarised in Table 6.1.

Table 6.1

Sample size	Population standard deviation	
	Known: standard error $= \dfrac{\sigma}{\sqrt{n}}$	Unknown: standard error $= \dfrac{s}{\sqrt{n}}$
Large	Normal tables	Normal tables
Small	Normal tables	*t*-tables

Do not be misled by Table 6.1 into thinking that the normal tables are used more often than the *t*-tables in estimation. We do not often know the population standard deviation, σ, and samples often are not as large as we would like, so the *t*-tables are more commonly used. We shall, however, first demonstrate the use of the normal tables before concentrating on the *t*-tables.

When using *t*-tables, just as with normal tables, we assume the population to be normally distributed. The convention is to assume, in the absence of the population data and for statistical reasons not discussed on this course, that if the sample is not extremely skewed the population is likely to be normal. If the data is not normal it is customary to work with medians rather than means.

6.6.1   Estimation of population mean when σ is known

If the population standard deviation, σ, is known we use the normal tables in the estimation of the population mean, μ. The formula for μ is:

$$\mu = \bar{x} \pm z \frac{\sigma}{\sqrt{n}} \tag{6.2}$$

where: μ is the unknown population mean to be estimated
$\bar{x}$ is the sample mean, that is, the point estimate for μ
z is the appropriate value from the normal tables
σ is the known population standard deviation
n is the sample size

EXAMPLE 6.4

For a **whole chain** of supermarkets it is **known** that the standard deviation of the hourly wages for part-time employees is £1.50.

A new supermarket is opened by the same chain in a new shopping precinct. The analysis of a random sample of the wages of 10 employees from this small supermarket gave a mean wage of £4.15 per hour. Assuming the same standard deviation (£1.50) calculate the 95% confidence interval for the average hourly wage for employees of the small branch and use it to see whether the figure could be the same as for the whole chain (£4.50).

95% CI

$\bar{x} = £4.15$, $\sigma = £1.50$, $n = 10$, $\alpha = 5\%$

From the condensed normal tables (Table D3) $z = 1.96$

$$\mu = \bar{x} \pm z\frac{\sigma}{\sqrt{n}} = 4.15 \pm 1.96 \times \frac{1.50}{\sqrt{10}} = 4.15 \pm 0.930$$

So the mean wage of the small supermarket is likely to be between £3.22 and £5.08 per hour.

$$£3.22 < \mu < £5.08$$

This interval includes the mean for the whole chain, £4.50, so the average hourly wage could be the same.

Note that the interval is rather wide because only a small sample was taken.

6.6.2   Estimation of population mean for large sample size and σ unknown

The calculation in this case is identical to that for Example 6.4. The usual practice is to use the normal tables. (If, however, you use the t-tables in error your result for a large sample will be the same!)

EXAMPLE 6.5

A random sample of 100 sales invoices was taken from a very large population of sales invoices. The average value was found to be £27.50 with a standard deviation of £7.50. Find a 90% confidence interval for the true mean value of all the sales.

90% CI

$\bar{x} = £27.50$, $s = £7.50$, $n = 100$, $\alpha = 10\%$

From the condensed normal tables $z = 1.64$

$$\mu = \bar{x} \pm z\frac{s}{\sqrt{n}} = 27.50 \pm 1.64 \times \frac{7.50}{\sqrt{100}} = 27.5 \pm 1.23$$

So the mean of the sales invoices for the whole population is likely to be between £26.27 and £28.73 per hour.

$$£26.27 < \mu < £28.73$$

6.6.3 Estimation of population mean for small sample size and σ unknown

The sample mean, $\bar{x}$, is used as the point estimate for μ as previously. The best estimate for the population standard deviation is s, the sample standard deviation, as produced by the σ_{n-1} button on the calculator in SD mode (see Section 3.4.4).

When using the t-tables: ν (nu) refers to the **degrees of freedom** of the sample. It equals $n - 1$ for single samples, as here. Looking at Table D2 (Appendix D), you can see that the value of t varies with ν and, therefore with the sample size. As the sample size increases, t approaches z, which is the value obtained from the normal tables.

EXAMPLE 6.6

An accountant at a small branch of a large company wishes to obtain some information about all its sales invoices. In order to obtain an estimate of this information, a sample of twenty-one invoices is randomly selected from the whole population.

Use the results in Table 6.2 to produce point estimates for μ and σ and then find a 99% confidence interval for all the branch's invoices. If the average invoice value for the whole company is £38.50, is this small branch in line with the rest of the company?

Table 6.2 Sample of invoices (£)

32.53	25.27	31.47	25.11	38.05	42.04	41.47
22.27	26.78	38.00	43.48	24.11	38.07	32.92
33.38	30.97	43.16	32.93	29.05	38.06	22.20

99% CI

From the calculator $\bar{x} = £32.92$, $s = £6.94$, $n = 21$, $\alpha = 1\%$

From the t-table for $\nu = n - 1 = 20$ degrees of freedom, two tails, 1%, $t = 2.85$

$$\mu = \bar{x} \pm t\frac{s}{\sqrt{n}} \Rightarrow 32.92 \pm 2.85 \times \frac{6.94}{\sqrt{21}}$$

$$= 32.92 \pm 4.32$$

$$£28.60 < \mu < £37.24$$

This interval does not include £38.50, so the small branch is out of line with the rest of the company. Its invoices are smaller.

How do we interpret the 99% confidence interval? If 100 similar samples were taken and analysed then we are confident that 99 of the intervals calculated would include the true population mean.

Make sure that you are happy with the use of the t-tables. The degrees of freedom, ν, is one less than the sample size and this determines which row of the table you use to find the required value of t. The column is determined by α (100 − the confidence level) and for confidence intervals we will always use two tails.

Computer analysis of Example 6.6 using Minitab and SPSS is shown in Section 6.12.

6.7 Confidence intervals for two independent means

We are going to extend the method to see if two populations could have the same mean or, alternatively, if two samples could have come from the same population as judged by their means. We assume that the standard deviations of both populations are the same.

There is a complicated formula for this but a simple approach can also be used. The confidence intervals for each sample mean can be found separately and compared to see if there is any overlap between them. If there is an overlap, the mean values could well be the same as they could both lie in the overlapping interval and so have a common value. If they do not overlap, then no common value exists and the samples are likely to have come from different populations. We assume, using this method, that both populations are normally distributed and independent of each other.

For example, if a supermarket chain wished to see whether a local advertising campaign had been successful they could sample customers' spending before and after the campaign and calculate confidence intervals for the mean spending of all customers at both times. If the intervals were found to overlap the means could be the same so the campaign may have had no effect. If, on the other hand, the intervals were quite separate, with the later sample giving the higher interval, then the campaign must have effectively increased sales.

EXAMPLE 6.7

The till slips of supermarket customers were sampled both before and after an advertising campaign and the results were analysed with the following results:

Before: $\bar{x}_B = £37.60$, $s_B = £6.70$, $n_B = 25$

After: $\bar{x}_A = £41.78$, $s_A = £5.30$, $n_A = 25$

Has the advertising campaign been successful in increasing the mean spending of all the supermarket customers? Calculate two 95% confidence intervals and compare the results.

For both, $n = 25$ so there are 24 degrees of freedom giving $t = 2.06$ for two tails, $\alpha = 5\%$.

$$\text{Before:} \quad \mu_B = \bar{x}_B \pm t\frac{s_B}{\sqrt{n_B}} \Rightarrow £37.60 \pm 2.06 \times \frac{6.70}{\sqrt{25}} = 37.60 \pm 2.76$$

$$£34.84 < \mu < £40.36$$

$$\text{After:} \quad \mu_A = \bar{x}_A \pm t\frac{s_A}{\sqrt{n_A}} \Rightarrow 41.78 \pm 2.06 \times \frac{5.30}{\sqrt{25}} \times == 41.78 \pm 2.18$$

$$£39.60 < \mu < £43.96$$

Interpretation

The sample mean had risen considerably but, because the confidence intervals overlap, the mean values for all the sales may still lie in the common ground. There may be no difference between the two means so we have not proved that the advertising campaign has been successful.

We shall improve on this method in the next example.

6.8 Confidence intervals for paired data

If two measures are taken from each case, that is, before and after, in every instance then the change, or difference, for each case can be calculated and a confidence interval for the mean of the changes calculated. If the data can be paired, that is, it is not independent, then this method should be used as a smaller interval is produced for the same sample size and percentage confidence.

$$\text{CI} \qquad \mu_d = \bar{x}_d \pm t \frac{s_d}{\sqrt{n_d}} \qquad\qquad (6.3)$$

$\bar{x}_x$, s_d and n_d refer to the calculated differences.

EXAMPLE 6.8

The supermarket statistician realised that there was a considerable range in customers' spending power and that the increases in individual customer's spending would show a smaller spread. In other words the 'before' and 'after' populations are not independent.

Before the next advertising campaign at the supermarket, he took a random sample of 10 customers, A to J, and collected their till slips. After the campaign, slips from the same 10 customers were collected and both sets of data recorded. Using the paired data, has there been any mean change at a 95% confidence level?

	A	B	C	D	E	F	G	H	I	J
Before	42.30	55.76	32.29	10.23	15.79	46.50	32.30	78.65	32.20	15.90
After	43.09	59.20	31.76	20.78	19.50	50.67	37.32	77.80	37.39	17.24

We first need to calculate the differences. The direction of subtraction does not matter but it seems sensible to take the earlier amounts away from the later ones to find the changes:

	A	B	C	D	E	F	G	H	I	J
Differences	0.79	3.44	−0.53	10.55	3.71	4.17	5.02	−0.85	5.19	1.34

We can now forget the original data sets and just work with the differences: $\bar{x}_d = £3.28$, $s_d = £3.37$, $n_d = 10$, $\alpha = 5\%$

$$\text{95\% CI} \quad \mu_d = \bar{x}_d \pm t \frac{s_d}{\sqrt{n_d}} \Rightarrow 3.28 \pm 2.26 \times \frac{3.37}{\sqrt{10}} \Rightarrow 3.28 \pm 2.41$$

$$£0.87 < \mu_d < £5.69$$

This interval does not include zero so the possibility of 'no change' has been eliminated. Because the mean amount spent after the campaign is greater than that before it, there has been a significant increase in spending.

If the confidence interval includes zero then there is a possibility that no change has taken place and the original situation has remained unchanged. If both limits have the same sign, as above, then zero is excluded and some change must have taken place.

When interpreting the change look carefully at the direction of the change as this will depend on your order of subtraction. In the above case it is obvious that there has been an increase in the average spending.

Computer analysis of Example 6.8 using Minitab and SPSS is shown in Section 6.12.

6.9 An extended example of confidence intervals

EXAMPLE 6.9

A large company was about to introduce a new training course for office recruits. A previous course had produced a pass rate of 74% on a standard test given to 1000 trainees and the company hoped that the new course would produce a better pass rate.

Find a 95% confidence interval for the percentage of trainees passing after the old training course

95% CI $\quad p = 74\%$, $n = 1000$, $\alpha = 5\%$

$$\pi = p \pm z \times \sqrt{\frac{p(100 - p)}{n}} \Rightarrow 74 \pm 1.96 \times \sqrt{\frac{74 \times 26}{1000}} \Rightarrow 74 \pm 2.72$$

$$\Rightarrow 71.3\% > \pi > 76.7\%$$

During the first month with the new test a random selection of 18 candidates were each given the standard test before training and a similar one after training so that their progress could be monitored. These test results are given in Table 6.3.

Table 6.3

Trainee	A	B	C	D	E	F	G	H	I
Before	42	56	64	57	45	43	62	51	39
After	56	73	87	68	59	62	79	62	60

Trainee	J	K	L	M	N	O	P	Q	R
Before	64	43	42	62	39	56	57	45	51
After	87	62	56	79	60	73	68	59	62

Use two separate 95% confidence intervals to see if there has been a mean improvement

Before the course:

$$\bar{x}_B = 51.0, \; s_B = 8.92, \; n_B = 18, \; t = 2.11 \text{ (by interpolation)}$$

$$\mu_B = x =_B \pm t \frac{s_B}{\sqrt{n_B}} \Rightarrow 51.0 \pm 2.11 \times \frac{8.92}{\sqrt{18}} \Rightarrow 51.0 \pm 4.44 \Rightarrow 46.6 < \mu < 55.4$$

After the course:

$$\bar{x}_A = 6.73, \; s_A = 10.1, \; n_A = 18, \; t = 2.11 \text{ (by interpolation)}$$

$$\mu_A = \bar{x}_A \pm t \frac{s_A}{\sqrt{n_A}} \Rightarrow 67.3 \pm 2.11 \times \frac{10.1}{\sqrt{18}} \Rightarrow 67.3 \pm 5.02 \Rightarrow 62.3 < \mu < 72.3$$

There is no overlap between these intervals, that is, no common ground, so the mean after the course must be different to the mean before the course and, looking at the two means, it is evident that an improvement has taken place. **Note**: this approach assumes that the two samples are independent. Although this assumption is incorrect in this example, the method serves as a useful indicator.

continued

EXAMPLE 6.9 *continued*

Assuming the data in Table 6.3 to be paired, use a 99% confidence interval for the mean improvement in the scores

Differences: 14, 17, 23, 11, 14, 19, 17, 11, 21, 23, 19, 14, 17, 21, 17, 11, 14, 11

From the sample: $\bar{x}_d = 16.3$, $s_d = 4.09$, $n_d = 18$, $t = 2.91$ (by interpolation)

$$\mu_d = \bar{x}_d \pm t \frac{s_d}{\sqrt{n_d}} \Rightarrow 16.3 \pm 2.91 \times \frac{4.09}{\sqrt{18}} \Rightarrow 16.3 \pm 2.81 \Rightarrow 13.5 < \mu < 19.1$$

Both limits are positive so there has definitely been an improvement in mean score.

Assuming the pass mark to be 60, find a point estimate for the percentage of the trainees who pass after the new course. This is only a small sample, but is there any evidence that the pass rate has improved?

From the sample: $p = \dfrac{14}{18} \times 100 = 77.8\%$

This is above the 71.3% to 76.7% interval for the old course so it is likely that the pass rate of the trainees has been improved by changing to the new course.

6.10 Interpretation of confidence intervals

We have interpreted individual confidence intervals within specific examples but will take a more general look at the situation.

The mean of a population is a constant figure. Its value may be unknown but it does not change. The variability is produced by the fact that each sample taken from the constant population is different, due to sampling error, and so produces different sample statistics, $\bar{x}$, s and n. These sample values are used to calculate a confidence interval for each sample and so these confidence intervals will vary from one sample to another. The confidence level is the percentage of confidence intervals, calculated from a very large number of samples, we would expect to include the true, constant population mean.

If we wish to be more sure of including the true value, but need to keep the sample size constant, then we have to use a higher confidence level (Example 6.2) but this can make the interval so wide that it is meaningless.

A preferable method is to keep the confidence level constant while increasing precision by taking larger samples (Example 6.3) but this can be expensive in both time and materials.

Figure 6.1

90%	← μ →	58–70
95%	← μ →	57–71
99%	← μ →	54.5–73.5

50 55 60 65 70 75

Figure 6.2

$n = 75$	← μ →	53–75
$n = 175$	← μ →	57–71
$n = 275$	← μ →	58–70

50 55 60 65 70 75

If we are comparing population parameters of independent populations by confidence intervals then our main interest centres on whether they overlap or not. If there is an overlap then there is common ground between them and the samples could have come from the same population. Assuming the same standard deviation, this indicates, of course, that there is no difference between the population means.

If we are comparing population parameters of dependent, paired data, then we are interested in whether the resulting confidence interval includes zero or not. If zero is included then there may be no difference between the populations, for example, in a 'before' and 'after' situation no change has taken place. If zero is excluded then some change has taken place and looking back at the direction of the calculated differences and the sign of their mean we can decide the direction of the change.

6.11 Further applications of estimations

Many decision-making applications involve estimating a population value from a sample taken from the same population. Estimations are widely used in quality control. Samples taken from a production line are analysed and the results used to estimate the quality of the whole of the production. These sample values, generally means, are plotted on a chart which is based on the expected distribution of the sample means when production is satisfactory. Confidence limits are drawn on these charts at 95% and 99% and act as warning and action limits for the standard of the production. More information can be found in advanced textbooks on quality control or decision making.

Chapter 13 describes how confidence intervals are often applied to forecasting. The quality of a forecasting model depends upon its likely errors, as judged by how well the model fits past data. These errors are used in the construction of the confidence interval so that the forecast can be stated with its expected precision.

Stock control is another useful application of confidence intervals to define the likely demand on stocks and indicate preferable stock-keeping levels.

6.12 Computer analysis of Examples 6.6 and 6.8

Example 6.6

```
Minitab   Variable   N   Mean   StDev   SE Mean   99.0  %   CI
          Invoices  21  32.92   6.94      1.51   (28.61,    37.23)
```

> 99% confidence interval
> from 28.6 to 37.2

SPSS

SPSS Descriptives			Statistic	Std. Error
INVOICES	Mean		32.9200	1.5135
	99% Confidence	Lower Bound	28.6135	
	Interval for Mean	Upper Bound	37.2265	
	5% Trimmed Mean		32.9296	
	Median		32.9200	
	Variance		48.107	
	Std. Deviation		6.9359	
	Minimum		22.20	
	Maximum		43.48	
	Range		21.28	
	Interquartile Range		12.0400	
	Skewness		−.029	.501
	Kurtosis		−1.193	.972

Example 6.8

```
Minitab   Variable   N   Mean   StDev   SE Mean    99.0  %   CI
          Invoices  10   3.28   3.37    1.06      (0.87,     5.69)
```

95% CI 0.87 to 5.6

SPSS

SPSS Descriptives			Statistic	Std. Error
DIFFS	Mean		3.2830	1.0649
	95% Confidence Interval for Mean	Lower Bound	.8739	
		Upper Bound	5.6921	
	5% Trimmed Mean		3.1089	
	Median		3.5750	
	Variance		11.341	
	Std. Deviation		3.3676	
	Minimum		−.85	
	Maximum		10.55	
	Range		11.40	
	Interquartile Range		4.6025	
	Skewness		.901	.687
	Kurtosis		1.376	1.334

Computer analysis of confidence intervals is included in Worksheets 15.2.3, 15.5.3 and 15.8.3.

6.13 Summary

In Chapter 6 we have introduced one of the most important concepts of statistics – estimating a population value from a sample taken from that population. We have looked at the inevitable sampling error introduced by this method but concluded that this is the best we can do in the circumstances because the truth about the whole population is unavailable. We accept that estimations may not be accurate so they are generally presented in the form of an interval which is expected to include the truth.

Confidence intervals can be calculated for all population parameters; in this chapter we have concentrated on means and percentages. We have used them as individual estimates, in pairs for comparing populations or to see if a particular value is acceptable as a likely population parameter.

Confidence intervals are centred on the point estimate of interest with the confidence limits defined by a certain number of standard errors on either side. The width of an interval depends upon the sample size, the variability of the data within the population and the confidence level employed. The confidence level is a measure of the probability that an interval does include the truth.

Table 6.4 summarises the use of different formulae. Do note that there are really only three formulae from which to choose by answering two questions:

- Is the parameter being estimated a mean or a percentage?
- If it is a mean, do we know the population standard deviation?

Table 6.4

Parameter	Number of samples	Population standard deviation	Data	Formula	Table
		known		$\bar{x} \pm z\dfrac{\sigma}{\sqrt{n}}$	normal table
	one large	unknown		$\bar{x} \pm z\dfrac{\sigma}{\sqrt{n}}$	normal table
		known		$\bar{x} \pm z\dfrac{\sigma}{\sqrt{n}}$	normal table
	one small	unknown		$\bar{x} \pm t\dfrac{s}{\sqrt{n}}$	t-table
Mean		unknown	paired	$\bar{x}_d \pm t\dfrac{s_d}{\sqrt{n_d}}$	t-table
	two small	unknown	unpaired	$\begin{cases} \bar{x}_1 \pm t\dfrac{s_1}{\sqrt{n_1}} \\ \bar{x}_2 \pm t\dfrac{s_2}{\sqrt{n_2}} \end{cases}$	t-table
Percentage → one large				$p \pm z\sqrt{\dfrac{p(100-p)}{n}}$	normal table

There are many other situations in which confidence intervals can be calculated (Wiemer, 1993, Chapter 9). We have confined ourselves in this chapter to those which are the simplest and most commonly used.

6.14 Tutorial 6 – Confidence intervals

Note: You may assume the populations to be normally distributed and of equal standard deviation where necessary.

6.1 A sample of 100 observations is taken from a population with unknown mean, μ, and **known** standard deviation, $\sigma = 4.5$. If the mean of the sample is 28.3, construct a confidence interval for μ for each of the following confidence levels.

(a) 90%   (b) 95%   (c) 99%

6.2 The management of a large national chain of motels decided to estimate the mean cost per room of repairing damage done by its customers during a holiday weekend. A random sample of 150 vacated rooms was inspected by the management and indicated a mean repair cost of £28.10 and a sample standard deviation of £12.40. Construct a 95% confidence interval for the mean repair cost, μ, of all its rooms.

6.3 Repeated assessments on a chemical determination of human blood during a laboratory analysis are known to be normally distributed. Ten assessments on a given sample of blood yielded the values:

1.002   0.958   1.014   1.009   1.041   0.962   1.058   1.024   1.019   1.020

Find a 99% confidence interval for the true chemical determination in the blood for repeated assessments of the sample.

6.4 A survey of 672 audited tax returns showed that 448 resulted in additional payments. Construct a 95% confidence interval for the true percentage of all audited tax returns that result in additional payments.

6.5 Firm A claims that it pays its clerical staff more per week on average than its rival, Firm B. Firm B disputes the claim so each examine a random sample of the salaries paid to their workers with the following results:

Firm A   Mean £343.00   Standard deviation £13.20 $n = 40$
Firm B   Mean £338.50   Standard deviation £14.30 $n = 50$

Calculate two 95% confidence intervals and compare them to see which firm is correct.

6.6 The same eleven workers performed a task using two different methods. The completion times, in minutes, for each task is given below:

Worker	1	2	3	4	5	6	7	8	9	10	11
Method A	15.2	14.6	14.2	15.6	14.9	15.2	15.6	15.0	16.2	15.7	15.6
Method B	14.5	14.8	13.8	15.6	15.3	14.3	15.5	15.0	15.6	15.2	14.8

Construct a 99% confidence interval for the average of the time differences and interpret your result.

6.7 The following data resulted from two independent random samples taken from two normal populations:

Sample 1: $n_1 = 11$, $\bar{x}_1 = 14$, $s_1 = 2$,   *Sample 2:* $n_2 = 9$, $\bar{x}_2 = 18$, $s_2 = 3$

Construct a 95% confidence interval for **each** sample. What does this imply about the populations?

6.8 A training manager wishes to see if there is any alteration in the aptitude of his trainees after they have been on a course. He gives each a test before they start the course and an equivalent one after they have completed it. Their scores are recorded below:

Trainee	A	B	C	D	E	F	G	H	I
Score before training	74	69	45	67	67	42	54	67	76
Score after training	69	76	56	59	78	63	54	76	75

Find the 95% confidence interval for the average **change** in score. Interpret your answer for the training manager.

6.9 In a survey carried out in a large city, 170 households out of a random sample of 250 owned at least one pet. Find the 95% confidence interval for the percentage of households in the city who own at least one pet.

   Does the result support a pet food manufacturer's claim that three quarters of all households have at least one pet?

6.10 The personnel department of a company developed an aptitude test for screening potential employees. The person who devised the test asserted that the mean mark attained would be 100. The following results were obtained with a random sample of applicants:

   $\bar{x} = 96$, $s = 5.2$, $n = 13$

Calculate a 95% confidence interval for the mean mark for all candidates and use it to see if the mean mark could be 100.

6.15 Supplementary exercise 6

Note: You may assume the populations to be normally distributed and of equal standard deviation where necessary.

6.11 The expected lifetime of electric bulbs produced by a given process was 1500 hours. A sample of 10, taken from a new batch, showed a lifetime of 1455 hours. The standard deviation of the production is known to be 90 hours. Use a 99% confidence interval to check the claim that the mean lifetime of the electric light bulbs has not changed.

6.12 Eleven cartons of sugar, each nominally containing 1 kg, were randomly selected from a large batch of cartons. The weights of sugar were:

1.02   1.05   1.08   1.03   1.00   1.06   1.08   1.01   1.04   1.07   1.00 kg

Using a 95% confidence interval, does this support the hypothesis that the mean weight for the whole batch is 1.00 kg?

6.13 A manufacturer wishes to assess the percentage of defective items in a large batch produced by a particular machine. He tests a random sample of 300 items and finds that 45 are defective. Calculate (a) a 95% confidence interval and (b) a 99% confidence interval for the percentage of defective items in the batch.

6.14 A sleeping drug and a neutral control were tested in turn on a random sample of ten patients in a hospital. The data below represent the **differences** between the number of hours sleep under the drug and the neutral control for each patient:

2.0   0.2   −0.4   0.3   0.7   1.2   0.6   1.8   −0.2   1.0

Calculate a 99% confidence interval and use it to test the claim that the drug would give more hours sleep on average than the control for all the patients in the hospital.

6.15 After treatment with a standard fertiliser, the average yield per hectare is 4.1 tonnes of wheat. A super fertiliser is developed and administered to 10 hectares. The yields were:

4.3   6.0   4.9   6.1   6.2   5.4   4.1   4.2   3.8   3.9 tonnes.

Use a 95% confidence interval to see whether this fertiliser has increased the average yield.

6.16 The times taken to complete a task were recorded for a sample of eight employees both before and after a period of training (min.):

Employee	1	2	3	4	5	6	7	8
Before training	15	14	18	14	15	17	13	12
After training	13	15	15	13	13	16	14	12

Use a 90% confidence interval to see if the training is effective or not.

6.17 A keyboard skills instructor uses two different training methods, A and B. At the end of the training period the **separate** groups being taught by these two methods were given the same test. The scores are shown below:

Method A	65	81	62	96	60	55	70	63	84	58
Method B	68	59	86	95	70	100	98	80	90	65

Assuming that these scores are normally distributed, is Method B better on average than Method A as judged by two 99% confidence intervals?

6.18 At the end of a course the same test was given to 100 male and 144 female trainees. The mean score for the males was 27.53 and the mean score for the females was 26.81. Assuming a common population standard deviation of 3.48, use a 99% confidence interval to see whether the groups performed differently?

6.19 In a large conglomerate the mean height of 50 security guards was 178 cm with a standard deviation of 5 cm, while that of 50 male office workers was 174 cm with a standard deviation of 7 cm. Use two confidence intervals, at the 95% level, to see if security officers have the same mean height as male office workers.

6.20 A new method of study for business management has been introduced. In order to test its effectiveness equivalent tests are given to the same students both before and after they have taken the course. Their test scores are shown below:

Student	A	B	C	D	E	F	G	H	I	J
Before	596	610	598	613	588	592	606	619	600	597
After	599	612	607	610	588	610	607	623	591	599

Assuming the score changes to be normally distributed, is this method of study effective as judged by a 99% confidence interval?

7 Hypothesis Testing

7.1 Objectives of this chapter

In Chapter 6 we used the analysis of samples taken from a population to estimate parameters, such as the unknown mean, of that population. In this chapter we use the value of the same sample statistic to see whether a corresponding figure claimed – hypothesised – for the whole population is likely to be true or not.

The uncertainty of using a sample value which required us to quote interval rather than point estimates in Chapter 6 now requires us to state that we are only, say, 95% sure that we have reached the right conclusion in rejecting the claim as being incorrect.

In this chapter we shall concentrate on the hypothesis tests concerned with means but will start, as we did with estimation, by looking at the general concept and then testing for hypothesised percentages. Having studied this chapter you should be able to understand the general concept of hypothesis testing; perform many of the simpler techniques; be aware of other techniques; and be able to interpret the results for non-statisticians in a business context.

7.2 General concept of hypothesis testing

When an estimate from a **sample** is used to test some belief, claim or **hypothesis** about the **population** the process is known as **hypothesis testing**. A hypothesis is tested at a particular **significance level**, α, so the technique may also be called **significance testing**. Some **conclusion** about the population is drawn from the **evidence** provided by the **sample**. The **conclusions** we reach following the **analysis of the sample** are based on **probability** and so, as with confidence intervals, there is always a small **chance of being incorrect**.

For example, a man who is charged with murder is assumed (hypothesised) to be innocent when he enters the courtroom. Clearly all the possible evidence will not be available (particularly if he is guilty!) so the jury have to reach a verdict (conclusion) from a sample. After the sample of evidence has been carefully considered he may be found 'beyond reasonable doubt', to be 'guilty' when he is actually innocent or 'not guilty' when he did, in fact, commit the crime. Two types of error could be made in reaching a conclusion but the stress is always on avoiding a miscarriage of justice, that is, in not finding an innocent man guilty. Note that the possible verdicts, in England, are 'guilty' and 'not guilty'; a man is never proved to be 'innocent'. The hypothesis of 'innocence' is either rejected – guilty – or not rejected – not guilty.

Similarly, in all hypothesis testing a claim, the **null hypothesis**, is stated and the conclusion which is most probably correct from the sample evidence is reached. The conclusion is always recorded with the probability of it being incorrect for the whole population. (The p-value from computer output is defined in Section 7.3). As in the courtroom the evidence is used to refute the hypothesised statement which will be allowed to stand unless the evidence is strong enough to cause its rejection.

As considered in Section 6.3, the problem of sampling error can never be eliminated completely when a sample is tested instead of the whole population. The same precautions are taken to make sure that the sample is as representative as possible of the population to which the conclusion applies.

The process of hypothesis testing is so widely used that a **common methodology** has been adopted.

7.3 Common methodology

Remember that a claim, or hypothesis, is made about the whole **population**. A **sample** is taken from that population and analysed. The results of the analysis are used to decide whether the claim is reasonable or not.

The common methodology for all hypothesis tests comprises six steps. Suppose a claim has been made that the mean male salary in a particular firm is £15 000.

1   State the **null hypothesis (H_0)**
    This is a statement about the population which may, or may not, be true. It will be in the form of an equation making some claim about the population.

    H_0: $\mu = £15\,000$ where μ is the population mean.

2   State the **alternative hypothesis (H_1)**
    This is the conclusion reached if the null hypothesis is rejected. It will include the terms 'not equal to' ($\neq$) for two tailed tests and 'greater than' (>) or 'less than' (<) for one tailed tests.

    H_1: $\mu \neq £15\,000$ or H_1: $\mu < £15\,000$, or H_1: $\mu > £15\,000$

3   State the **significance level (α) of the test**
    This is the proportion of the time you are willing to reject H_0 when it is in fact true. If not stated specifically a 5% (0.05) significance level is used. From computer output the p-value is the probability of H_0 being correct (see Section 7.12).

4   Find the **critical value**
    This is the value from the appropriate table which the test statistic is required to reach before we can reject H_0. It depends on the significance level and whether the test is one or two tailed.

5   Calculate the **test statistic**
    This value is calculated from the sample statistics, such as the mean and standard deviation, which are substituted into the appropriate formula to find the value of the test statistic. (Each formula is used in one specific type of hypothesis test only and so needs careful selection.)

6   Reach a **conclusion**
    Compare the values of the test statistic and the critical value. If the test statistic is greater than the critical value then we have enough evidence from the sample data to cause us to **reject the null hypothesis** and conclude that the alternative hypothesis is true; the mean salary is not £15 000. If the test statistic is not greater than the critical value then we do not have sufficient evidence and **so do not reject the null hypothesis**; the mean salary for the whole firm could be £15 000.

Note: We can prove that the null hypothesis is false but we can never prove it to be true because we only have a sample from all the evidence.

Figure 7.1 shows a graphical interpretation of the conclusion.

Figure 7.1

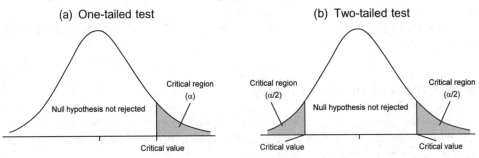

(a) One-tailed test

(b) Two-tailed test

If the test statistic falls into the critical region there is sufficient evidence for the null hypothesis to be rejected. Many students find the use of this type of diagram to be helpful in deciding whether or not to reject the null hypothesis. The total shaded area is the significance level, α (alpha), given as either a percentage (5%) or a decimal (0.05).

The methodology will seem simpler with specific examples so we shall first test some hypothesised proportions and then concentrate on means.

7.4 Tests for proportions

When testing for a population proportion much that we learnt in Section 6.5 needs to be remembered: take large samples; the normal tables are appropriate for the critical value; the same method applies for percentages and proportions.

Remember H_0 is shorthand for the null hypothesis, 'null' means nothing so in this context it means 'no difference from' whatever value is being claimed. H_1 is shorthand for the alternative hypothesis, or the conclusion we shall reach if we have to reject the null hypothesis.

H_0: $\pi = c$ where π is shorthand for the population proportion and c is its hypothesised value.

H_1: $\pi \neq c$, $\pi < c$ or $\pi > c$ (that is, anything but equal to c)

Significance level (α): as stated or 5% by default.

Critical value: from normal tables (Appendix D Table 3) using the appropriate number of tails and significance level.

Test statistic: calculated by $\dfrac{|p - \pi|}{\sqrt{\dfrac{\pi(100 - \pi)}{n}}}$ or $\dfrac{|p - \pi|}{\sqrt{\dfrac{\pi(1 - \pi)}{n}}}$ (7.1)

where p and π are the sample and population percentages or proportions, respectively

Conclusion: H_0 is rejected if the test statistic is so large that the sample could not have come from a population with the hypothesised proportion.

EXAMPLE 7.1

A company manufacturing a certain type of breakfast cereal claims that 60% of all housewives prefer that type to any other. A random sample of 300 housewives contains 165 who do prefer that type. At 5% significance is the true percentage as the company claims or lower?

continued

EXAMPLE 7.1 *continued*

Given: π is claimed to be 60%, $p = \dfrac{165}{300} \times 100 = 55\%$, $n = 300$

The claim is only wrong if the percentage is lower than 60%, so the test is one tailed.

H_0: $\pi = 60\%$ $\qquad$ H_1: $\pi < 60\%$

Significance level (α): 5% (0.05)

Critical value: normal tables, one tail, $z = 1.64$

Because the test is one tailed and 'less than', we know that the critical region is in the lower tail. Most normal tables include only positive values so we need to compare the absolute value of the test statistic with the always positive critical value.

Figure 7.2

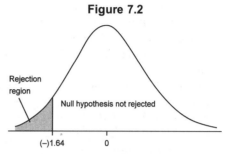

Rejection region

Null hypothesis not rejected

(−)1.64 $\qquad$ 0

Test statistic: $\dfrac{|p - \pi|}{\sqrt{\dfrac{\pi(100 - \pi)}{n}}} \Rightarrow \dfrac{|55 - 60|}{\sqrt{\dfrac{60(100 - 60)}{300}}} = \dfrac{5}{\sqrt{8}} = 1.77$

Conclusion: test statistic exceeds critical value so reject H_0. The percentage preferring the type manufactured by this company is lower than 60%.

EXAMPLE 7.2

An auditor claims that 10% of a company's invoices are incorrect. To test this claim a random sample of 200 invoices is checked and 24 are found to be incorrect. Test at the 1% significant level if the auditor's claim is supported by the sample evidence.

Given: π is claimed to be 10%, $p = \dfrac{24}{200} \times 100 = 12\%$, $n = 200$

The claim can be judged wrong in either direction so the test is two tailed.

H_0: $\pi = 10\%$ $\qquad$ H_1: $\pi \neq 10\%$

Significance level (α): 1% (0.01)

Critical value: normal tables, two tails, $\alpha = 0.01$, $z = 2.58$

Figure 7.3

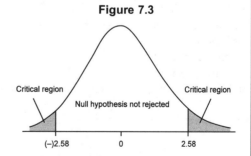

Critical region

Null hypothesis not rejected

Critical region

(−)2.58 $\qquad$ 0 $\qquad$ 2.58

Test statistic: $\dfrac{|p - \pi|}{\sqrt{\dfrac{\pi(100 - \pi)}{n}}} \Rightarrow \dfrac{|12 - 10|}{\sqrt{\dfrac{10(100 - 10)}{200}}} = \dfrac{2}{\sqrt{4.5}} = 0.943$

Conclusion: test statistic is less than critical value so H_0 is not rejected. The percentage of incorrect invoices is consistent with the auditor's claim of 10%.

For each of these examples we have worked through the six steps described in Section 7.3. Had we decided to use proportions, rather than percentages, the method would have been the same except that $(100 - p)$ would have been replaced by $(1 - p)$ in the formula and both the values for p and π would have been decimal values between 0 and 1 rather than percentages between 0 and 100.

7.5 Testing for one mean

The methods described in this section require the population to be measured on interval or ratio scales and to be normally distributed. You may assume this to be so for any data presented here. The treatment of non-normal data will be covered in Section 7.9.

As with Section 6.6 on confidence intervals we have to ask whether the sample size is large or small and whether the population standard deviation is known or has to be estimated from the sample before deciding which test to use. The methods are basically the same but the answers to these questions, as in Section 6.6, determine the formula and table to be used (see Table 7.1).

Table 7.1

| | Population standard deviation | |
Sample size	Known: standard error $= \dfrac{\sigma}{\sqrt{n}}$	Unknown: standard error $= \dfrac{s}{\sqrt{n}}$
Large	Normal tables	Normal tables
Small	Normal tables	t-tables

7.5.1 Method of testing for one mean

A **mean value** is hypothesised for the population. A sample is taken from that population and its mean value calculated. The sample mean is then used to see if the value hypothesised for the population is reasonable or not. If the population standard deviation is not known then the sample standard deviation is calculated and used to estimate it. The appropriate test to use depends on whether this estimated value has been used or not.

$H_0: \mu = c$ } where μ is the population mean and c is the hypothesised

$H_1: \mu \neq c, \mu < c$ or $\mu > c$ } value

Significance level: $\alpha = 5\%$, or as stated in the question.

Critical value: From normal (z) table or t-tables, significance level, number of tails, degrees of freedom.

The normal table is used if we know the population standard deviation and do not need to estimate it. If we need to estimate the population standard deviation then a slightly less stringent critical value is found from the t-table.

Test statistic: σ known, $z = \dfrac{|\bar{x} - \mu|}{\sigma/\sqrt{n}}$ \hfill (7.2)

or σ unknown so s is needed $t = \dfrac{|\bar{x} - \mu|}{s/\sqrt{n}}$ \hfill (7.3)

where $\bar{x}$ and μ are the means of the sample and population respectively and s and σ are their standard deviations.

Conclusion: Compare test statistic with critical value.
Decide whether to reject H_0 or not.
Conclude in terms of question.

7.5.2   *Testing for one mean when σ is known*

The population standard deviation is known so the z formula and the normal table are appropriate.

EXAMPLE 7.3

A packaging device is set to fill detergent packets with a mean weight of 150 g. The standard deviation is **known** to be 5.0 g. It is important to check the machine periodically because if it is overfilling it increases the cost of the materials, whereas if it is underfilling the firm is liable to prosecution. A random sample of 25 filled boxes is taken and weighed, giving a mean net weight of 152.5 g. Can we conclude that the machine is no longer producing the mean net weight of 150 g?
   Use a 5% significance level (0.05 significance level).

Given $\mu = 150$ g? $\sigma = 5$ g, $n = 25$, $\bar{x} = 152.5$ g

The machine can 'no longer produce the mean net weight of 150 g' by producing packets that are too heavy or too light, therefore the appropriate test is two tailed.

H_0: $\mu = 150$ g H_1: $\mu \neq 150$ g

Significance level (α): 5% (0.05)

Critical value: σ is known therefore use normal tables, 5%, two tailed, critical value is 1.96.

Figure 7.4

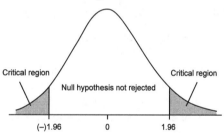

Test statistic: $z = \dfrac{|\bar{x} - \mu|}{\sigma/\sqrt{n}} \Rightarrow \dfrac{152.5 - 150}{5/\sqrt{25}} = \dfrac{2.5}{1} = 2.5$

Conclusion: The test statistic exceeds the critical value so reject H_0 and conclude that the mean weight produced is no longer 150 g.

7.5.3   *Testing for one mean when σ is not known and the sample is large*

Because the sample is large the estimation of the population standard deviation will be accurate so the z formula and the normal tables are appropriate.

EXAMPLE 7.4

The mean and standard deviation of the weights produced by the packaging device set to fill detergent packets with a mean weight of 150 g, are known to drift upwards over time due to the normal wearing of some bearings. Obviously it cannot be allowed to drift too far so a large random sample of 100 boxes is taken and the contents weighed. This sample has a mean weight of 151.0 g and a standard deviation of 6.5 g. Can we conclude that the mean weight produced by the machine has increased? Use a 5% significance level (0.05 significance level).

continued

EXAMPLE 7.4 *continued*

Given $\mu = 150$ g? $n = 100$, $\bar{x} = 151.0$ g, $s = 6.5$ g

We are only interested in whether the mean weight has increased or not so a one tailed test is appropriate.

H_0: $\mu = 150$ g $\qquad$ H_1: $\mu > 150$ g

Significance level (α): 5% (0.05)

Critical value: σ is unknown but the sample is large therefore use normal tables, 5%, one tailed, critical value = 1.64.

Figure 7.5

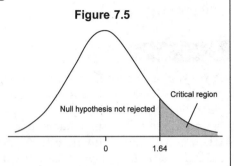

Critical region

Null hypothesis not rejected

0 $\qquad$ 1.64

Test statistic: $z = \dfrac{|\bar{x} - \mu|}{s/\sqrt{n}} \Rightarrow \dfrac{|151.0 - 150|}{6.5/\sqrt{100}} = \dfrac{1.0}{0.65} = 1.54$

Conclusion: The test statistic does not exceed the critical value so we do not reject H_0 but conclude that the machine may still be producing a mean weight of 150 g.

7.5.4 Testing for one mean when σ is not known and the sample is small

Since the population standard deviation is unknown it has to be estimated from the sample standard deviation. Because the sample is small, this estimate will not be very accurate and so the t-formula and tables are appropriate. This group of tests are referred to as t-tests and are the most widely used type of hypothesis tests.

Remember from Chapter 6 that the t-tables (Appendix D Table 2) require the use of degrees of freedom. For a single sample this is one less than the sample size, $n - 1$.

EXAMPLE 7.5 One sample t-test

The personnel department of a company has developed an aptitude test for screening potential employees. The person who devised the test asserted that the mean mark attained would be 100. The following results were obtained with a random sample of applicants: $\bar{x} = 96$, $s = 5.2$, $n = 13$. Test the hypothesis that the mean mark is 100 against the alternative that the mean mark is less than 100, at the 1% level.

Given: $\mu = 100$? $\bar{x} = 96$, $s = 5.2$, $n = 13$

H_0: $\mu = 100$ $\qquad$ H_1: $\mu < 100$

Significance level (α): 1% (0.01)

Critical value: σ is unknown so use t-tables at 1% significance, one tail, $n - 1 = 12$ degrees of freedom, critical value $= 2.68$

Figure 7.6

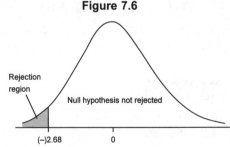

Rejection region

Null hypothesis not rejected

(–)2.68 $\qquad$ 0

Test statistic: $t = \dfrac{|\bar{x} - \mu|}{s/\sqrt{n}} \Rightarrow \dfrac{|96 - 100|}{5.2/\sqrt{13}} = \dfrac{4}{1.44} = 2.77$

Conclusion: The test statistic is larger than the critical value so reject H_0 and conclude that the mean mark is likely to be less than 100.

7.6 Test for two independent means

Note: This section may, or may not, be included at the discretion of your lecturer.

If we have **two independent sets of data** we can test whether the difference between their means could be zero in a similar manner to the way we tested whether the mean from a single set of data could have a particular population value. In other words, could both samples have come from the same population?

The first four steps of the method of hypothesis testing are the same as those listed in Section 7.3: state the null hypothesis and alternative hypothesis, state the significance level and calculate the critical value. The test statistic needs to incorporate the parameters of both samples and is calculated from a different formula. Again, the null hypothesis is rejected if the test statistic is greater than the critical value.

7.6.1 Testing the difference between two means where σ_1 and σ_2 are known

In this case we know the standard deviations of the populations which may, or may not, be the same. We do not need to estimate the standard deviations, so we use the normal table to find the critical value.

H_0: $\mu_1 - \mu_2 = 0$ (or c) or H_0: $\mu_1 = \mu_2$ H_1: $\mu_1 - \mu_2 \neq 0$ (or c) or $\mu_1 \neq \mu_2$

Significance level: as stated in question or $\alpha = 5\%$ by default

Critical value: from normal tables since population standard deviations are known

Test statistic: $z = \dfrac{|\bar{x}_1 - \bar{x}_2|}{\sqrt{\dfrac{\sigma_1^2}{n_1} + \dfrac{\sigma_2^2}{n_2}}}$ (7.4)

where $\bar{x}_1$, $\bar{x}_2$, are the sample means, σ_1, σ_2 are the known standard deviations, n_1, n_2 are the sample sizes.

Conclusion: H_0 is rejected if the test statistic is so large that the two samples could not have come from the same population.

EXAMPLE 7.6

A retailing company wishes to know whether there is any difference between the average size of the customer accounts in its Leeds and Bradford stores. Past experience has shown that the standard deviations for the two stores are £16 and £20 respectively.

Samples of 100 accounts taken from each branch gave mean values of £66.20 at Leeds and £70.40 at Bradford. Does this provide evidence, at 5% significance, that the mean account size at the two branches is different?

'Different' can be in either direction so a two tailed test is appropriate.

Given: $\bar{x}_L = £66.20$, $\sigma_L = £16.00$, $\bar{x}_B = £70.40$,

       $\sigma_B = £20.00$, $n_L = n_B = 100$

H_0: $\mu_L = \mu_B$ H_1: $\mu_L \neq \mu_B$

Significance level: not stated so $\alpha = 5\%$ used by default.

Critical value: from normal tables since both σ values are known, two tails, 5%, critical value is 1.96

Figure 7.7

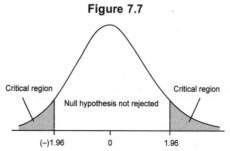

Critical region   Critical region

Null hypothesis not rejected

(−)1.96   0   1.96

continued

EXAMPLE 7.6 *continued*

Test statistic: $z = \dfrac{|\bar{x}_1 - \bar{x}_2|}{\sqrt{\dfrac{\sigma_1^2}{n_1} + \dfrac{\sigma_2^2}{n_2}}} \Rightarrow \dfrac{70.40 - 66.20}{\sqrt{\dfrac{16^2}{100} + \dfrac{20^2}{100}}} = \dfrac{4.20}{2.561} = 1.64$

Conclusion: H_0 not rejected as the test statistic is less than the critical value. The two samples could have come from the same population so the mean sales of the two stores could be the same.

7.6.2 Testing the difference between two means where σ_1 and σ_2 are unknown

Assumptions: the use of this test requires the samples to come from normal populations and equal variance.

We must first test whether the standard deviations of the two sets of data are not too different from each other as indicated by the F-test.

An **F-test** is generally used to test for equality of sample variances, which are (standard deviation)^2. This is a test for checking the ratio of the two variances against a table value to ensure that it is not too far from unity.

F-test

H_0: $\sigma_1 = \sigma_2$ H_1: $\sigma_1 \neq \sigma_2$

Significance level: as stated in question or $\alpha = 5\%$ by default

Critical value: from the F-tables (Table D4) with $(n_1 - 1)$, $(n_2 - 1)$ degrees of freedom.

Test statistic: $F = \dfrac{s_1^2}{s_2^2}$ $\hspace{4cm}$ (7.5)

where s_1 and n_1 refer to the sample with the larger standard deviation so that F is always greater than 1.

Conclusion: If the test statistic is less than the critical value then the variances can be assumed to be the same. If the sample variances can be assumed to be the same, the standard deviations can be combined, or pooled, in order to get a better estimate of the population standard deviation. If the data fails the F-test then a Mann–Whitney test should be used rather than a two sample t-test (see Section 7.8).

Most students prefer to calculate the pooled standard deviation separately so that a single figure can be substituted for the standard deviation, s_p, in the formula for the test statistic.

The formula used for pooling the standard deviations is:

$$s_p = \sqrt{\dfrac{(n_1 - 1)s_1^2 + (n_2 - 1)s_2^2}{n_1 + n_2 - 2}} \hspace{3cm} (7.6)$$

where s_1 and s_2 are the standard deviations of samples 1 and 2 respectively.

This is really combining the sums of squares which we used to calculate the separate standard deviations.

Two sample t-test

H_0: $\mu_1 - \mu_2 = 0$ or alternatively $\mu_1 = \mu_2$ $(\mu_1 - \mu_2 = c)$

H_1: $\mu_1 - \mu_2 \neq 0$ or alternatively $\mu_1 \neq \mu_2$ $(\mu_1 - \mu_2 \neq c)$

Significance level: as stated or $\alpha = 5\%$ by default.

Critical value: from t-tables, since population standard deviations are not known, with $(n_1 + n_2 - 2)$ degrees of freedom.

Test statistic: calculated by $t = \dfrac{|\bar{x}_1 - \bar{x}_2|}{s_P\sqrt{\dfrac{1}{n_1} + \dfrac{1}{n_2}}}$ or $t = \dfrac{||\bar{x}_1 - \bar{x}_2| - c|}{s_P\sqrt{\dfrac{1}{n_1} + \dfrac{1}{n_2}}}$ $\qquad$ (7.7)

where s_P is the pooled standard deviation.

Conclusion: H_0 is rejected if the test statistic is larger than the critical value, that is, so large that the two samples could not have come from populations with mean difference of zero (or c) as hypothesised.

EXAMPLE 7.7

Firm A claims that it pays its clerical staff on average at least £10 per week more than its rival, Firm B. Firm B disputes the claim so each company examines a random sample of the salaries paid to their workers with the following results:

$\quad$ Firm A $\quad$ Mean £343.00 $\quad$ Standard deviation £13.20 $\quad$ $n = 40$
$\quad$ Firm B $\quad$ Mean £338.50 $\quad$ Standard deviation £14.30 $\quad$ $n = 50$

What conclusion can be drawn from this evidence at the 5% level of significance?

First carry out an F-test to check that the standard deviations can be pooled.

H_0: $\sigma_A = \sigma_B$ $\qquad\qquad$ H_1: $\sigma_A \neq \sigma_B$

Significance level: $\alpha = 5\%$

Critical value: from the F-tables with $(n_1 - 1)$, $(n_2 - 1)$ degrees of freedom
$\qquad\qquad$ $F_{0.05}(39, 49) = 1.83$ (See Appendix D, Table 4)

Test statistic: $\dfrac{s_1^2}{s_2^2} = \dfrac{14.3^2}{13.2^2} = 1.174$

Conclusion: The test statistic is less than the critical value. H_0 is not rejected as there may be no difference in the population variances. These may be combined to give an improved estimate of a common population value.

Next pool the standard deviations:

$$s_P = \sqrt{\dfrac{n_1 - 1)s_1^2 + (n_2 - 1)s_2^2}{n - n_2 - 2}} \Rightarrow \sqrt{\dfrac{39 \times 13.2^2 + 49 \times 14.3^2}{88}} = £13.82$$

This figure, s_P, is now used as the estimated common standard deviation for the population.

continued

EXAMPLE 7.7 *continued*

H_0: $\mu_A - \mu_B = £10$

H_1: $\mu_A - \mu_B < £10$

Significance level: $\alpha = 5\%$

Critical value: from t-tables, since population standard deviations are not known, with 88 degrees of freedom, one tailed test, critical value = 1.66

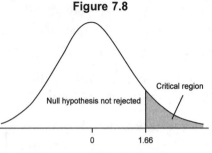

Figure 7.8

Test statistic: calculated by $t = \dfrac{|(343 - 338.5) - 10|}{13.82\sqrt{\dfrac{1}{40} + \dfrac{1}{50}}} = \dfrac{5.5}{2.93} = 1.87$

Conclusion: test statistic > critical value so reject H_0, the difference is less than £10.

7.7 Testing for means of paired data

We may need to say whether there is any difference between two sets of **paired data** or whether both sets could have come from the same population. As with confidence intervals (Section 6.8), if the two sets of data represent two measurements on each case then a paired t-test is appropriate. In this test the 'difference' between each pair of data points is first calculated and then these differences are treated as a single set of data in order to consider whether there has been any significant change, or whether the differences could have occurred by chance.

7.7.1 Hypothesis test for the difference of means of paired data

If we have 'pairs' of measurements, then the differences between each 'pair' can be calculated and the mean of the resulting values compared to zero, or some other hypothesised value, using the t-test for a single sample as used previously.

This test is known as the **paired t-test**.

H_0: $\mu_d = 0$ where μ_d is the mean of the differences.

H_1: $\mu_d \neq 0$, $\mu_d < 0$, or $\mu_d > 0$

Alternatively: H_0: $\mu_d = c$, where c is the value of the hypothesised change

Significance level: $\alpha = 5\%$, or as stated in question.

Critical value: t-table, degrees of freedom, significance level.

Test statistic: $t = \dfrac{\bar{x}_d - 0}{s_d / \sqrt{n_d}}$ (7.8)

Conclusion: Compare the test statistic with the critical value.
Decide whether to reject H_0 or not.
Conclude in terms of question.

EXAMPLE 7.8

A training manager wishes to see if there has been any alteration in the ability of his trainees after they have been on a course. The trainees take an aptitude test before they start the course and an equivalent one after they have completed it. The scores are recorded in Table 7.2. Has any change taken place at a 5% significance level?

Table 7.2

Trainee	A	B	C	D	E	F	G	H	I
Score before training	74	69	45	67	67	42	54	67	76
Score after training	69	76	56	59	78	63	54	76	75

First the 'changes' are computed and then a simple *t*-test is carried out on these differences.

Changes: $-5, +7, +11, -8, +11, +21, 0, +9, -1$

From sample changes $\bar{x}_d = 5.0$, $s_d = 9.206$, $n_d = 9$

H_0: $\mu_d = 0$; H_1: $\mu_d \neq 0$

Significance level (α): 5% (0.05)

Critical value: *t*-table, 8 degrees of freedom, 5%, two tailed, critical value = 2.31

Figure 7.9

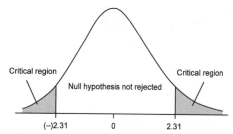

Critical region   Null hypothesis not rejected   Critical region

$(-)2.31$ 0   2.31

Test statistic: $t = \dfrac{\bar{x}_d}{s_d/\sqrt{n_d}} = \dfrac{5.0}{9.206/\sqrt{9}} = \dfrac{5.0}{3.07} = 1.63$

Conclusion: The test statistic is less extreme than the critical value so do not reject H_0. There may be no change due to the training.

7.8 An extended example

EXAMPLE 7.9

A large company was about to introduce a new training course for office recruits. 74% of the previous trainees had passed the aptitude test taken after the end of the previous course and the company hoped that the new course would produce a better pass rate. The pass mark for the test is 60%. (The same data was used in Example 6.8 for confidence intervals.)

During the first month with the new test a random selection of 18 candidates were each given a standard test before training and a similar one after training so that their progress could be monitored. These results are given in Table 7.3.

continued

EXAMPLE 7.9 *continued*

Table 7.3

Trainee	A	B	C	D	E	F	G	H	I
Before	42	56	64	57	45	43	62	51	39
After	56	73	87	68	59	62	79	62	60

Trainee	J	K	L	M	N	O	P	Q	R
Before	64	43	42	62	39	56	57	45	51
After	87	62	56	79	60	73	68	59	62

A random selection of 50 results later in the year gave a pass rate of 84%.

We shall use this data to test the following hypotheses:

- The pass rate has improved at the 1% significance level
- The average mark after training is 75%, using $\alpha = 0.05$
- The average increase in marks is more than 10%, using $\alpha = 0.01$
- If the data were not paired, the increase in mean marks would be more than 10%, using $\alpha = 0.01$.

The pass rate has improved at the 1% significance level

$\pi = 74\%, p = 84\%, n = 50$

$H_0: \pi = 74\%,$ $\qquad$ $H_1: \pi > 74\%$

Critical value: Proportion, z-table, 1%, 1 tailed, critical value is 2.33

Test statistic: $z = \dfrac{|p - \pi|}{\sqrt{\dfrac{\pi(100 - \pi)}{n}}} \Rightarrow \dfrac{|84 - 74|}{\sqrt{\dfrac{74 \times 26}{50}}} = \dfrac{10}{6.20} = 1.61$

Conclusion: The test statistic is less than the critical value so H_0 cannot be rejected. The pass rate might still be 74% and so it might not have increased for all the trainees.

The average mark after training is 75%, use $\alpha = 0.05$

$\mu = 75\%$? From sample: $\bar{x}_A = 67.3$, $s_A = 10.1$, $n_A = 18$

$H_0: \mu = 75,$ $\qquad$ $H_1: \mu \neq 75$ (The claim can be proved incorrect at either end.)

Critical value: small sample, σ unknown, 5% two tails, 17 degrees of freedom, critical value is 2.11

Test statistic: $t = \dfrac{|\bar{x} - \mu|}{s/\sqrt{n}} \Rightarrow \dfrac{|67.3 - 75|}{10.1/\sqrt{18}} = \dfrac{7.7}{2.38} = 3.23$

Conclusion: The test statistic exceeds the critical value so H_0 is rejected. The mean mark after training is not 75%. (Be careful not to conclude that it is less than 75% because that was not the alternative hypothesis.)

The average increase in marks is more than 10%, use $\alpha = 0.01$

Differences: 14, 17, 23, 11, 14, 19, 17, 11, 21, 23, 19, 14, 17, 21, 17, 11, 14, 11

From the sample: $\bar{x}_d = 16.3$, $s_d = 4.09$, $n_d = 18$

continued

EXAMPLE 7:9 *continued*

Paired t-test

H_0: $\mu_d = 10$, (No matter how the claim is phrased H_0 is always of equality)

H_1: $\mu_d > 10$ (H_0 can be proved incorrect only at the upper end.)

Critical value: small sample, σ unknown, 1% one tail, 17 degrees of freedom, critical value is 2.57

Test statistic: $t = \dfrac{|\bar{x}_d - \mu_d|}{s_d/\sqrt{n_d}} \Rightarrow \dfrac{|16.3 - 10|}{4.09/\sqrt{18}} = \dfrac{6.3}{0.964} = 6.54$

Conclusion: The test statistic exceeds the critical value so H_0 is rejected. The mean increase is over 10%

If the data were not paired, the increase in mean marks would be more than 10%, use $\alpha = 0.01$

Treating the scores before and after the course as independent samples, we first need their individual summary statistics.

Two-sample t-test

Before the course: $\bar{x}_B = 51.0, s_B = 8.92, n_B = 18$

After the course: $\bar{x}_A = 67.3, s_A = 10.1, n_A = 18$

Check that the standard deviations are similar enough to be pooled

$\dfrac{s_A^2}{s_B^2} = \dfrac{10.1^2}{8.92^2} = 1.282$

From the F-tables at 5% significance with $(n_1 - 1)$, $(n_2 - 1)$ degrees of freedom, $F_{0.05}(17, 17) = 2.28$ (see Appendix D, Table D4). The standard deviations pass the F-test.

Pool the standard deviations:

$s_P = \sqrt{\dfrac{(n_B - 1)S_B^2 + (n_A - 1)S_A^2}{n_B + n_A - 2}} \Rightarrow \sqrt{\dfrac{17 \times 8.92^2 + 17 \times 10.1^2}{34}} = 9.53$

This figure, s_P, is now used as the estimated common standard deviation.

Carry out the hypothesis test

H_0: $\mu_A - \mu_B = 10\%$ $\qquad\qquad$ H_1: $\mu_A - \mu_B > 10\%$

Significance level: $\alpha = 1\%$

Critical value: from t-tables, since population standard deviations are not known, with 34 degrees of freedom, one tailed test, critical value = 2.44

Test statistic: $t = \dfrac{|\bar{x}_A - \bar{x}_B| - c}{s_P\sqrt{\dfrac{1}{n_A} + \dfrac{1}{n_B}}} = \dfrac{|(67.3 - 51.0) - 10|}{9.53\sqrt{\dfrac{1}{18} + \dfrac{1}{18}}} = \dfrac{6.3}{3.18} = 1.98$

Conclusion: The test statistic is less than the critical value so H_0 is not rejected. The increase could be 10%, that is, it has not been shown to be significantly more than 10%.

This extended example demonstrates that the paired test is better able to reject the null hypothesis and so should always be used when appropriate.

7.9 Non-parametric tests

These tests are not part of the course syllabus but are included here for completeness. If the **sample** is not normally distributed then we cannot assume that the **population** has a normal distribution. Alternatively if the information is only ordered, that is, ordinal, instead of being interval we cannot use the parametric tests which **assume interval data and normality in the population**.

For this reason alternative tests have been produced which are less **powerful** but do not need the population to be normal. These non-parametric tests are also called 'distribution free' tests because no assumptions are made about the distribution of the parent population and they are valid for ordinal as well as quantitative data.

Each of the parametric tests that we use has a non-parametric equivalent. The most common ones are described briefly, with a single worked example of each, below.

- The **sign test**, or the **Wilcoxon Signed rank test**, is used instead of the one sample *t*-test.
- The **Wilcoxon matched pairs test** is used instead of the paired *t*-test
- The **Mann–Whitney U-test** is used instead of the two sample *t*-test. This is also known as the **Wilcoxon rank sum test**.

If your data are ordinal then non-parametric tests are always appropriate because conclusions drawn from parametric tests will not be valid.

Non-parametric tests are mainly used for data which cannot be assumed to be normally distributed. Normality can be checked by examination of a histogram or a box plot of the sample data. If using a computer package a Kolmogorov–Smirnov, or equivalent, test for normality should be carried out.

Parametric tests are more **powerful** than their non-parametric equivalents and should always be used in preference if the data do not infringe any of the necessary assumed conditions.

Do note that for non-parametric – as opposed to parametric – tests, the smaller of the two totals is the test statistic. The rejection region is therefore that which is smaller than the table value.

7.9.1   The sign test

This test, which is not powerful, compares the **sample median** with a **hypothesised median** by seeing how many sample members are above it (positive) and how many are below it (negative). If the sample median is close to the hypothesised median then there will be approximately the same number of **positive** and **negative** results.

Because orderings rather than actual measurements are involved, the sign test is acceptable if the distribution is not symmetrical, that is, when the mean would not be an appropriate measure of centrality.

The sign test is also used to detect significant **change** by comparing the number of **positive changes** with the number of **negative changes**. If no change has taken place for the whole population then the numbers of small random positive and negative changes would be expected to be nearly the same.

EXAMPLE 7.10

Pre- and post-test scores after a particular training course are known to be non-normal in their distribution. A sample of the scores, with the calculated changes, is given in Table 7.4.

Table 7.4

Pre-test	67	71	83	69	68	36	52	72	56
Post-test	58	62	84	67	72	38	63	72	55
Changes	−9	−9	+1	−2	+4	+2	+11	0	−1
Pre-test	64	76	83	69	68	36	52	72	56
Post-test	59	76	84	69	72	38	63	74	66
Changes	−5	0	+1	0	+4	+2	+11	+2	+10

The sign test will be used to see if any significant change has taken place. **Equal values are ignored**.

H_0: There is no difference between the scores for the pre-test and the post-test.

H_1: There is a difference between them.

Significance level (α): 5% (0.05)

Critical value: Sign tables, Appendix D, Table 8, number of changes = 15, two tailed, $S \leq 3$

Test statistic: The number of positive changes is 10. The number of negative changes is 5. The test statistic, usually given the symbol S, is the smaller of these two totals, that is, $S = 5$

Conclusion: For 15 changes the totals needed to be more different, that is, 3 and 12, for a significant change to have taken place. In this case they were less extreme, 10 and 5, so we can conclude that no significant change has taken place.

7.9.2 *Wilcoxon matched pairs (signed rank) test*

The non-parametric equivalent of the paired *t*-test is the Wilcoxon matched pairs test. This test is carried out on the ranks of the differences between the pairs of data points. It is often used to identify a change in behaviour following an event such as an advertising campaign.

The basic premise is that the rankings of individual changes will be random if there has been no overall change. Where there has been an overall change then the rankings of those changes in a positive direction will be different from changes in a negative direction.

EXAMPLE 7.11

A small panel of 8 members has been asked about their perception of a product before and after they had an opportunity to try it. Their perceptions, measured on an ordinal scale, gave the results in Table 7.5.

Table 7.5

Member	A	B	C	D	E	F	G	H
Before	8	3	6	4	5	7	6	7
After	9	4	4	1	6	7	9	2

Have the perception scores changed, at 5%, after trying the product?

H_0: There is no difference in perception.

H_1: There is a difference in perception.

Significance level (α): 5% (0.05)

Critical region: Wilcoxon matched pairs, Table 9, 5%, two tailed, $n = 8$, critical region ≤ 3.

Test statistic: Find the difference between the two scores and rank these differences in absolute size. There are seven differences so the smallest differences is ranked 1 and the largest ranked 7. Ties are given the means of their rankings.

Table 7.6

Member	Before	After	Difference	Rank
A	8	9	+1	2
B	3	4	+1	2
C	6	4	−2	4
D	4	1	−3	5.5
E	5	6	+1	2
F	7	7	0	ignore
G	6	9	+3	5.5
H	7	2	−5	7

Sums of ranks: $T+ = 11.5$; $T- = 16.5$; the smaller is the test statistic, $T = 11.5$

Conclusion: The test statistic is less extreme than the critical value. Do not reject H_0 – there has been no change after trying the product.

7.9.3 Mann–Whitney U test (Wilcoxon rank sum test)

The Mann–Whitney U test is used if two samples have unequal variance, as judged by the F-test (Section 7.6.2). This test is also appropriate if the data are only ordinal.

The basic premise of the Mann–Whitney U test is that if both samples come from populations with the same medians and if all the values from the two samples are put into a single ordered list, then the members of Sample 1 and Sample 2 will be ranked at random. If the two samples come from different populations, then the rankings of the values from the samples will not be random and there will be a tendency for one of the samples to have lower ranks than the other.

The smallest sum of ranks possible is $\dfrac{n(n+1)}{2}$ where n is the number of items being ranked. (Try this for the numbers one to five – they add up to 15 which is $(5 \times 6)/2$.)

Test statistic: $U = R - \dfrac{n_1(n_1+1)}{2}$ (7.9)

where R is the smaller sum of ranks and n_1 the size of the same sample.

The test statistic measures its deviation from the smallest possible sum, that is, the most extreme position.

EXAMPLE 7.12

Samples have been taken from two branches of a chain of stores. The samples relate to the daily takings of both branches which are situated in city centres. We wish to find out if there is any difference in turnover between the two branches. (With such small samples it cannot be assumed that the data are normally distributed.)

| Branch 1 | £235 | £255 | £355 | £195 | £244 | £240 | £236 | £259 | £260 |
| Branch 2 | £240 | £198 | £220 | £215 | £245 | | | | |

H_0: Both samples come from the same population and so have the same median.

H_1: The two samples come from different populations and have different medians.

Significance level (α): 5% (0.05)

Critical value: Mann–Whitney, Table 10, 5%, sample sizes 5 and 9, 2-tailed test (α_2), $U \leq 7$

Test statistic: All the sample values are ranked in one ordering (Table 7.7).

Table 7.7

Branch 1	Order	Branch 2	Order
235	5	240	7.5
255	11	198	2
355	14	220	4
195	1	215	3
244	9	245	10
240	7.5		
236	6		
259	12		
260	13		

Sum of ranks of branches: $R_1 = 78.5$, $R_2 = 26.5$, so $R = 26.5$ (smaller one).

$$U = R - \frac{n_1(n_1+1)}{2} = 26.5 - \frac{5(5+1)}{2} = 11.5$$

Conclusion: test statistic, 11.5 > critical value, 7, so the situation is not so extreme that we need to reject H_0. We can conclude that the two samples could come from the same population and that there is no difference between the turnovers of the two branches.

With non-parametric tests the data has to be very extreme before the null hypothesis will be rejected; we were not able to reject any of the null hypotheses above. This is because these tests are less powerful than the parametric ones and should only be used when the assumptions needed for the parametric tests are not true (Weimer, 1993, Chapter 15).

7.10 Other hypothesis tests

We shall cover more hypothesis tests in the next three chapters. In Chapter 8 you will study **analysis of variance** with which we shall investigate the differences between more than two means. Chapter 9 covers **Chi-squared tests** which look for associations between two categorical variables and in Chapter 10 we shall look for significant **correlation** between two continuous variables before identifying the relationship between them in the form of a **regression equation**.

There are numerous other non-parametric tests which have been developed comparatively recently. Many have been produced independently by more than one statistician and, like the test described in Section 7.8.3, bear more than one name. Some statisticians have been prolific in their production of tests and so have numerous tests named after them. This can lead to some confusion so if you are looking for a particular test be very careful!

In this course we have so far studied only single variables. Later we shall study bivariate data but will not venture into the realms of multivariate analysis. Many of the simpler tests used have multivariate equivalents which are only appropriate for analysis by computer packages such as Minitab, SPSS and SAS.

7.11 Further considerations

There are various other considerations common to all types of hypothesis tests which you should be aware of but need not study in detail on this course.

7.11.1 Types of error

When testing any hypothesis there are four possible outcomes, as illustrated in Table 7.8.

Table 7.8

	H_0 is true	H_0 is not true
Reject H_0	Incorrect decision – Type I error	Correct decision
Do not reject H_0	Correct decision	Incorrect decision – Type II error

A **Type I error** occurs if the null hypothesis is rejected when it is actually true. This is the most common situation and has been illustrated in all the examples. In the courtroom example it is the case when the accused is found 'guilty' when in fact he is 'not guilty'. The probability of committing a Type I error is the familiar **significance level** and is usually symbolised by the Greek letter α (alpha). If the probability of committing a Type I error is α, then the probability of not committing it is $(1 - \alpha)$ which is, of course, the familiar **confidence interval**. In this course we are only concerned with Type I errors.

A **Type II Error** occurs if the null Hypothesis is not rejected when it is in fact false. The conclusion of 'not guilty' when in fact the man is 'guilty'. This leaves the status quo unchanged and is considered preferable to making a Type I error.

7.11.2   The power of a test

The main purpose of hypothesis testing is to reject the null hypothesis when it is incorrect so we need **powerful tests**. Remember that parametric tests are more powerful than their non-parametric equivalents so should always be used if the data are appropriate. The power of a test is the ability of that test correctly to reject the null hypothesis, that is, to avoid Type I errors. Any test must of course be valid for the given circumstances.

7.11.3   The validity of a test

For a test to be **valid** it must assess what it is intended to assess.

Among other things, the validity of a test depends on the data to which it is being applied. Are they quantitative, qualitative, interval, ordinal or nominal? Are they normally distributed or skewed?

Tests are available for any type of data but they will only be valid so long as the data are appropriate for that particular test because validity depends on the data being appropriate to the standard probability distribution giving the critical value.

The importance of using non-parametric tests when the data are not interval or not normally distributed has already been stated but not fully explained. Each hypothesis test has its own set of assumptions based on the distribution from which the test statistic is assumed to come. Each test has a particular probability associated with its value if the null hypothesis is correct.

Similarly if the data are skewed or with large kurtosis (peakedness) the probability associated with any particular test statistic is not the same as for the normal distribution.

Another obvious point is that the probability changes with the number of tails, so the number used in the conclusion must agree with that in the alternative hypothesis, for example, we cannot infer a direction from the results of a two tailed test. Both the null and the alternative hypothesis should be established **before** any evidence is collected or any given data analysed.

You should now understand the importance of selecting appropriate tests so that you have confidence in any conclusions you reach.

7.12 Summary

In this chapter we first considered the concepts common to all hypothesis tests and then studied many different tests in more detail. The reason for the formal method of hypothesis testing with its six essential steps and its logical ordering should now be evident.

- The two hypotheses establish the framework for the whole test
- The critical value assumes a certain distribution and defines the region of rejection of the null hypothesis with a predetermined probability
- The test statistic establishes whether rejection is appropriate or not
- The conclusion states which of the two hypotheses is most likely to be true.

At this stage you are probably thinking that the main problem is the selection of the appropriate test to use in any given circumstances. Figure 7.10 summarises the situation for all of the tests considered on this course. All the tests, apart from the chi-squared test, need continuous data.

Figure 7.10 Selection of a hypothesis test

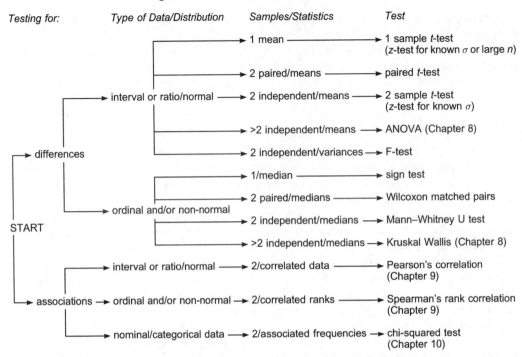

These tests all share the same overall methodology but differ mainly in the calculation of the test statistic and the tables from which the critical value is obtained. The required formulae and distribution tables needed for each are given on p. xi and in Appendix D.

Finally, if the analysis has been carried out by a computer package, such as Minitab or SPSS, the output will include a p-value, which is the probability of H_0 being correct. If testing at 5% (0.05) this needs to be < 0.05 if H_0 is to be rejected.

7.13 Computer output for Example 7.9

t-test of the mean

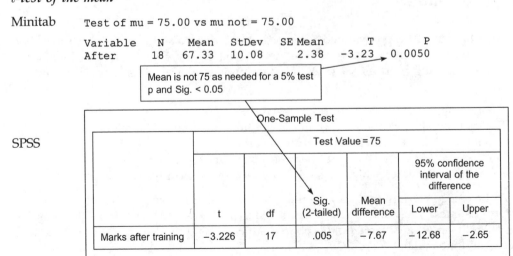

Paired t-test and confidence interval

Minitab

```
Paired T for After - Before

Variable     N    Mean   StDev   SE Mean
After       18   67.33   10.08      2.38
Before      18   51.00    8.92      2.10
Difference  18   16.333   4.087    0.963

99% CI for mean difference: (13.451, 19.125)
T-Test of mean difference = 10 (vs > 10): T-Value = 6.57 P-Value = 0.000
```

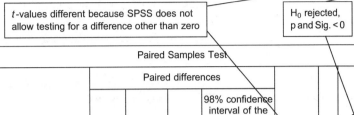

t-values different because SPSS does not allow testing for a difference other than zero

H_0 rejected, p and Sig. < 0

SPSS

Paired Samples Test

	Paired differences							
				98% confidence interval of the difference				
	Mean	Std. deviation	Std. error mean	Lower	Upper	t	df	Sig. (2-tailed)
Pair 1 Marks before training – marks after training	−16.33	4.09	.96	−18.81	−13.86	−16.954	17	.000

Two sample t-test and confidence interval

Minitab

```
Two sample T for After vs Before

         N    Mean   StDev   SE Mean
After   18    67.3   10.1      2.4
Before  18    51.00   8.92     2.1

95% CI for mu After - mu Before: (9.9, 22.8)
T-Ttest mu After = mu Before (vs >): T = 5.15   p = 0.0000   DF = 33
```

A significant change has taken place
Both p and Sig. < 0.05

SPSS

Independent Samples Test

	Levene's test for equality of variances		t-test for equality of means						
								95% confidence interval of the difference	
	F	Sig.	t	df	Sig. (2-tailed)	Mean diff.	Std. error diff.	Lower	Upper
Marks Equal variances assumed	.147	.704	−5.148	34	.000	−16.33	3.17	−22.78	−9.89
Equal variances not assumed			−5.148	33.501	.000	−16.33	3.17	−22.78	−9.88

Hypothesis testing using statistical computer packages is included in Worksheets 15.2.3, 15.5.3 and 15.8.3

7.14 Tutorial 7 – Hypothesis testing

7.1 A newspaper article stated that students at a particular university spend an average of £95 per term on beer. A student investigator who believed this average was too high polled a random sample of 50 students and found that $\bar{x} = £92.25$ and $s = £10$. Use these results to test at a 5% significance level the statement made by the newspaper.

7.2 Clerical officers are expected to spend 30% of their time on the telephone. Pamela, who was suspected of spending longer, was found on the phone during 90 out of 200 random spot checks. Test at the 5% level whether she did use the phone more often than expected.

7.3 Eleven cartons of sugar, each nominally containing 1 kg, were randomly selected from a large batch of cartons. The weights of sugar they contained were:

1.02   1.05   1.08   1.03   1.00   1.06   1.08   1.01   1.04   1.07   1.00 kg

Does this support the hypothesis, at 5%, that the mean weight for the whole batch is over 1.00 kg?

7.4 The expected lifetime of electric bulbs produced by a given process was 1500 hours. To test a new batch a sample of 10 was taken. This showed a mean lifetime of 1455 hours. The standard deviation of the production is **known** to be 90 hours. Test the hypothesis, at 1% significance, that the mean lifetime of the electric light bulbs has not changed.

7.5 A sleeping drug and neutral control were tested in turn on a random sample of 10 patients in a hospital. The differences between the number of hours each patient slept under the drug and the neutral control were:

2.0   0.2   −0.4   0.3   0.7   1.2   0.6   1.8   −0.2   1.0 hours

Test, at 5%, the hypothesis that the drug would give more hours sleep on average than the control for all the patients in the hospital.

7.6 A coin is suspected of being biased. It is tossed 200 times and 114 heads occur. Carry out a hypothesis test to see if the coin is indeed biased at 1% significance.

7.7 The times taken to complete a task were recorded for a sample of eight employees before and after a period of training (min):

Employee	1	2	3	4	5	6	7	8
Before training	15	14	18	14	15	17	13	12
After training	13	15	15	13	13	16	14	12

Test at 5% to see if the training is effective or not.

7.8 A dairy advertises that a tub of ice-cream produces on average 84 scoops. An ice-cream seller who buys wholesale from the dairy found that an average of 81.5 scoops were obtained from 72 tubs. The standard deviation was found to be 11.43 scoops and so he thinks that the claimed quantity is too high. Carry out a test at the 5% level of significance to see who is correct.

7.9 After treatment with a standard fertiliser, the average yield per hectare is 4.2 tonnes of wheat. A super fertiliser is developed and administered to 10 hectares. The yields from the treated areas were:

4.3 6.0 4.9 6.1 6.2 5.4 4.1 4.2 3.8 and 3.9 tonnes.

Test the hypothesis that this fertiliser would improve a farmer's yields at 1% significance.

7.10 A new method of study for management has been introduced. In order to test its effectiveness equivalent tests are given to the same students before and after they have taken the course. Their test scores are:

Student	A	B	C	D	E	F	G	H	I	J
Before	596	610	598	613	588	592	606	619	600	597
After	599	612	607	610	588	610	607	623	591	599

Assuming the score changes to be normally distributed, is this method of study effective at 5% significance?

7.15 Supplementary exercise 7

Note: All data may be assumed normal.

7.11 In a city centre shopping precinct the average number of shoplifting incidents has been established as 130 per day with a standard deviation of 20 incidents. The security staff think the level is rising and obtain an average of 134 incidents from 50 days. Are they correct at 1% significance?

7.12 Seven applicants for a job were interviewed by two personnel officers who were asked to mark one aspect of their performance on a scale of 1 to 10.

Candidate	1	2	3	4	5	6	7
Interviewer A	8	7	6	9	7	5	8
Interviewer B	7	4	6	8	5	6	7

Test to see if there was a significant difference between the standards being applied by the two interviewers at the 5% level. Assume data are normally distributed and measured on an interval scale.

7.13 A company manufacturing a certain brand of washing-up liquid claims that 60% of all housewives prefer it to any other. A random sample of 200 housewives contains 108 who do prefer the brand. Is the true percentage lower than the company claims?

7.14 Coal trucks arriving at a power plant are contracted to carry 10 tonnes of coal per load. A sample of 15 loads showed $\bar{x} = 9.5$ tonnes and $s = 0.9$ tonnes. If the distribution of weights is assumed to be normal, do these results indicate that the loads are as contracted on average or are they lighter, at 1% level?

7.15 An experiment was conducted to compare the performance of two varieties of wheat, A and B. Seven farms were randomly chosen for the experiment and the yields (in tonnes per hectare) for each variety on each farm were:

Farm number	1	2	3	4	5	6	7
Yield of variety A	4.6	4.8	3.2	4.7	4.3	3.7	4.1
Yield of variety B	4.1	4.0	3.5	4.1	4.5	3.2	3.8

(a) Why do you think both varieties were tested on each farm, rather than testing variety A on seven farms and variety B on seven other farms?

(b) Assuming normal distributions, carry out a hypothesis test at 5% significance to test whether the mean yields are the same for the two varieties.

7.16 The management of a small supermarket claims that at least 70% of housewives in the local community shop with them once a week. Out of a random sample of 350 households in the community 235 admitted shopping there weekly. Is the supermarket's claim upheld at 1% significance?

7.17 A drug company wants to see if the application of a new drug causes any change in the temperature of the patients who use it. The patients' temperatures (in °F) before and after using the drug are:

Patient	1	2	3	4	5	6	7	8
Temperature before	96.7	98.3	98.8	99.2	99.7	99.5	98.2	98.0
Temperature after	103.2	98.6	99.1	98.9	101.3	99.0	99.4	100.7

Patient	9	10	11	12	13	14	15	16
Temperature before	97.8	98.8	98.4	98.2	99.8	99.6	98.4	99.4
Temperature after	97.4	99.7	98.0	98.2	102.4	102.0	98.6	99.0

Assuming the distributions to be normal, test at the 5% level the null hypothesis that there has been no increase in temperature.

7.18 In a Gallup poll before a general election 64% of a sample of 250 voters stated that they would vote for Labour. Is this percentage low enough to refute Labour's claim that at least 70% of the electorate would vote for the party in the general election?

7.19 The percentage scores of 10 students on a computing examination were:

33   51   57   60   64   66   69   75   84   71

Assuming these scores are from a normal distribution, test at the 5% level of significance that the mean score is 60%.

Note: The remaining questions make use of the **two sample *t*-test**. Attempt them only if it has been included in your syllabus.

7.20 A keyboard skills tutor used two different learning systems, A and B, for two separate groups. At the end of the learning period the students were given the same ability test. Their scores are:

| *Method A* | 58 | 65 | 81 | 62 | 96 | 60 | 55 | 70 | 63 | 84 |
| *Method B* | 65 | 68 | 59 | 86 | 95 | 70 | 100 | 98 | 80 | 90 |

Does method B give better results on average, at 5% significance, than method A?

7.21 Two randomly selected groups, each of 50 employees, of a very large firm are taught an assembly operation by two different methods. If the first group averaged 140 points with a standard deviation of 10 points while the second group averaged 135 points with a standard deviation of 8 points, are the mean performances of the two groups significantly different at the 5% level?

7.22 A firm believes that tyres produced by process A last longer on average than tyres produced by process B. To test this belief, random samples of tyres produced by the two processes were tested and the results are:

Process	*Sample size*	*Average lifetime*	*Standard deviation*
A	50	22 400 miles	1000 miles
B	50	21 800 miles	1000 miles

Is there evidence at a 5% level of significance that the firm is correct in its belief?

7.23 Samples of 400 men and 200 women sit an accountancy exam. The men have a mean mark of 51.2% while the women have a mean mark of 53.7%. The standard deviations are 11.14% and 10.0% respectively. Does this indicate that women on average have better marks? (Use 1% level of significance)

7.24 Mr Brown and Mr Green work at the same office and live next door to each other. Each day they leave for work together but travel by different routes. Mr Brown maintains that his route is quicker, on average, by at least 4 minutes. Both men time their journeys, in minutes, over 10 weeks of 5 journeys per week. The results obtained were:

Mr Brown: mean 21 min,   standard deviation 3.2 min.
Mr Green: mean 24 min, standard deviation 2.8 min.

Assuming equal variance and normality, test the truth of Mr Brown's claim, at 1%.

8 Analysis of Variance

8.1 Objectives of this chapter

In Chapter 7 we investigated variation among cases in terms of group means. Do males and females have different earnings in a particular company? Do students' aptitude marks improve after training? We calculated the summary statistics for each group from the samples and then used them to answer questions about the population

In this chapter we continue with the same theme but extend it to investigate more than two groups of cases. If a factory works shifts, is there any difference between the production of the morning, afternoon and night shifts? Is the production level higher on any day of the week? Production can also be analysed using the shifts and days of the week in combination. Is Friday afternoon production worse than that on any other shift?

Analysis of variance, or ANOVA, can be quite a complex topic. We will use it in its simplest form, **one-way ANOVA**, to investigate the variation between three or more groups. We will use **two-way ANOVA** to split variation between two sets of groups then briefly discuss more complex analysis. Having completed this chapter you should be able to do the simpler analysis and be aware of the method's potential for carrying out more detailed work.

8.2 Introduction – why do we need analysis of variance?

We cannot just carry out repeated t-tests on pairs of the variables. If many independent tests are carried out pairwise then the **probability of being correct for the combined results is greatly reduced**. For example, if we compare the average marks of two students at the end of a semester to see if their mean scores are significantly different we would have, at a 5% level, 0.95 probability of being correct. Three students need three pairwise tests, and so on. Table 8.1 shows how the probability of being correct decreases, even for a small number of students.

Table 8.1

Students	Pairwise tests	P(all correct)	P(at least one incorrect)
2	1	0.95	0.05
3	3	$0.95^3 = 0.857$	0.143
10	45	$0.95^{45} = 0.1$	0.90 etc.

For a large group of n students this progess clearly produces a very high probability of being incorrect.

We need to use methods of analysis which will allow the variation between **all n means to be tested simultaneously** giving an **overall** probability of 0.95 of being correct at the 5% level. This type of analysis is referred to as analysis of variance or ANOVA. It measures the overall variation within a variable; finds the variation between the group means; combines these to calculate a single test statistic and then uses this to carry out a hypothesis test in the standard manner.

The traditional terminology of ANOVA reflects its origins in agriculture. It refers to 'levels of treatment', 'blocking factors', etc. This book aims to avoid these terms as much as possible, calling treatments and blocks by names specific to a particular example.

8.3 One-way analysis of variance

8.3.1 Assumptions to be met for ANOVA

As with the two sample t-test,

- The population should be normally distributed
- The groups should be independent of each other
- The groups should be of equal variance.

The distribution of the sample can be checked by drawing a histogram or carrying out a Kolmogorov-Smirnov test for normality if a computer package is available. The need for independence is usually satisfied by the random selection of the samples. The equality of variance can be checked by the F-test as described in Section 7.6.2. In practice, the method is fairly tolerant of departures from the ideal situation.

8.3.2 The one-way ANOVA model

The total variation between all the cases is split between **variation due to difference between groups** and the **remainder** or **residual error** which is due to chance.

Figure 8.1

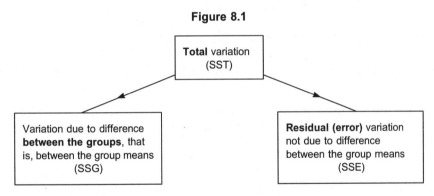

where SST = total sum of squares; SSG = between groups sum of squares; SSE = error sum of squares.

The method of measuring this variation is **variance** (see Section 3.6.2).

Total variance = variance between groups + variance due to the errors

It follows that:

$$\text{Total sum of squares (SST)} = \text{Sum of squares between the groups (SSG)} + \text{Sum of squares due to the errors (SSE)}$$

If we find any two of the three sums of squares then the other can be found by difference. In practice, we calculate SST and SSG and then find SSE.

The method will be explained in stages by reference to a numerical example. Examples 8.1 to 8.4 use the same data.

8.3.3 Sums of squares as a measure of deviation from the mean

The sum of squares is the total of the squares of the deviations from the mean, that is $\sum(x - \bar{x})^2$, where x is the value for each case and $\bar{x}$ is the mean. The classical method for calculating the sum of squares is to tabulate the values; subtract the mean from each value; square the results; and finally sum the squares. It is easier to use a statistical calculator! Both the outputs below give identical answers.

In Section 3.4.3 we saw that the standard deviation is calculated by:

$$s = \sqrt{\frac{\sum(x - \bar{x})^2}{n}} \text{ so } \sum(x - \bar{x})^2 = ns^2 \text{ with } s \text{ from the calculator using } [x\sigma_n]$$

$$\text{or } s_{n-1} = \sqrt{\frac{\sum(x - \bar{x})^2}{n - 1}} \text{ so } \sum(x - \bar{x})^2 = (n - 1)s_{n-1}^2 \text{ with } s \text{ from the calculator using } [x\sigma_{n-1}]$$

EXAMPLE 8.1

One important factor in selecting software for word processing and database management systems is the time required to train. In order to evaluate three file management systems, a firm devised a test to see how many training hours were needed for five of its word processing operators to become proficient in each of three systems.

Table 8.1

System A	16	19	14	13	18
System B	16	17	13	12	17
System C	24	22	19	18	22

Using a 5% level, is there any difference between the training time needed for the three systems?

In this case the groups are the three database management systems, A, B and C. Differences between the groups account for some of the variance but the remainder is due to errors.

Method

Calculate the total sum of squares (SST)

Input all the data individually and output the values for n, $\bar{x}$ and s_n from the calculator in SD mode. Use these values to calculate s_n^2 and ns_n^2.

n	$\bar{x}$	s_n	s_n^2	ns_n^2
15	17.33	3.419	11.69	175.3 = SST

Calculate the sum of squares between groups (SSSys)

Calculate n and $\bar{x}$ for each of the systems separately:

	n	$\bar{x}$
System A	5	16
System B	5	15
System C	5	21

continued

EXAMPLE 8.1 *continued*

Input as frequency data, that is, using a frequency of five, in your calculator and output n, $\bar{x}$ and s_n. Use the values to calculate s_n^2 and ns_n^2.

n	$\bar{x}$	s_n	s_n^2	ns_n^2
15	17.33	2.625	6.889	$103.3 = \text{SSSys}$

Find the sum of squares due to errors (SSE)

SSE is found by difference $\text{SSE} = \text{SST} - \text{SSSys} = 175.3 - 103.3 = 72.0$

8.3.4 ANOVA table

Table 8.3 shows the general format of an analysis of variance table. You may find it helps you to follow the sequence of calculations.

Table 8.3 ANOVA table (for k groups, total sample size N)

Source	Sum of squares (SS)	Degrees of freedom (df)	Mean sums of squares (MSS)	Test statistic (F)
Between groups	SSG	$k - 1$	$\dfrac{\text{SSG}}{k-1} = \text{MSG}$	$\dfrac{\text{MSG}}{\text{MSE}} = \text{F}$
Errors	SSE	$(N-1) - (k-1)$	$\dfrac{\text{SSE}}{N-k} = \text{MSE}$	
Total	SST	$N - 1$		

Method

Complete the ANOVA table.

- Calculate the total sum of squares, SST, and the sum of squares between groups, SSG; find the sum of squares due to the errors, SSE, by difference.
- The degrees of freedom, df, for the total and the groups are one less than the total number of values and the number of groups respectively. Find the errors df by difference.
- The mean sums of squares, MSS, is found in each case by dividing the sum of squares, SS, by the corresponding degrees of freedom, df.
- The test statistic, F, is the ratio of the mean sum of squares due to the differences between the group means (MSG) and that due to the errors (MSE).

EXAMPLE 8.1 *continued*

In this example $k = 3$ systems, $n = 15$ values

Table 8.4

Source	SS	df	MSS	F
Between systems	103.3	$3 - 1 = 2$	$103.3/2 = 51.65$	$51.65/6.00 = 8.61$
Errors	72.0	$14 - 2 = 12$	$72.0/12 = 6.00$	
Total	175.3	$15 - 1 = 14$		

8.3.5 The hypothesis test

The methodology for carrying out the hypothesis test is described in Section 7.3.

Null hypothesis, H_0, is that all the group means are equal. H_0: $\mu_1 = \mu_2 = \mu_3 = \mu_4$ etc.

Alternative hypothesis, H_1, is that at least two of the means are different.

Significance level is as stated or 5% by default.

Critical value is from the F-tables, $F_\alpha(\nu_1, \nu_2)$ with the two degrees of freedom being those of the groups, ν_1, and the errors, ν_2.

Test statistic is the F-value calculated from the sample in the ANOVA table.

Conclusion is reached by comparing the test statistic with the critical value and rejecting the null hypothesis if the test statistic is the larger of the two.

EXAMPLE 8.1 *continued*

H_0: $\mu_A = \mu_B = \mu_C$ H_1: At least two of the means are different

Critical value: $F_{0.05}(2, 12) = 3.89$ (df from between systems is 2 and from errors is 12)

Test statistic: 8.61

Conclusion: test statistic > critical value so reject H_0. There is a difference between the mean times of at least two of the three systems.

8.3.6 Where does any difference lie?

We can calculate a critical difference, CD, which depends on the mean sum of squares due to errors (MSE), the sample sizes and the significance level. Any difference between means that exceeds the CD is significant and any difference that is less than the CD is not significant.

This critical difference formula is

$$CD = t\sqrt{MSE\left(\frac{1}{n_1} + \frac{1}{n_2}\right)}$$

t has the error degrees of freedom and one tail (see Table 2).

EXAMPLE 8.1 *continued*

$$CD = t\sqrt{MSE\left(\frac{1}{n_1} + \frac{1}{n_2}\right)} \Rightarrow 1.78\sqrt{6.00\left(\frac{1}{5} + \frac{1}{5}\right)} = 2.76$$

From the samples $\bar{x}_A = 16$, $\bar{x}_B = 15$, $\bar{x}_C = 21$.

System C takes significantly longer to learn than Systems A and B which have similar training times.

EXAMPLE 8.2

A company, intending to alter its logo, sent questionnaires to a sample of its employees asking their opinions about three possibilities. The employees were asked to award each of the three logos (A, B and C) a score out of five on six different aspects of design, colour, and so on. The total scores awarded by the eight employees are given in Table 8.5.

continued

EXAMPLE 8.2 *continued*

Table 8.5

Logos	Employees							
	1	*2*	*3*	*4*	*5*	*6*	*7*	*8*
A	22	19	14	18	21	18	23	20
B	24	22	18	20	21	21	18	19
C	20	16	16	19	18	15	19	18

Is there a significant difference between logo preferences?

Sums of squares

Total SS   Putting all the individual values into the calculator gives the following summary statistics: $n = 24, \bar{x} = 19.125, s_n = 2.403 \Rightarrow ns_n^2 = 138.63$

Between logos SS   The mean scores are $\bar{x}_A = 19.375$, $\bar{x}_B = 20.375$ and $\bar{x}_C = 17.625$. Each of these means came from 8 values so inputting the means with a frequency of 8 gives: $n = 24$, $\bar{x} = 19.125$, $s_n = 1.1365 \Rightarrow ns_n^2 = 31.00$ (n and $\bar{x}$ for checking)

Error SS   138.63 − 31.00 = 107.63

ANOVA table

In this example $k = 3$ logos, $N = 24$ values.

Table 8.6

Source	SS	df	MSS	F
Between logos	31.00	3 − 1 = 2	31/2 = 15.50	15.50/5.13 = 3.02
Errors	107.63	23 − 2 = 21	107.63/21 = 5.13	
Total	138.73	24 − 1 = 23		

Hypothesis test

H_0: $\mu_A = \mu_B = \mu_C$ H_1: At least two of them are different.

Critical value: $F_{0.05}(2, 21) = 3.47$

Test statistic: 3.02

Conclusion: test statistic < critical value so H_0 not rejected. There is no difference between employee preference for the logos.

8.4 Two-way analysis of variance

In Section 8.3, we used one-way ANOVA to investigate whether there was a difference in the time taken to learn three different database management systems. We found that System C took longer to learn than either System A or System B which took similar lengths of time. System C took, on average, at least 5 hours longer and since the standard error of the difference between the means – the critical difference – was 2.76 we concluded that System C was significantly more difficult to learn.

We might suspect that some of the variation left in the errors from one-way analysis of variance was not, in fact, due to random chance but to some other measurable factor. For instance, in Example 8.1 we might feel instinctively that some of the variation in time needed to learn a database management system was due to the different learning ability of the operators. If so, this accountable variation was erroneously included in the error sum of squares (SSE) and caused the mean error sum of squares (MSE) to be too large. The calculated F-value would then be too small and would make rejection of the null hypothesis more unlikely.

Two-way analysis of variance can be used in various ways. We can:

- Explore just one factor of interest in a more realistic manner by removing the accountable variation and allowing a truer conclusion to be reached by this more powerful test
- Investigate two factors of interest at the same time by also testing the difference in means between levels of the second set of groups
- Consider any interaction between the two variables. In Example 8.1 do particular operators relate better to particular systems?

We shall look at these three uses in turn, but you should be aware that analysis of variance is a very powerful analytical tool which can be used effectively with very large sets of data in computer packages.

8.4.1 Randomised block design

In this section we shall treat the two-way ANOVA method as an extension of one-way ANOVA but also include a blocking factor to remove the unwanted accountable variation which we shall assume to be of no interest. (The term 'blocking' comes from the agricultural origins when each trial would have been applied to each 'block' of ground, such as those having different degrees of slope.)

This design ensures that each group is measured under the same conditions by removing the variation due to these conditions by the use of a blocking factor. In the case of the database management systems in Example 8.1 each system would be learned by all the operators in the sample so removing the variation due to differing operator ability and giving a better indication of the amount which is genuinely due to random errors.

We shall again consider the theory in tandem with the calculations in order to make the method easier to follow.

Two-way random blocked ANOVA model

Figure 8.2

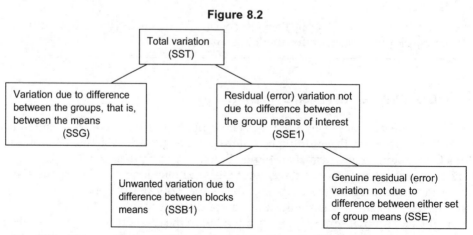

where SST = total sum of squares; SSG = treatment sum of squares between the groups; SSBI = blocks sum of squares; SSE = sum of squares of errors.

EXAMPLE 8.3

Example 8.3 uses the same data as Example 8.1 but the operators have been identified.

Since operator variability was believed also to be a significant factor, each of the five operators was trained on each of the three database management systems. The training hours needed for each are as shown in Table 8.7.

Use the system means calculated in Example 8.1 and calculate mean time for each operator.

Table 8.7

| | Operators | | | | | |
	1	2	3	4	5	Means
System A	16	19	14	13	18	16.00
System B	16	17	13	12	17	15.00
System C	24	22	19	18	22	21.00
Means	18.67	19.33	15.33	14.33	19.00	17.33

In this two-way model

$$\text{Total variance} = \text{between systems variance} + \text{between operator variance} + \text{error variance}$$

It follows that:

$$\begin{array}{l} \text{Total sum} \\ \text{of squares} \\ \text{(SST)} \end{array} = \begin{array}{l} \text{Sum of squares} \\ \text{between systems} \\ \text{(SSSys)} \end{array} + \begin{array}{l} \text{Sum of squares} \\ \text{between Operators} \\ \text{(SSOps)} \end{array} + \begin{array}{l} \text{Sum of squares} \\ \text{of errors (SSE)} \end{array}$$

SST (from the individual data, as Example 8.1) $= 175.3$

SSSys (inputting treatment means as frequency data, as Example 8.1) $= 103.3$

SSOps Inputting the operator means as frequency data (frequency $= 5$) gives:

n	$\bar{x}$	s_n	s_n^2	ns_n^2
15	17.33	2.078	4.317	64.7 $=$ SSOps

General ANOVA table for k treatments, b blocks and total sample size, N

Table 8.8

Source	S	df	MSS	F
Between groups	SSG	$k-1$	$SSG/(k-1) = MSG$	MSG/MSE
Between blocks	SSBl	$b-1$		
Errors	SSE	$(k-1)(b-1)$	$SSE/(k-1)(b-1) = MSE$	
Total	SST	$N-1$		

Note: Error df generally calculated as: $(N-1) - \{(k-1) + (b-1)\}$, that is, the remainder.

EXAMPLE 8.3 *continued*

The two-way ANOVA table, including both systems and operators, is shown in Table 8.9.

Table 8.9

Source	SS	df	MSS	F
Between systems	103.3	$3 - 1 = 2$	$103.3/2 = 51.65$	$51.65/0.91 = 56.8$
Between operators	64.7	$5 - 1 = 4$		
Errors	7.3	$14 - 6 = 8$	$7.3/8 = 0.91$	
Total	175.3	$15 - 1 = 14$		

Hypothesis test method as Example 8.1 (assuming no interest in operator difference).

H_0: $\mu_A = \mu_B = \mu_C$ H_1: At least two of them are different.

Critical value: $F_{0.05}(2,8) = 4.46$

Test statistic: 56.8 (Note how much larger this is than for the one-way analysis.)

Conclusion: test statistic > critical value so reject H_0. There is a difference between at least two of the times needed for training on the different systems.

8.4.2   Main effects only

In this model we assume that there are two factors of interest but no interaction between them. The only difference from the previous model is that the 'blocks' are now of interest and so the second factor is also tested for significance.

Table 8.10

Source	S	df	MSS	F
Between groups	SSG	$k - 1$	$SSG/(k - 1) = MSG$	MSG/MSE
Between blocks	SSBl	$b - 1$	$SSBl/(b - 1) = MSBl$	MSBl/MSE
Errors	SSE	$(k - 1)(b - 1)$	$SSE/(k - 1)(b - 1) = MSE$	
Total	SST	$N - 1$		

Note: Error df are generally calculated as: $(N - 1) - \{(k - 1) + (b - 1)\}$, that is, the remainder.

EXAMPLE 8.4

Example 8.4 continues Example 8.3 by testing for significance of operator difference.

Two-way ANOVA table, including both systems and operators

Table 8.11

Source	SS	df	MSS	F
Between systems	103.3	$3 - 1 = 2$	$103.3/2 = 51.65$	$51.65/0.91 = 56.8$
Between operators	64.7	$5 - 1 = 4$	$64.7/4 = 16.18$	$16.18/0.91 = 17.8$
Errors	7.3	$14 - 6 = 8$	$7.3/8 = 0.91$	
Total	175.3	$15 - 1 = 14$		

We test now for two separate hypotheses, one that the systems can be learnt in the same time and the second that the operators take the same mean time to learn.

continued

EXAMPLE 8.4 *continued*

Hypothesis test for systems as for Example 8.3

H_0: $\mu_A = \mu_B = \mu_C$ H_1: At least two of them are different.

Critical value: $F_{0.05}(2, 8) = 4.46$

Test statistic: 56.8

Conclusion: test statistic > critical value so reject H_0. There is a difference between at least two of the mean times needed for training on the different systems.

Hypothesis test for operators

H_0: $\mu_1 = \mu_2 = \mu_3 = \mu_4 = \mu_5$ H_1: At least two of them are different.

Critical value: $F_{0.05}(4, 8) = 3.84$

Test statistic: 17.8

Conclusion: test statistic > critical value so reject H_0. There is a difference between at least two of the operators in average time needed for learning the systems.

   Where does this difference lie? The calculations are as in Example 8.1, but the degrees of freedom and mean square errors are different.

t has the error degrees of freedom $= 8$, one tail only, giving 1.86

$$CD = 1.86\sqrt{0.91\left(\frac{1}{3} + \frac{1}{3}\right)} = 1.45$$

Table 8.12

	n	$\bar{x}$
Operator 1	3	18.67
Operator 2	3	19.33
Operator 3	3	15.33
Operator 4	3	14.33
Operator 5	3	19.00

Absolute differences between operator mean training times

Table 8.13 shows that it is not necessary to list all the possible pairs.

Table 8.13

Operators	1	2	3	4	5
1	0				
2	0.66	0			
3	3.33	4.00	0		
4	4.33	5.00	1.00	0	
5	0.33	0.33	3.66	4.66	0

This is not easy to interpret. It looks as though operators 1, 2 and 5 are very similar. Operators 3 and 4 are not significantly different from each other but they are different from the others.

We conclude that operators 3 and 4 are significantly quicker learners than operators 1, 2 and 5.

EXAMPLE 8.5

Example 8.5 uses the same data as Example 8.2 but we are interested now in employees as well as logos. One-way ANOVA found no significant difference between logo preferences. Can this more powerful method detect any? Is there any difference between the scoring of the different employees. Are some more generous than others?

Table 8.14

Logos	Employees							
	1	2	3	4	5	6	7	8
A	22	19	14	18	21	18	23	20
B	24	22	18	20	21	21	18	19
C	20	16	16	19	18	15	19	18

As calculated for Example 8.2:

Total SS $= 138.63$ Between logos SS $= 31.00$

Between employees SS

$\bar{x}_1 = 22.0, \bar{x}_2 = 19.0, \bar{x}_3 = 16.0, \bar{x}_4 = 19.0, \bar{x}_5 = 20.0, \bar{x}_6 = 18.0, \bar{x}_7 = 20.0, \bar{x}_8 = 19.0$

Sums of squares

n	$\bar{x}$	s_n	s_n^2	ns_n^2
24	19.13	1.62	2.61	$62.63 = SSOps$

ANOVA table

Table 8.15

Source	SS	df	MSS	F
Between logos	31.00	$3 - 1 = 2$	$31/2 = 15.50$	$15.50/3.21 = 4.83$
Between employees	62.63	$8 - 1 = 7$	$62.63/7 = 8.95$	$8.95/3.21 = 2.79$
Errors	45.00	$23 - 9 = 14$	$45.0/14 = 3.21$	
Total	138.63	$24 - 1 = 23$		

Hypothesis test for logos

$H_0: \mu_A = \mu_B = \mu_C$ H_1: At least two of them are different.

Critical value: $F_{0.05}(2, 14) = 3.74$

Test statistic: 4.83

Note that this test statistic is much larger than that produced by one-way ANOVA.

Conclusion: test statistic > critical value so H_0 is now rejected. There is a difference between logo preferences. This test has been powerful enough to reject the null hypothesis which was not rejected by one-way ANOVA.

Hypothesis test for employees

$H_0: \mu_1 = \mu_2 = \mu_3 = \mu_4 = \mu_5 = \mu_6 = \mu_7 = \mu_8$ H_1: At least two of them are different

Critical value: $F_{0.05}(7, 14) = 2.76$

Test statistic: 2.79

Conclusion: test statistic > critical value so H_0 is rejected. There is a difference between employee scores.

continued

EXAMPLE 8.5 *continued*

The critical difference can be calculated and the means inspected as in Example 8.2 to see which logo was significantly preferred and which employees scored more generously than the rest. For eight employees a matrix of means like Table 8.13 is definitely recommended!

8.4.3 Main effects and interactions

You are not expected to carry out this type of analysis by hand as it can be more conveniently executed by means of a computer package. However, you need to know that replicate data values are always needed for the analysis. For single values, the method assumes that any variation not due to the main effects is due to their interaction so the value of the error sum of squares would be zero. This means that the ANOVA table cannot be completed and so no conclusion can be reached. It is always necessary therefore to collect duplicate or triplicate samples if the interaction between the main effects is of interest.

What do we mean by interactions? In Example 8.4 we concluded that System C took longer to learn than the other two and in Example 8.5 that Operators 3 and 4 were significantly quicker learners than Operators 1, 2 and 5. It is possible that a particular operator might have related better to one of the systems, even though the rest had trouble with it, and he might have had problems with a different one.

A graph of the situation may make it easier to understand.

Figure 8.3   Interactions between operators and systems

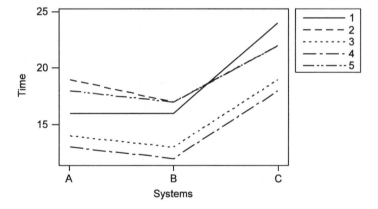

We can see that systems A and B were mastered by the operators in the same order; operator 4 finished first, followed by 3, 1, 5 and 2. System C followed the same pattern except that Operator 1 seemed to have problems with it. In other words, there was an interaction between Operator 1 and System C which accounted for some of the variation between the main effects.

In a sketch of this type parallel lines indicate no interactions but marked differences in gradient or lines crossing each other indicate some interaction has upset the pattern. If the lines were drawn for the systems, rather than the operators, it would be seen that all three are parallel except for the section for System C which would have a different gradient between operators 1 and 2.

8.5 Further analysis using ANOVA techniques

If a large amount of data is available it is more sensible to use a computer package for these more advanced techniques. It is, however, difficult to know exactly what is happening between putting in the data and looking at the ANOVA table so a few examples are produced here.

We have only considered two sets of main effects but many more can be investigated by computer analysis providing that sufficient data are available. The main effects and interactions of interest can be selected so that the models do not become too cumbersome. Try to avoid the 'throw everything in and see what comes out' attitude because it can lead to some very difficult interpretation.

More than one variable can also be considered simultaneously in MANOVA – multivariate analysis of variance (but not on this course.)

8.5.1 Factorial model

The factorial model has been discussed briefly in Section 8.4.3. We shall now work through a question by hand.

EXAMPLE 8.6

The transport manager in a haulage company wished to improve the fuel consumption of his fleet. He knew that there were a variety of fuel additives on the market which might improve the performance of his vehicles. Four different additives were used on long journeys with three different types of vehicle.

There are simultaneously three different hypotheses under test:

H_0 (1): There is no difference between the mean fuel consumption produced by the four different additives.

H_0 (2): There is no difference between the mean fuel consumption of the three different types of vehicle.

H_0 (3): There is no interaction between the different vehicles and the different additives.

H_1, in each case, is that at least two of the mean fuel consumptions are different.

The experiment

In this experiment the average consumption for 24 long journeys was measured. Three different types of vehicle were used. Duplicate journeys were recorded for each combination of additive and vehicle, giving the data in Table 8.16.

Table 8.16 Table of fuel consumption (mpg)

Vehicle type	Fuel additive			
	1	2	3	4
A	34.0	30.1	29.8	29.0
	32.7	32.8	26.7	28.9
B	32.0	30.2	28.7	27.6
	33.2	29.8	28.1	27.8
C	28.4	27.3	29.7	28.8
	29.3	28.9	27.3	29.1

continued

EXAMPLE 8.5 *continued*

First calculate the mean values for each additive, each vehicle, each interaction and the overall mean. Add them to the table.

Table 8.17 Fuel consumption (mpg)

Vehicle type	Fuel additive				
	1	2	3	4	
A	34.0 (33.35) 32.7	30.1 (31.45) 32.8	29.8 (28.25) 26.7	29.0 (28.95) 28.9	30.500
B	32.0 (32.60) 33.2	30.2 (30.00) 29.8	28.7 (28.40) 28.1	27.6 (27.70) 27.8	29.675
C	28.4 (28.85) 29.3	27.3 (28.10) 28.9	29.7 (28.50) 27.3	28.8 (28.95) 29.1	28.600
Mean	31.600	29.850	28.383	28.533	29.952

Next the sums of squares are all calculated. The main effects of additive and vehicle are input and calculated as in previous examples.

For the interaction sum of squares the mean of each cell is input with a frequency of 2 since two values contributed to it. The figure produced from the standard deviation includes the main effects sums of squares which then have to be subtracted from it.

Sums of squares
Table 8.18

	n	$\bar{x}$	s_n	s_n^2	ns_n^2	
Total	24	29.592	1.9545	3.8200	91.68	= SST
Vehicles	24	29.592	0.7779	0.6051	14.52	= SSVehicles
Additives	24	29.592	1.2925	1.6704	40.09	= SSAdds
Interactions	24	29.592	1.7885	3.1987	76.77	
Vehicles * additives			$76.77 - (14.52 + 40.09) = 22.16$ = SS(vehicles * adds)			

Note: * indicates 'interaction between'.

ANOVA table, including both vehicles and additives
Table 8.19

Source	SS	df	MSS	F
Between vehicles	14.52	2	$14.52/2 = 7.26$	$7.26/1.24 = 5.85$
Between additives	40.09	3	$40.09/3 = 13.36$	$13.36/1.24 = 10.77$
Between vehicles * adds	22.16	6	$22.16/6 = 3.69$	$3.68/1.24 = 2.97$
Errors	14.91	12	$14.91/12 = 1.24$	
Total	91.68	23		

F-table values for comparison: $F_{0.05}(2, 12) = 3.89$, $F_{0.05}(3, 12) = 3.49$, $F_{0.05}(6, 12) = 3.00$

continued

EXAMPLE 8.5 *continued*

Since the interaction proves to be insignificant the small amount of variance accounted for by it should be included with the error variance and the F-values recalculated.

Table 8.20

Source	SS	df	MSS	F
Between vehicles	14.52	$3 - 1 = 2$	7.26	3.52
Between additives	40.09	$4 - 1 = 3$	13.36	6.49
Errors	$14.91 + 22.16 = 37.07$	$23 - 5 = 18$	2.06	
Total	91.68	$24 - 1 = 23$		

F-table values for comparison: $F_{0.05}(2, 18) = 3.55$, $F_{0.05}(3, 18) = 3.16$

There is a significant difference between effects of the additives but not between the types of vehicle.

Additives: $CD = 1.73 \times \sqrt{2.06 \left(\frac{1}{6} + \frac{1}{6} \right)} = 1.43$

Table 8.21

Absolute differences	1	2	3
2	1.75		
3	3.22	1.47	
4	3.07	1.32	0.15

Additive 1 is significantly different from (better mileage than) additives 2, 3 and 4 and 2 is better than 3.

8.5.2 Latin square model

The Latin square model is a very efficient method of resource allocation. The experimental area, or its theoretical equivalent, is divided into rows and columns and each treatment must appear once in each row and once in each column. The most important property of this arrangement is that any comparison of treatments is unaffected by the average differences which exist between rows or between columns since all treatments have been applied to each row and each column. This design is technically described as being 'fully balanced'.

The analysis follows the normal procedure of analysing the differences between rows, columns and treatments.

EXAMPLE 8.7

The same transport manager as in Example 8.6 wants to test the relative efficiency, in miles per gallon, with the four different additives A, B, C and D using four different types of vehicle (Mini, Volkswagen, Rover, Porsche) on four different types of road (country lane, city street, trunk road and motorway).

Test to see, at the 5% level if there is any difference between the fuel consumption of the different brands, vehicle makes or road types.

continued

EXAMPLE 8.7 *continued*

A Latin square experiment was carried out and the results in Table 8.22 were obtained. (Note that each additive appears in every row and every column.)

Table 8.22

Type of car	Type of road			
	Country lane	City street	Trunk road	Motorway
Mini	(A) 30	(B) 33	(C) 36	(D) 40
Volkswagen	(B) 32	(C) 32	(D) 35	(A) 38
Rover	(C) 24	(D) 26	(A) 23	(B) 26
Porsche	(D) 23	(A) 21	(B) 23	(C) 24

Means (miles per gallon)

Table 8.23

Cars	Mini	Volkswagen	Rover	Porche
Means	34.75	34.25	24.75	22.75

Roads	Country lane	City street	Trunk road	Motorway
Means	27.25	28.00	29.25	32.00

Brands	A	B	C	D
Means	28.00	28.50	29.00	31.00

Sums of squares

Table 8.24

	n	$\bar{x}$	s_n	s_n^2	ns_n^2
Total	16	29.125	5.925	35.109	561.75 = SSTotal
Cars	16	29.125	5.424	29.422	470.75 = SSCars
Roads	16	29.125	1.807	3.266	52.25 = SSRoads
Brands	16	29.125	1.139	1.297	20.75 = SSBrands

ANOVA table

Table 8.25

Source	SS	df	MSS	F
Between Cars	470.75	3	156.92	52.31
Between Roads	52.25	3	17.42	5.81
Between Brands	20.75	3	6.92	2.31
Errors	18.00	6	3.00	
Total	561.75	15		

F-table values for comparison: $F_{0.05}(3,6) = 4.76$

The main source of variation is between the types of car used and there is also some between the type of roads travelled but none between the additive brands.

continued

EXAMPLE 8.7 *continued*

Which cars are different?

Cars: $\quad CD = 1.94 \times \sqrt{3.00\left(\frac{1}{4} + \frac{1}{4}\right)} = 2.37$

Observed differences between means

Table 8.26

	Mini	VW	Rover
VW	0.5		
Rover	10.0	9.5	
Porsche	12.0	11.5	2.0

We clearly have two pairs of cars in terms of petrol consumption: the Mini and the Volkswagen are more economical then the Rover and the Porsche.

8.6 An extended example

In this example we shall carry out

- A one-way analysis of variance
- A two-way analysis of variance where only the main factor is of interest
- A two-way analysis of variance where both factors are of interest but interaction is not
- A two-way analysis of variance where both main effects and the interaction is of interest – a factorial design.

EXAMPLE 8.8

A component is produced by a process which involves it being baked at a fairly high temperature for a short time. The component may be baked in any one of four ovens, each of which tends to run at a different temperature.

The production manager in charge of this process suspects that the working lifetime of the components may depend upon the temperature at which they are baked and runs an experiment to investigate.

Duplicate sample components are baked at each of three controlled temperatures in each of the four ovens and their working lifetimes found in a testing laboratory. We shall analyse the results by the different methods of analysis of variance in order to see if the production manager is correct.

Table 8.27   Working lifetime of component in hours

Temperature °C	Oven			
	1	2	3	4
250	220	207	218	253
	224	252	229	222
275	187	181	232	246
	208	179	198	273
300	174	198	178	206
	202	194	213	219

continued

EXAMPLE 8.8 *continued*

Does the baking temperature have any effect on a component's working lifetime?

One-way analysis of variance

Table 8.28 Mean lifetimes for each temperature and overall mean

Temperature	250	275	300	All
Mean	228.1	213.0	198.0	213.0

Sums of squares

Table 8.29

	n	$\bar{x}$	s_n	s_n^2	ns_n^2
Total	24	213.0	25.32	641.0	15383 = SSTotal
Temperatures	24	213.0	12.29	151.0	3624 = SSTemps

ANOVA table

Table 8.30

Source	SS	df	MSS	F
Between temperatures	3624	2	1812	3.24
Errors	11759	21	560	
Total	15383	23		

Hypothesis test for temperatures

H_0: $\mu_{250} = \mu_{275} = \mu_{300}$ H_1: At least two of the means are different.

Critical value: $F_{0.05}(2, 21) = 3.47$

Test statistic: 3.24

Conclusion: test statistic < critical value so H_0 is not rejected. There is no difference between the lifetimes of the components baked at the different temperatures.

Does the baking temperature have any effect on a component's working lifetime if the effect of the different ovens is removed from the analysis?

Two-way ANOVA using a blocked design

Table 8.31 Mean lifetimes for each temperature, each oven and overall

Temperature	250	275	300	All
Mean	228.1	213.0	198.0	213.0
Oven	1	2	3	4
Mean	202.5	201.8	211.3	236.5

Sums of squares

Table 8.32

	n	$\bar{x}$	s_n	s_n^2	ns_n^2
Total	24	213.0	25.32	641.0	15383 = SSTotal
Temperatures	24	213.0	12.29	151.0	3624 = SSTemps
Ovens	24	213.0	14.06	197.7	4745 = SSOvens

continued

EXAMPLE 8.8 *continued*

ANOVA table

Table 8.33

Source	SS	df	MSS	F
Between temperatures	3624	2	1812	4.65
Between ovens	4745	3		
Errors	7014	18	390	
Total	15383	23		

Hypothesis test for temperatures

H_0: $\mu_{250} = \mu_{275} = \mu_{300}$ H_1: At least two of the means are different.

Critical value: $F_{0.05}(2, 18) = 3.55$

Test statistic: 4.65

Conclusion: test statistic > critical value so now H_0 is rejected. There is a significant difference between the mean lifetimes of the components baked at the different temperatures. The lower the temperature of baking the longer the life, within the range of temperatures tested.

Is there a significant difference between the mean working life of components baked in the different ovens?

Completing the ANOVA table for the ovens as well as for the temperatures:

ANOVA table

Table 8.34

Source	SS	df	MSS	F
Between temperatures	3624	2	1812	4.65
Between ovens	4745	3	1582	4.06
Errors	7014	18	390	
Total	15383	23		

Hypothesis test for ovens

H_0: $\mu_1 = \mu_2 = \mu_2 = \mu_4$ H_1: At least two of the means are different.

Critical value: $F_{0.05}(3, 18) = 3.16$

Test statistic: 4.06

Conclusion: test statistic > critical value so H_0 is rejected. There is a significant difference between the lifetimes of the components baked in different ovens. Oven 4 seems preferable to the others in terms of life expectancy.

Is there a significant interaction between the ovens and the temperature of baking as regards life expectancy?

Table 8.35 Working lifetime of component in hours – cell means

| Temperature °C | Oven | | | |
	1	2	3	4
250	222.0	229.5	223.5	237.5
275	197.5	180.0	215.0	259.5
300	188.0	196.0	195.5	212.5

continued

EXAMPLE 8:8 *continued*

Sums of squares

Table 8.36

	n	$\bar{x}$	s_n	s_n^2	ns_n^2
Total	24	213.0	25.32	641.0	$15383 = $ SSTotal
Temperatures	24	213.0	12.29	151.0	$3624 = $ SSTemps
Ovens	24	213.0	14.06	197.7	$4745 = $ SSOvens
$T + Ov + T * Ov$	24	213.0	21.95	481.6	11560
Interaction			$11560 - (3624 + 4745) = 3191 = $ Temperature*OvenSS

ANOVA table

Table 8.37

Source	SS	df	MSS	F
Between temperatures	3624	2	1812	5.69
Between ovens	4745	3	1582	4.97
Temperature * oven	3191	6	532	1.67
Errors	3823	12	318.6	
Total	15383	23		

Checking the significance of the interactions: $F_{0.05}(6, 12) = 3.00$

Since 1.67 is less than this there is no interaction between the ovens and the temperature at which they are run. The final analysis is therefore that shown in Table 8.34.

8.7 Summary of analysis of variance

The technique known as ANOVA can be employed at a range of levels. The simpler methods make up most of this chapter with the more complex variations confined to Section 8.5.

We used one-way ANOVA to see if there was a significant difference between three or more group means, that is, the three file management systems in Example 8.1. We then used two-way ANOVA to remove any accountable variation which might prove a nuisance during analysis in a blocked design. If the second group of factors, such as the operators in Example 8.3, was itself of interest then it was analysed simultaneously with the main factor and both were tested for significance.

Any interaction between the two factors could be tested for significance using a factorial design but that method is beyond the scope of this course and has been confined to the further analysis.

Groebner and Weimer both have plenty of ANOVA examples but both calculate sums of squares by tabulation.

8.8 Computer analysis

Example 8.1

Minitab

```
One-way analysis of variance
```

┌─────────────────────────┐
│ H_0 rejected, $p<0.05$ │
└─────────────────────────┘

```
Analysis of Variance for Times
Source   DF       SS       MS       F       P
System    2    103.33    51.67    8.61    0.005
Error    12     72.00     6.00
Total    14    175.33
```

┌──────────────────────────┐
│ Level 3 (C)   │
│ significantly different │
│ from A and B   │
└──────────────────────────┘

```
                        Individual 95% CIs For Mean
                        Based on Pooled StDev
Level   N     Mean   StDev   --------+--------+--------+---+----
1       5   16.000   2.550        (-------*-------)
2       5   15.000   2.345   (-------*-------)
3       5   21.000   2.449                        (-------*-------)
                             --------+--------+--------+--------
Pooled StDev = 2.449              15.0     18.0     21.0
```

SPSS

	ANOVA				
Training hours					
	Sum of Squares	df	Mean Square	F	Sig.
Between Groups	103.333	2	51.667	8.611	.005
Within Groups	72.000	12	6.000		
Total	175.333	14			

┌──────────────────────────────┐
│ H_0 rejected, Sig. <0.05 │
└──────────────────────────────┘

Multiple Comparisons

┌──────────────────────────────┐
│ C significantly different   │
│ from A and B   │
└──────────────────────────────┘

Dependent variable: Training hours
LSD

(I) File management system	(J) File management system	Mean difference (I−J)	Std. Error	Sig.	95% Confidence Interval	
					Lower Bound	Upper Bound
A	B	1.0000	1.5492	.531	−2.3754	4.3754
	C	−5.0000*	1.5492	.007	−8.3754	−1.6246
B	A	−1.0000	1.5492	.531	−4.3754	2.3754
	C	−6.0000*	1.5492	.002	−9.3754	−2.6246
C	A	5.0000*	1.5492	.007	1.6246	8.3754
	B	6.0000*	1.5492	.002	2.6246	9.3754

Example 8.3

Minitab
```
Analysis of Variance for Times
Source      DF        SS        MS       F       P
System       2    103.333    51.667   56.36  0.000
Operators    4     64.667    16.167   17.64  0.000
Error        8      7.333     0.917
Total       14    175.333
```

> Systems and operator both show significant difference

Tests of Between-Subjects Effects

Dependent Variable: Training hours

Source	Type III Sum of Squares	df	Mean Square	F	Sig.
Corrected Model	168.000[a]	6	28.000	30.545	.000
Intercept	4506.667	1	4506.667	4916.364	.000
SYSTEMS	103.333	2	51.667	56.364	.000
OPERATOR	64.667	4	16.167	17.636	.000
Error	7.333	8	.917		
Total	4682.000	15			
Corrected Total	175.333	14			

[a] R Squared = .958 (Adjusted R Squared = .927)

SPSS

Multiple Comparisons

Dependent variable: Training hours
LSD

> Still only C which is significantly different

(I) File management system	(J) File management system	Mean difference (I−J)	Std. Error	Sig.	95% Confidence Interval Lower Bound	95% Confidence Interval Upper Bound
A	B	1.0000	.6055	.137	−.3964	4.3964
	C	−5.0000*	.6055	.000	−8.3964	−1.6036
B	A	−1.0000	.6055	.137	−2.3964	.3964
	C	−6.0000*	.6055	.000	−7.3964	−4.6036
C	A	5.0000*	.6055	.000	3.6036	6.3964
	B	6.0000*	.6055	.000	4.6036	7.3964

Example 8.5

Minitab   Analysis of Variance for Consumpt, using Sequential SS for Tests

Source	DF	Seq SS	Adj SS	Seq MS	F	P
Vehicle	2	14.326	14.326	7.163	5.75	0.018
Additive	3	39.871	39.871	13.290	10.67	0.001
Vehicle*Additive	6	22.447	22.447	3.741	3.00	0.050

Vehicles and additivies both significantly different. Interaction not significant at 5% level

SPSS

Tests of Between-Subjects Effects

Dependent Variable: Fuel consumption (mpg)

Source	Type III Sum of Squares	df	Mean Square	F	Sig.
Corrected Model	76.645[a]	11	6.9680	5.595	.003
Intercept	21021.920	1	21021.920	16879.428	.000
ADDITIVE	39.871	3	13.290	10.671	.001
VEHICLE	14.326	2	7.163	7.751	.018
ADDITIVE*VEHICLE	22.447	6	3.741	3.004	.050
Error	14.945	12	1.245		
Total	21113.510	24			
Corrected Total	91.590	23			

[a] R Squared = .837 (Adjusted R Squared = .687)

The use of computer packages for analysis of variance is included in Worksheets 15.2.4, 15.5.4 and 15.8.4

8.9 Tutorial 8 – Analysis of variance

8.1   The accompanying table contains the number of words typed per minute by four office trainees at five different times using the same word processor.

A	B	C	D
82	55	69	87
79	67	72	61
75	84	78	82
68	77	83	61
65	71	74	72

At the 5% significance level, determine whether the typing speeds of the four trainees differ. Summarise your findings in an ANOVA table.

8.2 Three equivalent training courses were taught by three different instructors. A common final examination was given. The test scores are given in the table below:

Instructor 1	Instructor 2	Instructor 3
75	90	17
91	80	33
83	89	55
45	93	70
82	53	61
75	87	43
68	76	50
62	58	73
47	82	73
95	98	93
38	78	58
79	64	81
	80	70
	81	
	79	

Assume that the populations of test scores are normally distributed with equal variance. By using the 0.5 significance level, test to determine whether there is a difference in the average marks gained by the students of the three instructors. Summarise your calculations in an ANOVA table.

8.3 Four laboratories, A, B, C and D, are used by food manufacturing companies for making nutrition analyses of their products. The following data are the fat contents (in grams) of the same weight of three similar types of peanut butter.

	Laboratory			
Peanut butter	A	B	C	D
Brand 1	16.6	17.7	16.0	16.3
Brand 2	16.0	15.5	15.6	15.9
Brand 3	16.4	16.3	15.9	16.2

Analyse the data at 5% significance by (a) carrying out a one-way ANOVA to see if there is a difference between the fat content of the three brands; (b) performing a two-way ANOVA to see if there is any difference between the brands using the laboratories as blocks; (c) do you think there is any evidence that the results were - not reasonably consistent between the four laboratories?

8.4 An electronics manufacturing firm operates 24 hours a day 5 days a week. Three 8-hour shifts are used, and the workers rotate shifts each week. A management team conducted a study to determine whether there is a difference in the mean number of 14" video monitors produced when employees work on the various shifts. A random sample of five workers was selected and the number of 14" video monitors they produce for each shift is recorded overleaf.

	Monitors produced		
Employee	Morning	Afternoon	Night
A	10	4	14
B	12	5	12
C	7	3	9
D	9	8	7
E	7	5	6

Is there a difference in the mean production by worker and/or the mean production by shift? Use a two-way analysis of variance for both variables which you may assume to exhibit no interaction. Test at the 5% level.

8.5 The manager of a large department store conducted an experiment to determine whether there is a difference between the average weekly sales of three members of the staff in the same department. The following data indicate sales (in £100) for seven consecutive weeks for the three employees.

		Employee	
Week	A	B	C
1	27.6	28.7	26.4
2	31.2	29.3	30.3
3	28.8	28.4	28.0
4	30.6	29.8	28.7
5	30.0	31.0	32.3
6	28.4	29.9	29.6
7	30.9	29.5	31.1

(a) Carry out a one-way ANOVA to see whether there is any difference between the sales of the three employees.

(b) Carry out a two-way ANOVA to see whether there is any difference between the sales of the three employees when using the weeks as blocks.

(c) If you find a significant result, test pairwise to see where the difference lies.

8.10 Supplementary exercise 8

The first five questions assume no interactions.

8.6 Carry out a one-way ANOVA on the following packing times (min) in a warehouse to see if there is any significant difference between them at 5% significance.

	Packers		
1	2	3	4
10	7	6	6
5	4	3	2
9	5	8	6
8	5	6	5

8.7 Carry out a two-way ANOVA on the following packing times to see if there is a significant difference between either/or packers and shifts.

Packers	Shifts		
	A	B	C
1	9	7	7
2	5	6	9
3	2	3	1
4	6	8	7

8.8 In an effort to expand its services, a regional transport authority conducted an experiment to determine which of four routes to take from an airport to the centre of the business district of the city. The following data indicate the travel times (in minutes) along each of the four routes.

Day	Route			
	1	2	3	4
Monday	20	22	22	24
Tuesday	23	24	26	26
Wednesday	22	25	27	25
Thursday	27	23	30	27
Friday	28	26	30	27

Carry out a two-way ANOVA on days and routes. If either are significant, carry out a pairwise test in order to see where the difference lies.

8.9 Four kinds of fertiliser, A, B, C, and D, could be used to increase the yield of peas. The ground is divided into twelve plots of the same size with three blocks each containing four homogenous plots. The yields (in kg per plot) are as follows.

Block	Fertiliser			
	A	B	C	D
1	52.8	49.4	58.6	42.9
2	60.1	48.1	61.0	50.3
3	62.0	56.4	63.3	61.2

(a) Carry out a one-way ANOVA to see if there is any difference between the four fertilisers.

(b) Carry out a two-way ANOVA to see if there is any difference between the four fertilisers.

(c) If you find a significant result, test pairwise to see where the difference lies.

Question 8.10 includes interactions – ignore it if you have not covered them.

8.10 A study was made to determine if humidity conditions have an effect on the force required to break cotton rope made with different structures. Three different structures of rope, A, B and C, were tested using four different levels of humidity. The forces, in Newtons, are given as follows:

Rope structure	Humidity			
	30%	50%	70%	90%
A	39.0	33.1	33.8	33.0
	42.8	37.8	30.7	32.9
B	36.9	27.2	29.7	28.5
	41.0	26.8	29.1	27.9
C	27.4	29.2	26.7	30.9
	30.3	29.9	32.0	31.5

(a) Test the hypotheses of no difference between the strengths of the ropes of the different structures and also no interaction at 5%.

(b) Perform a similar analysis using only rope structures A and B and again test for an interaction.

8.11 A Latin square is used in this question. The atmosphere in five different districts of a large town was sampled, each district being sampled at five different heights. Each sample was tested by one of five different tests for the presence of a certain type of pollution. The arrangement shown in the table gives a measure of the weight of the chemical as determined by the tests. The different tests are denoted by different letters.

Heights	1		2		Districts 3		4		5	
1	10	(C)	12	(B)	20	(A)	6	(D)	4	(E)
2	9	(D)	10	(C)	24	(B)	0	(E)	5	(A)
3	12	(B)	3	(E)	25	(C)	7	(A)	2	(D)
4	16	(A)	6	(D)	18	(E)	4	(C)	6	(B)
5	14	(E)	8	(A)	23	(D)	9	(B)	3	(C)

Is there any evidence of significant variation from district to district or between heights? Are the results from the different methods of analysis consistent?

9 Correlation and Regression

9.1 The objectives of this chapter

So far we have only been interested in one variable at a time. In this chapter we consider two quantitative variables and look for any association between them. If a relationship is found to exist then the next step is to describe it both graphically and by an equation which can be used for predictive purposes.

Having completed this chapter you should be able to describe bivariate data graphically; represent them by an equation describing the dependent variable as a function of the independent one; use the equation for predictive purposes and give an indication of the expected accuracy of the prediction.

9.2 Introduction

If we have information available on more than one variable, we might be interested in seeing if there is any connection – any association – between them. The method for doing this depends upon the type of data we have. Are they nominal, ordinal or interval?

Methods for analysing the association between two **nominal** variables will be described in the next chapter by the use of contingency tables and chi-squared tests. In this chapter we will first consider pairwise association between **interval** data using scatter diagrams, and Pearson's method of correlation. We will then look at associations between **ordinal** variables using Spearman's method.

If a pairwise correlation is found to be significant, the relationship between the variables will be investigated by producing a regression model in the form of a linear equation. If we wish to use the regression equation for making predictions we also need to know how good our predictions are likely to be. On the assumption that the lack of fit for the predicted values will be similar to that for the data from which the regression model was constructed, we shall analyse the residuals (the lack of fit) and quote estimates of accuracy with the predictions.

Each section of theory is followed by an example.

EXAMPLE 9.1

An ice-cream manufacturer wishes to estimate how much he is likely to be able to sell in the coming month. Common sense suggests that his sales vary with the climatic conditions and now that long-term weather forecasts are available, he realises he can obtain an estimate of the average temperature for one month ahead. Can he find an association between average monthly temperature and his sales in the past, then use this association to predict his likely sales for the coming month?

continued

EXAMPLE 9.1 *continued*

In order to help him we need to find out:

- If there is any association between average monthly temperature and ice-cream sales
- If there is an association, is it strong enough to be useful to him
- If so, what form the relationship between the two variables takes
- How we can make use of that relationship for predictive purposes, that is, forecasting
- How good any predictions about his sales will be.

The sample of information collected by the manufacturer about his sales for the previous twelve months and the corresponding average monthly temperatures from the weather office for his locality are recorded in Table 9.1.

Table 9.1

Month	Average temperature (°C)	Sales (£000)	Month	Average temperature (°C)	Sales (£000)
January	4	73	July	16	134
February	4	57	August	17	139
March	7	81	September	14	124
April	8	94	October	11	103
May	12	110	November	7	81
June	15	124	December	5	80

9.3 Scatter diagrams

Some initial insight into the relationship between two continuous variables can be obtained by plotting a **scatter diagram** and looking at the resulting graph. Does there appear to be any relationship between the two variables?

Figure 9.1 Scatter diagrams for various correlation coefficients (r)

(a) $r = +1$

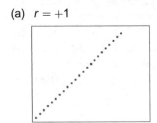

(c) $r \cong +0.7$

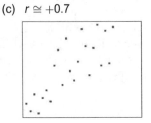

(e) $r = 0$

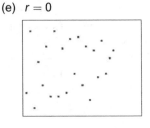

(b) $r = -1$

(d) $r \cong -0.7$

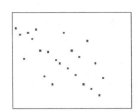

(f) $r = 0$, but a relationship is evident

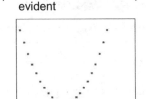

We are looking for a **linear** relationship with the bivariate points lying reasonably close to a line of best fit. Scatter diagrams are usually plotted on graph paper and, although at this stage no causality is implied, it makes sense to use the same diagram for the addition of the regression line later. The dependent variable, y, should be identified at this stage and plotted on the vertical axis with the independent variable, x, on the horizontal.

9.3.1 Independent and dependent variables

The decision as to which variable is which sometimes causes problems. Often the choice is obvious, as in Example 9.1 because it would make no sense to suggest that monthly temperature could be dependent on ice-cream sales! The temperature has to be the independent variable, x, and the ice-cream sales the dependent variable, y.

If you are unsure, here are some pointers that might be of use:

- If you have control over one of the variables then that is the independent, x. For example, a manufacturer can decide how much to spend on advertising and expect his sales to be dependent upon how much he spends
- If there is any lapse of time between the two variables being measured, then the latter must depend upon the former, it cannot be the other way round
- If you want to predict the values of one variable from your knowledge of the other variable, the variable to be predicted must be dependent on the known one.

EXAMPLE 9.1 *continued*

Plot a scatter diagram with ice-cream sales as the dependent variable and average temperature as the independent variable.

Figure 9.2 seems to indicate a straight line relationship, with all points fairly close to a line of best fit. The strength of the relationship can be quantified by calculating the coefficient of correlation which will then be tested for significance.

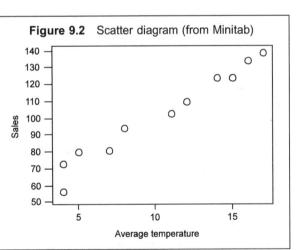

Figure 9.2 Scatter diagram (from Minitab)

9.4 Pearson's product moment correlation coefficient

Pearson's product moment correlation coefficient is generally just referred to as the correlation coefficient, r. It describes the strength of a linear relationship between two variables measured on an interval or ratio scale.

Pearson's correlation coefficient compares how the variables vary together with how they each vary individually and is independent of the origin or units of measurement. Note that it is not concerned with cause and effect. Perfect correlation would give a value of $r = 1$.

9.4.1 Calculation of Pearson's correlation coefficient

The value of the correlation coefficient, r, is most easily found using a calculator in linear regression (LR) mode. (See Section 9.14 or, preferably, consult your calculator booklet for the method.)

The tutorial sheet (Section 9.16) will provide practice in the use of your calculator. Make sure that you are happy and confident in its use. If not, ask for help from your lecturer or tutor. (If you do not have a calculator capable of carrying out correlation and regression calculations use the formulae in Section 9.15.)

EXAMPLE 9.1 *continued*

For the ice-cream data the value of the correlation coefficient from the calculator is
$$r = 0.9833$$

Is the size of the correlation coefficient large enough to claim that there is a **significant** relationship between average monthly temperature and sales of ice-cream?

The test statistic seems very close to 1, but is it close enough to decide that the amount of association between the two variables justifies the use of temperature to estimate sales?

We need to compare the correlation coefficient with a table value to see if it was significantly high. The correlation table is reproduced as Table D6 in Appendix D. The table (critical) value is found by using $(n - 2)$ degrees of freedom, 5% significance and two tails, where n is the number of data pairs in the sample.

If you have studied Chapter 7 on hypothesis testing you should carry out the formal test in Section 9.4.2. If not, just compare the sample correlation coefficient with the table value. If the value from the sample is higher than the table value the correlation is significant. If it is lower then any association between the two variables is not significant and could have occurred by chance.

9.4.2 Hypothesis test for a Pearson's correlation coefficient

Null hypothesis H_0: There is no association (correlation) between the two variables.

Alternative hypothesis H_1: There is an association (correlation) between them.

Critical value: Pearson's correlation tables, usually 5% (0.05), two tails, $n - 2$ degrees of freedom, where n is the number of data pairs in the sample.

Test statistic: the sample correlation coefficient.

Conclusion: Compare the test statistic with the critical value. If the test statistic is larger, reject the null hypothesis and conclude that the correlation is significant. If it is smaller, accept the null hypothesis that there is no significant correlation.

EXAMPLE 9.1 *continued*

Null hypothesis H_0: There is no association between ice-cream sales and temperature.

Alternative hypothesis H_1: There is an association between them.

Critical value: 5%, $(12 - 2) = 10$ degrees of freedom, critical value is 0.576

Test statistic: 0.983

continued

EXAMPLE 9.1 *continued*

Conclusion: The test statistic exceeds the critical value so we reject the null hypothesis and conclude that there is a significant association between ice-cream sales and temperature.

Because we have found significant association between average monthly temperature and ice-cream sales it is reasonable to try to identify this relationship by a regression model in the form of a linear equation. This can then be used to estimate sales.

9.5 Regression equation (least squares)

As we now know there is a significant relationship between the two variables, the next step is to define it by a 'least squares regression' equation. We can then draw the line described by the equation on the scatter diagram and use it to estimate a value for the dependent variable from a given value of the independent.

The term 'least squares regression' comes from the method of calculating the equation (see Section 9.15). It is the method used by the calculator even though we are not aware of it!

The **regression line** is described, in general, as the straight line with the equation:

$$y = a + bx$$

where x and y are the independent and dependent variables, respectively, a is the intercept on the y-axis, and b is the slope of the line. (You may be more familiar with a straight line equation in the form $y = mx + c$, in which c is the intercept on the y-axis, and m the slope of the line.)

As with the correlation coefficient, the coefficients a and b of the regression equation can be found directly from the calculator in LR mode or calculated (see Section 9.15).

To draw the regression line on the scatter diagram, plot any three points and join them up. The points should be widely spaced on your diagram in the region of the observed data, so choose one low value of x and one high value of x, substitute them in your equation and find the corresponding values of y. For any value of x the corresponding value of y can be calculated from the equation. Alternatively, while the data is still in your calculator, inputting any value of x and pressing the key $(\hat{y})$ will produce the corresponding value of y. The centroid $(\bar{x}, \bar{y})$, which can be found directly from your calculator in LR mode, is often plotted as the third point, but any third point will do.

EXAMPLE 9.1 *continued*

Plot the regression line to find the expected value of ice-cream sales for a forecast average temperature.

The values of a and b produced from a calculator in linear regression (LR) mode are $a = 45.52$ and $b = 5.448$, giving the regression equation (when rounded off to three significant figures):

$$y = 45.5 + 5.45x$$

That is, the predicted ice cream sales (£000) are:

45.5 + 5.45 × average monthly temperature (°C)

continued

EXAMPLE 9.1 *continued*

To draw this line on the scatter diagram, give x a low value and a high value and calculate the corresponding y values, for example:

If $x = 5$ then $y = 45.5 + 5.45 \times 5 = 72.8$
If $x = 15$ then $y = 45.5 + 5.45 \times 15 = 127.3$

Alternatively, while the data is still in your calculator, inputting the value of 5 for x and pressing key $(\hat{y})$ will produce the corresponding value of y, 72.8.

The centroid $(\bar{x}, \bar{y})$ is the point (10.0, 100.0). Plot these three points on your graph and join them with a straight line.

Scatter diagram with regression line added (Minitab)

Figure 9.3   Sales against average monthly temperature

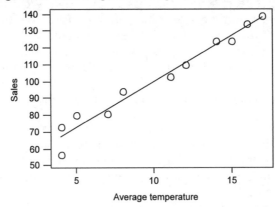

9.5.1   Interpretation of regression model

The constant, a, is interpreted as the value of the dependent variable, y, if the independent variable, x, is zero, that is, the intercept on the y-axis. The gradient, b, can be interpreted as the marginal increase in the dependent variable, that is, the change in the dependent variable, y, per unit change in the independent variable, x. The model is only applicable within the range of the sample data.

EXAMPLE 9.1 *continued*

Mathematically we interpret the coefficients of the equation $y = 45.5 + 5.45x$ as:

- For a month during which the average temperature is 0°C we would expect sales of £45 500.
- For every extra 1°C in average monthly temperature we can expect an extra £5450 in sales.

These interpretations do not necessarily apply in real life. An average temperature of 0°C is a most unlikely situation in this country! Also zero is outside the range of the sample data.

9.6 Goodness of fit

How well does the regression line fit the data? Goodness of fit is measured by $(r^2 \times 100)\%$ and indicates the percentage of the variation in the dependent variable that is attributed to the variation in the independent variable.

EXAMPLE 9.1 *continued*

For the ice-cream data the correlation coefficient, r, was 0.983 so we have a goodness of fit of $(0.983)^2 \times 100 = 96.6\%$ fit. This high value indicates that any predictions made about the sales from a value of the average monthly temperature will be good.

The variation in the average monthly temperature accounts for 96.6% of the variation in sales leaving only 3.4% to be accounted for by other unknown factors.

9.7 Using the regression model for prediction or estimation

All predictions lie on the regression line so the **regression equation** is used to calculate their values. Substituting the known or estimated value of the independent variable, x, into the equation allows the calculation of the corresponding dependent value, y.

Sales can also be estimated directly from your graph using the regression line. For any given value of x, what is the value on the line of the corresponding value of y? The corresponding value of y for any value of x can be produced directly from the calculator in LR mode by typing in the x value and pressing key $(\hat{y})$ to find the estimated value of y.

EXAMPLE 9.1 *continued*

The ice-cream manufacturer knows that the estimated average temperature for the following month is 14°C, what would he expect his sales to be?

By substitution

$$\text{Estimated sales} = 45.5 + 5.45 \times \text{average temperature}$$
$$= 45.5 + 5.45 \times 14$$
$$= 121.8$$

Expected sales would be £122 000 (only 3 significant figures are appropriate for this data).

From the graph

What is the value on the line of y when the x value is 14?

You will find that is about 122. The number of significant figures to which you can read the value depends on the scale of your graph.

Using a calculator

While the original data is still in your calculator type in 14 and then press $(\hat{y})$. This will produce the value of 121.8 giving estimated sales of £122 000.

9.7.1 Accuracy of predictions

Correlation coefficients can be used directly for comparing the degree of association of bivariate variables provided the sample sizes are the same.

In order to quantify the accuracy of predictions a fairly involved calculation is necessary. However, a rough idea of its value can be obtained by producing a computer-generated graph showing the line of best fit with its confidence interval and prediction interval. The confidence interval describes what is expected to happen on average and the prediction interval indicates the range of values expected to be taken by individual predictions. Figure 9.4 shows the graph for Example 9.1.

Figure 9.4 Sales against average monthly temperature

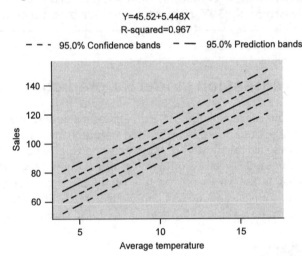

9.8 Residual analysis

The residual is the difference between the measured value and the predicted value, that is the value on the regression line:

Residual = Sales – Predicted (Fitted) value

The size of the residuals are a measure of the 'misfit' of the model. In each case the residual is the bit not accounted for by the regression model. Graphically it is the vertical distance between the plotted point (the actual value) and the regression line (the model value). These residuals therefore need to be small, as is the case when the points on the scatter diagram are all nearly on the line. They also need to be randomly scattered about zero with a much smaller standard deviation than that of the dependent variable, normally-distributed and random when plotted against the dependent variable.

A package such as Minitab or SPSS is usually employed for residual analysis. If you are not using a computer package on this course use 'goodness of fit' as a measure of the accuracy of your model in comparison to others. Obviously the higher the goodness of fit value, the better the model.

EXAMPLE 9.1 continued

Analysis of the residuals from the ice-cream model in Minitab produced the following:

```
              N        MEAN       STDEV
Sales        12       100.00      26.41
RESI1        12       000.00      04.80
```

We can see that the mean is zero and the standard deviation is much smaller than that of the original sales. Also from Figure 9.5 the residuals appear to be random against sales and approximately normally distributed. (Remember that this is only a very small sample.)

Figure 9.5

(a) Residuals against sales

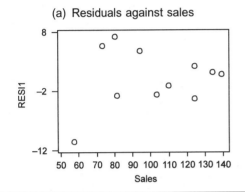

(b) Histogram of residuals

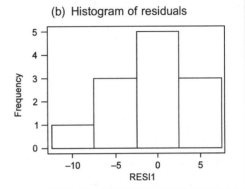

9.9 An extended example

EXAMPLE 9.2

The gross monthly sales volume for a corporation is not subject to substantial seasonal variation. We wish to see if a relationship exists between sales volume and the amount spent on advertising in the previous months and, if so, how we can use this amount to predict sales.

The data in Table 9.2 represent a sample of advertising expenditures and sales volumes for ten randomly selected months.

Table 9.2

Month	Advertising, X (£0000s)	Sales volume, Y (£0000s)
1	1.2	101
2	0.8	92
3	1.0	110
4	1.3	120
5	0.7	90
6	0.8	82
7	1.0	93
8	0.6	75
9	0.9	91
10	1.1	105

continued

EXAMPLE 9.2 *continued*

Scatter plot

Plot a scatter diagram by hand on graph paper. You will see that the result suggests a fairly loose linear relationship. In general the larger the amount spent on advertising the larger the sales volume.

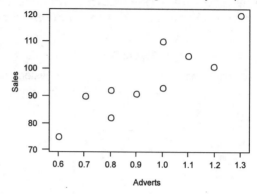

Figure 9.6   Sales against average monthly temperature

Correlation coefficient

The correlation coefficient, r, from the calculator is 0.8754

Testing it for significance:

H_0: There is no association between advertising expenditure and sales volume.

H_1: There is an association between them.

Critical value: 5%, $(10 - 2) = 8$ degrees of freedom, critical value 0.632

Test statistic: 0.875

Conclusion: The test statistic exceeds the critical value so we reject the null hypothesis and conclude that there is a significant association between advertising expenditure and sales volume.

Regression equation

From the calculator $a = 46.5$, $b = 52.6$ so the regression equation $y = 46.5 + 52.5x$ is calculated from the sample to estimate

Sales $= 46.5 + 52.5 \times$ advertising expenditure for the whole corporation

Plot the line

To plot the line: $y = 46.5 + 52.6x$ by hand:

Plot the centroid $(\bar{x}, \bar{y})$: $(0.94, 95.9)$

Plot a point for a low value of x:

$x = 0.60$ $y = 46.5 + 52.6 \times 0.60 = 78.1$ $(0.60, 78.06)$

Plot a point for a high value of y:

$x = 1.30$ $y = 46.5 + 52.6 \times 1.30 = 114.9$ $(1.30, 114.9)$

By eye, the regression line shows a reasonable fit (see Figure 9.7).

continued

EXAMPLE 9.2 *continued*

Figure 9.7 Sales against average monthly temperature

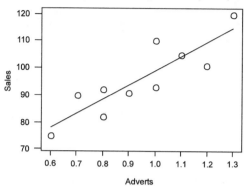

Adverts

Interpretation of coefficients

We need to interpret the coefficients of the equation $y = 45.5 + 52.6x$. If no money were to be spent on advertising we would expect sales to be £455 000. For every extra £10 000 spent on advertising we expect an extra £526 000 in sales – not bad!

Goodness of fit

$r = 0.875$ gives a goodness of fit measurement of $0.875^2 \times 100 = 76.6\%$

Estimating values

What value would you estimate for the gross monthly sales if you decided to spend £12 000 on advertising in a particular month?

Substitute $x = 1.2$ in the equation and calculate the corresponding value of y:

$$y = 46.5 + 52.6x \Rightarrow y = 46.5 + 52.6 \times 1.2 \Rightarrow y = 109.6$$

By spending £12 000 on advertising the firm would expect, on average, sales of £1 100 000

Residual analysis

	N	MEAN	STDEV
Sales	10	95.90	13.34
RESI1	10	0.00	6.45

The residuals have a mean of zero, low standard deviation, are random and normal.

Figure 9.8

(a) Residuals against sales

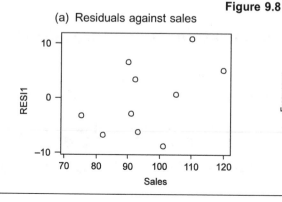

Sales

(b) Histogram of residuals

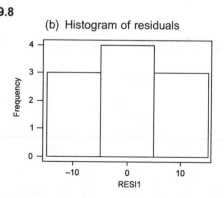

RESI1

9.10 Spearman's rank correlation coefficient, r_s

If data are not interval or ratio but can be ranked in some manner, such as in qualitative replies to questionnaires, then the use of Spearman's rank correlation coefficient, r_s, is preferable to Pearson's coefficient.

9.10.1 Calculation of Spearman's rank correlation coefficient

The formula for calculating Spearman's rank correlation coefficient is:

$$r_s = \frac{6\sum d^2}{n(n^2-1)}$$

where d is the difference in rankings and n the sample size.

The coefficient is then tested against a table value from the Spearman's rank correlation table (Table D7). As for Pearson's correlation, the amount of correlation is considered to be significant if the correlation coefficient exceeds the table value.

If hypothesis testing (Chapter 7) has been included in your course, then the hypothesis test should be carried out. If not just compare the two values: if the test statistic is larger then the correlation is significant.

9.10.2 Hypothesis test for a Spearman's correlation coefficient (r_s)

Null hypothesis, H_0: There is no association (correlation) between the two variables.

Alternative hypothesis, H_1: There is an association (correlation) between them.

Critical value: Spearman's correlation tables, usually 5%, for n pairs of data points.

Test statistic: the sample correlation coefficient.

Conclusion: Compare the test statistic with the critical value.
If the test statistic is larger, reject the null hypothesis and conclude that the correlation present is significant. If it is smaller, accept the null hypothesis that there is no significant correlation present.

This test is not as powerful as Pearson's test because the original data values are not taken into consideration. However, it is always better to carry out a valid test rather than a more powerful one that is invalid. See Groebner, 1993, Chapter 13, for more detail.

9.11 Further methods and applications with regression

Simple linear regression can be extended in three ways:

- As non-linear regression which deals with 'curved' data, that is, data which cannot be fitted by a straight line
- As multiple regression in which there is more than one independent variable
- As log-linear regression in which categorical variables can be investigated

Linear regression can also be used in the analysis of a time series and the resulting model used for forecasting (see Chapter 13).

9.11.1 Non-linear regression

If a scatter diagram indicates that a curved line would fit the data better than a straight one then the problem is deciding what function best describes the line. Is it quadratic or cubic? Is a logarithmic function better than either of these? Fortunately the answer can be readily found in SPSS.

Using the non-linear curve-fitting facility in SPSS, a variety of functions can be tried very quickly. The graphs of the trial equation are plotted from the data so that an assessment of their fit can be made. The goodness of fit can also be compared numerically. By this method it is easy to see which non-linear equation best suits your data.

9.11.2 Multiple regression

It may be preferable to use more than one predictor variable, if available, in predicting a value for the dependent variable. Explaining the behaviour of one dependent variable in terms of several independent variables often produces a much better-fitting model.

The use of a computer is essential for this technique or the mathematics becomes very cumbersome. With the use of Minitab or SPSS any number of predictor variables can be introduced into the equation, the contribution of each to the overall model compared and the quality of the selected model assessed.

9.11.3 Log-linear regression

Log-linear regression is an extension of the two dimensional contingency table for more than two categorical or ordinal variables in which frequencies are examined for independence. By taking logs the ratios are converted into a linear combination of the variables so that a model similar to that used in regression can explore the relationships between the original variables. See Groebner, 1993, Chapter 14 for more detail.

9.12 Summary

In this chapter

- We have considered the association between two variables measured on a continuous scale.
- We drew a scatter diagram to check that the data seemed to follow a straight line. If it did not, correlation methods of analysis are not appropriate.
- We calculated Pearson's correlation coefficient, r, if the variables were measured on an interval scale, or Spearman's correlation coefficient, r_s, if the data were only ordinal.
- We tested the correlation coefficient for significance using a hypothesis test (or just compared the sample correlation coefficient to a table value).
- For interval data with Pearson's correlation coefficient shown to be significant:
  - We carried out regression analysis in order to produce the best fitting model in the form of a regression equation.
  - We plotted the regression line on the original scatter diagram.
  - We used the regression model to estimate the value of the dependent variable, y, for a given value of the independent variable, x.
  - We checked, roughly, how good this estimation was likely to be.
  - We analysed the residuals from the model in order to check that they were random, with a smaller standard deviation than the dependent variable, normally-distributed and random when plotted against the dependent variable.

9.13 Regression analysis by computer – Example 9.1

Minitab regression output

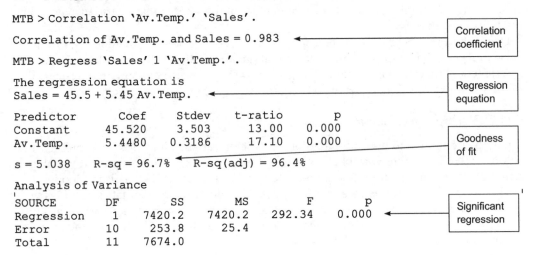

```
MTB > Correlation 'Av.Temp.' 'Sales'.
Correlation of Av.Temp. and Sales = 0.983
MTB > Regress 'Sales' 1 'Av.Temp.'.
The regression equation is
Sales = 45.5 + 5.45 Av.Temp.

Predictor     Coef     Stdev    t-ratio        p
Constant     45.520     3.503      13.00    0.000
Av.Temp.      5.4480    0.3186      17.10    0.000

s = 5.038     R-sq = 96.7%     R-sq(adj) = 96.4%

Analysis of Variance
SOURCE        DF        SS         MS         F        p
Regression     1     7420.2     7420.2    292.34    0.000
Error         10      253.8       25.4
Total         11     7674.0
```

Correlation
coefficient

Regression
equation

Goodness
of fit

Significant
regression

SPSS regression output

Correlations		Average monthly temperature	Ice cream sales (£000)
Average monthly temperature	Pearson correlation Sig. (2 tailed) N	1.000 . 12	.983* .000 12
Ice cream sales (£000)	Pearson correlation Sig. (2 tailed) N	.983* .000 12	1.000 . 12

*Correlation is significant at the 0.1 level (2 tailed)

Coefficients[a]	Unstandardised coefficients		Standardised coefficients		
Model	B	Std. error	Beta	t	Sig.
1 (Constant)	45.520	3.503		12.996	.000
Average monthly temperature	5.448	.319	.983	17.098	.000

[a] Dependent variable: ice cream sales (£000)

Regression equation
$y = 45.5 + 5.45x$

Regression analysis using computer packages is included in Worksheets 15.2.5, 15.5.5 and 15.8.5

9.14 Calculator use and practice

Note: The procedures are for Casio calculators with linear regression mode. Refer to handbook for other makes.

The data are entered as pairs of numbers. Within the many memories of the calculator these numbers and their squares are accumulated, the correlation coefficient and the values of a and b in the regression equation are then calculated from these stored sums using formulae 9.1 and 9.2 .

The following method produces the correlation coefficient, r, the regression coefficients, a and b, and estimated values of y for given values of x.

Data in

1	Clear all memories	Shift AC
2	Enter linear regression mode	Mode 3, 1
3	Input variables x and y together for each case Repeat to end of data.	x, y DT

Results out

4	Check number of pairs entered	RCL Red C
5	Output correlation coefficient (r)	(r) Shift (
6	Output intercept (a) and slope (b) of regression line	(A) Shift 7, (B) Shift 8
7	To get value of y $(\hat{y})$ for plotting line when $x = 15$	15 $(\hat{y})$ Shift –

Practice

For each set of numbers calculate:

- The value of the correlation coefficient
- The regression equation
- The value of y when $x = 8$

1	x	3	5	4	7	8	6	9	10	12
	y	5	6	9	8	11	13	14	16	19

2	x	15	13	9	10	7	6	4	5	3
	y	7	7	9	9	11	15	14	13	18

3	x	4	5	4	7	6	6	10	5	2
	y	5	6	7	8	4	8	9	6	7

4	x	7	4	4	10	11	8	7	9	14
	y	10	6	9	15	9	12	13	15	20

Answers

1	$r = 0.898$	$y = 1.03 + 1.43x$	$y = 12.5$
2	$r = -0.922$	$y = 18.3 - 0.858x$	$y = 11.4$
3	$r = 0.470$	$y = 4.86 + 0.331x$	$y = 7.51$
4	$r = 0.781$	$y = 3.77 + 1.01x$	$y = 11.9$

9.15 Formulae for correlation and regression coefficients

Pearson's product moment correlation coefficient

The value of the correlation coefficient, r, is best produced directly from a calculator in LR mode. Otherwise the following calculations are necessary.

The formula used to find the Pearson's product moment correlation coefficient is (least squares method):

$$r = \frac{S_{xy}}{\sqrt{S_{xx}S_{yy}}} \qquad (-1 \le r \le +1) \qquad (9.1)$$

where $\quad S_{xx} = \sum x^2 - \dfrac{\sum x \sum x}{n}$

$$S_{yy} = \sum y^2 - \frac{\sum y \sum y}{n}$$

$$S_{xy} = \sum xy - \frac{\sum x \sum y}{n}$$

where $\sum x$ (sigma x) means the sum of all the x values, and so on.

Regression equation

As with the correlation coefficient, the regression equation can be produced directly from a calculator in LR mode. Otherwise, further use is made of the values of Σx, Σy, Σx^2, Σy^2, Σxy, n.

The regression line is described, in general, as the straight line with the equation:

$$y = a + bx$$

where x and y are the independent and dependent variables respectively, a the intercept on the y-axis, and b the slope of the line.

The gradient, b, is calculated from:

$$b = \frac{S_{xy}}{S_{xx}} \qquad (9.2)$$

where $\quad S_{xy} = \sum xy - \dfrac{\sum x \sum y}{n}$

and $\quad S_{xx} = \sum x^2 - \dfrac{\sum x \sum x}{n}$

Since the regression line passes through the centroid, both means, its equation can be used to find the value of a, the intercept on the y-axis:

$$a = y - b\bar{x}$$

EXAMPLE 9.3

Ice-cream sales per month against mean monthly temperature (Celsius) are shown in Table 9.3. The sums of the columns, $\sum x$, $\sum y$, $\sum x^2$, $\sum y^2$, $\sum xy$ are also calculated.

Table 9.3

Month	Average temperature (x)	Ice cream sales (y)	x^2	y^2	xy
January	4	73	16	5329	292
February	4	57	16	3249	228
March	7	81	49	6561	567
April	8	94	64	8836	752
May	12	110	144	12100	1320
June	15	124	225	15376	1860
July	16	134	256	17956	2144
August	17	139	289	19321	2363
September	14	124	196	15376	1736
October	11	103	121	10609	1133
November	7	81	49	6561	567
December	5	80	25	6400	400
Sums $\sum$	120	1200	1450	127674	13362

Correlation coefficient

$\sum x = 120$, $\sum y = 1200$, $\sum x^2 = 1450$, $\sum y^2 = 127674$, $\sum xy = 13362$, $n = 12$

$$S_{xx} = 1450 - \frac{120 \times 120}{12} = 250$$

$$S_{yy} = 127674 - \frac{1200 \times 1200}{12} = 7674$$

$$S_{xy} = 13362 - \frac{120 \times 120}{12} = 1362$$

Therefore $\quad r = \dfrac{1362}{\sqrt{250 \times 7674}} = 0.9833$

Regression equation

Assume sales are dependent on temperature.

$S_{xy} = 1362 \quad S_{xx} = 250$

so $b = \dfrac{1362}{250} = 5.448$

$$a = \frac{1200}{12} - 5.448 \times \frac{120}{12} = 45.52$$

The values of a and b are therefore 45.5 and 5.45, respectively, giving the regression equation:

$$y = 45.5 + 5.45x$$

9.16 Correlation and regression tutorial

9.1 A small retail business has determined that the correlation coefficient between monthly expenses and profits for the past year, measured at the end of each month, is $r = 0.56$. Assuming that both expenses and profits are approximately normal, test at the 5% (0.05) level of significance the null hypothesis that there is no correlation between them.

9.2 Plot a scatter diagram and calculate the correlation coefficient for the following data.

Firm	Annual percentage increase in advertising expenditure	Annual percentage increase in sales revenue
A	1	1
B	3	2
C	4	2
D	6	4
E	8	6
F	9	8
G	11	8
H	14	9

If appropriate find the least squares regression line, plot it on your graph and use it to estimate the increase in sales revenue expected from an increase in advertising expenditure of 7.5%.

9.3 The following data relates to the annual sales of petrol at 8 garages and their expenditure on coupons to give away to customers.

Expenditure on coupons (£000s)	Sales of petrol (0 000 gallons)
15	35
5	40
25	30
30	45
20	40
40	50
50	25
55	55

(a) Plot a scatter diagram. (First decide which variable is independent.)
(b) Calculate the correlation coefficient and see if it is significantly high.
(c) If appropriate find the least squares regression line.
(d) Calculate percentage goodness of fit.
(e) Use your graph or the regression equation to estimate the sales of petrol if £25 000 is spent on coupons.

9.4 A trainee manager wondered whether the length of time his trainees revised for an examination had any effect on the marks they scored. Before the exam, he asked a random sample of them to estimate honestly how long, to the nearest hour, they had spent revising. After the examination he investigated the relationship between the two variables.

Trainee	A	B	C	D	E	F	G	H	I	J
Revision time	4	9	10	14	4	7	12	22	1	17
Exam mark	31	58	65	73	37	44	60	91	21	84

(a) Plot the scatter diagram in order to inspect the data.

(b) Calculate the correlation coefficient and test it for significance.

(c) If significant calculate the regression model to fit the data and interpret its coefficients.

(d) Plot the regression line on the scatter diagram.

(e) Calculate the percentage goodness of fit.

(f) Predict the examination mark for a trainee who revises for 15 hours.

(g) Predict the examination mark for a trainee who revises for 35 hours.

(h) Do you have any reservations about your answer to (g)?

9.5 In an effort to determine the relationship between annual wages, in £000, for employees and the number of days absent from work due to sickness, a large corporation studied the personnel records for a random sample of twelve employees. The paired data are:

Employee	Annual wages (£000)	Days missed
1	15.7	4
2	17.2	3
3	13.8	6
4	24.2	5
5	15.0	3
6	12.7	12
7	13.8	5
8	18.7	1
9	10.8	12
10	11.8	11
11	25.4	2
12	17.2	4

Determine the correlation coefficient and test to see if the number of days missed is related to annual wages at the 5% level of significance. If it is, find the regression equation for predicting the likely absence in days. Interpret its coefficients and use it to predict the likely absence of an employee earning £15 000.

9.6   The turnover and profit levels of ten companies in a particular industry are (£ million):

Company	A	B	C	D	E	F	G	H	I	J
Turnover	30.0	25.5	6.7	45.2	10.5	16.7	20.5	21.4	8.3	70.5
Profit	3.0	2.8	1.1	5.3	0.6	2.1	2.1	2.4	0.9	7.1

Test whether the variables are significantly correlated at the 1% level.

If they are correlated calculate the regression line for predicting expected profit from turnover and explain the coefficients of your equation.

9.17 Supplementary exercise 9

9.7   Two departmental managers ordered ten trainees according to this perceived ability. The ratings are given below:

Trainee	A	B	C	D	E	F	G	H	I	J
Manager A	1	9	6	2	5	8	7	3	10	4
Manager B	3	10	8	1	7	5	6	2	9	4

Calculate an appropriate correlation coefficient to measure the consistency of the ratings and test to see if there is significant association between them.

9.8   The manager of a small shop is hopeful that his sales are rising significantly week by week. Treating the sales for the previous six weeks as a typical example of this rising trend, he recorded them in £000 and analysed the results. Has the rise been significant ?

Week	1	2	3	4	5	6
Sales	2.69	2.62	2.80	2.70	2.75	2.81

(a) Find the correlation coefficient between sales and week and test it for significance at 5%.

(b) If appropriate, calculate the regression equation which will tell him the weekly rate at which his sales are rising and use this equation to tell him what his sales are expected to be for weeks 7 and 8.

9.9   A dress manufacturer is interested in predicting how many dresses will be sold of each style, colour and size. If the manufacturer could make a good prediction of sales after a new item has been delivered to salesman for 5 weeks, then total production could be suitably adjusted. In order to investigate the possibility he collected data from a random sample of the sales of similar garments. This is shown in the table overleaf.

Total sales	Sales after five weeks	Total sales	Sales after five weeks
3920	2350	3140	1590
1900	1220	1400	750
740	340	2350	1400
3070	1960	1880	1270
2000	1210	1420	890
1850	1270	2530	1890
2910	1770	960	700
1910	1250	980	640

(a) Plot a scatter diagram

(b) Calculate the correlation coefficient and test for its significance, at 5%.

(c) Find the least squares regression line and plot it on the graph.

(d) Calculate the goodness of fit.

(e) If the sales after five weeks are found to be 1000, what would you expect total sales to be?

9.10 A company is introducing a job evaluation scheme in which all jobs are graded by points for skill, danger, responsibility, and so on. Monthly pay scales are then drawn up according to the number of points allocated and other factors, such as experience and local conditions. To date, the company has applied this scheme to 10 jobs:

Job	A	B	C	D	E	F	G	H	I
Points	50	250	70	190	100	120	150	280	160
Pay (£)	1000	3050	1250	2500	1500	1600	2000	3250	2100

(a) Draw a scatter diagram of monthly pay against points

(b) If appropriate, find the least squares regression line for linking pay to points. Plot it on your graph and interpret your answer.

(c) Estimate the monthly pay for a job graded by 200 points and assess the likely reliability of your answer.

9.11 In your main office some keyboard operators, who were already ranked on their speed, were also ranked by their supervisor on accuracy. The results were as follows:

Operator	A	B	C	D	E	F	G	H	I	J
Speed	1	2	3	4	5	6	7	8	9	10
Accuracy	7	9	3	4	1	6	8	2	10	5

Calculate the appropriate correlation coefficient between speed and accuracy, and test whether it is significant at a 5% level of significance.

9.12 The sales manager of a nationwide chain of bookshops needed to investigate whether there was any association between the sales area of a shop and its annual sales. He took a random sample of 15 shops and recorded their sales for the previous year, with the following results:

Area (000 m^2)	10	4	12	21	14	6	8	18	14	10	17	8	14	20	22
Sales (£ million)	0.4	0.1	1.0	1.5	0.9	0.6	0.6	1.0	0.6	0.8	1.0	0.4	1.4	1.2	1.9

(a) Is there any significant association between the size of the sales area of a shop and the volume of its sales?

(b) If there is, calculate the regression equation for estimating the volume of sales of a shop from its known floor area. Interpret your calculated coefficients.

(c) What sales would be expected from a shop with a sales area of 10 000 m^2?

9.13 Your personnel department is interested in comparing the rankings of job applicants when measured by a variety of standard tests. The rankings of 9 applicants by interviews and standard psychological tests are shown below:

Applicant	A	B	C	D	E	F	G	H	I
Interview	5	2	9	4	3	6	1	8	7
Standard test	8	1	7	5	3	4	2	9	6

Calculate Spearman's rank correlation coefficient.

Test for significance and interpret your result.

10 The Chi-squared Test for Categorical Data

10.1 Objectives of this chapter

In Chapter 9 we looked for association between measurements on two continuous variables. We calculated the correlation coefficient between the two variables and then tested it to see if there was a significant association between them.

In this chapter we shall again look for association but now between categorical variables. The calculations are based on the frequencies in the cells of a cross-tabulation, as in Chapter 4 on probability. This is a very useful technique as it deals with the type of bivariate data often collected from questionnaires for which correlation is not appropriate as the data are often only categorical or, at best, ordinal.

Having completed this chapter you will be able to construct cross-tabulations from given information, test to see if a significant association exists between the two variables and you will have revised some of the previous work on probability.

10.2 Introduction

In this type of analysis we have two characteristics, such as gender and eye colour, which cannot be measured but which can be used to group people by variations within them. These characteristics may be associated in some way or they may be completely independent of each other. How can we decide?

We can take a random sample from the population, note which variation of each characteristic is appropriate for each case and cross-tabulate the data. It is then analysed in order to see if the proportions of each characteristic in the subsamples are the same as the overall proportions – easier to do than to describe! For example, if there is no relationship between gender and eye colour we would expect similar proportions of males and females to have blue eyes.

The variables are usually nominal (described by name only) and the frequencies may be cross-tabulated by each category within each variable. Ordinal variables may be used if there are only a few orders so that each one can be classified as a separate category. Continuous variables may be grouped and then tabulated similarly, although the results will then vary according to the grouping categories and also useful information may be lost.

10.3 Contingency tables (cross-tabs)

You have met this type of table before as a contingency table when calculating probabilities. Cases are allotted to categories and their frequencies cross-tabulated. In the gender/eye colour example there might be blue-eyed males, blue-eyed females, brown-eyed males and brown-eyed females. These tables are known as contingency tables. All possible contingencies are included in the cells which are themselves mutually exclusive. The table is completed by calculating the row totals, the column totals and the grand total.

An on-going example will be used to illustrate each stage of the process.

EXAMPLE 10.1

Table 10.1, compiled by a personnel manager, relates to a random sample of 180 staff taken from the whole workforce of the supermarket chain. We shall test for association between a member of staff's gender and his/her type of job, at the 5% level of significance.

Table 10.1

	Male	Female
Supervisor	20	15
Shelf stacker	20	30
Till operator	10	35
Cleaner	10	40

Cross tabulated data

Completing the row and column totals, as with the work on probability, gives the full table.

Table 10.2

	Male	Female	Total
Supervisor	20	15	35
Shelf stacker	20	30	50
Till operator	10	35	45
Cleaner	10	40	50
Total	60	120	180

10.4 Chi-squared (χ^2) test for independence

The hypothesis test which is carried out in order to see if there is any association between categorical variables, such as gender and eye colour, is known as the chi-squared (χ^2) test.

10.4.1 Expected values

If the two variables are completely independent, the proportions within the subtotals of the contingency table would be expected to be the same as those of the group totals for each variable. In practice we work with frequencies rather than proportions, distinguishing between observed and expected frequencies by putting expected frequencies in brackets. If gender and eye colour are independent and if one-third of the population has blue eyes, we would expect one-third of males to be blue-eyed and one-third of females to be blue-eyed.

These proportions are obviously contrived so as to be easy to work with. How can we cope with more awkward numbers? In Example 10.1 the proportions are first calculated as fractions which are then multiplied by the total frequency to find the expected individual cell frequencies. This produces a formula which is applicable in all cases.

For any cell the expected frequency is calculated by:

Row total × Column total

Overall total

where the relevant row and column are those crossing in that particular cell.

EXAMPLE 10.1 *continued*

We randomly selected a sample of 180 supermarket staff and found that 120 of them were female and 60 male, that is, two-thirds were female, one-third were male. Assuming there is no association between gender and job category and finding that we have 45 till operators, we would expect two-thirds (30) of them to be female and one-third (15) of them to be male.

Note that these figures add up to one-quarter of the total for each gender, which checks because till operators form one-quarter of the total staff.

We could calculate the other expected frequencies from the probabilities and put them into the table (see Section 4.8):

P(Supervisor) $= 35/180$

P(Male) $= 60/180$

P(Supervisor and male) $= 35/180 \times 60/180$ assuming independence.

Therefore the expected number of male supervisors $= \dfrac{35}{180} \times \dfrac{60}{180} \times 180 = 11.67$

This is the expected frequency for members of staff who are both male and a supervisor. Note that the frequency is a theoretical number and does not have to be an integer.

Alternatively the expected frequency in each cell is:

$$\frac{\text{Row total} \times \text{Column total}}{\text{Overall total}} = \frac{35 \times 60}{180} = 11.67$$

Calculate the other expected frequencies and insert them in the table (in brackets):

Table 10.3

	Male		Female		Total
Supervisor	20	(11.67)	15	(23.33)	35
Shelf stacker	20	(16.67)	30	(33.33)	50
Till operator	10	(15.00)	35	(30.00)	45
Cleaner	10	(16.67)	40	(33.33)	50
Total		60		120	180

These are the frequencies that would be expected if there were no association between gender and job category at the supermarket.

If the expected frequencies are observed to occur then we can deduce that the two variables are indeed independent. In practice, we would obviously not expect to get exact agreement between the observed and the expected frequencies. Some critical amount of difference is allowed and we compare the difference from our observations with that allowed by the use of a standard table. Are the values observed so different from those expected that we must reject the idea of independence? Are the results just due to sampling errors, with the variables actually being independent? You should recognise the need for a hypothesis test!

10.4.2 The chi-squared (χ^2) hypothesis test

To find the answer, we analyse the data and compare the result to a standard table. We carry out a formal hypothesis test at 5% significance: **the chi-squared test**.

Method

1   State the null hypothesis (no association) and alternative hypothesis

2   Record observed frequencies, O, in each cell of the contingency table.

3   Calculate row, column and grand totals.

4   Calculate expected frequency, E, for each cell:

$$E = \frac{\text{row total} \times \text{column total}}{\text{grand total}}$$

   Note: The test is invalid if any expected frequency is less than 1 or the number of expected frequencies below 5 is more than 20% of the total number of cells.

5   Find the critical value from the chi-squared table (Table D5) with $(r-1) \times (c-1)$ degrees of freedom where r and c are the number of rows and columns respectively.

6   Calculate the test statistic:

$$\sum \frac{(O-E)^2}{E}$$

7   Compare the two values and decide whether the variables are independent or not.

In Example 10.1, we have already completed steps 2, 3 and 4 by calculating the expected values. Whether these are calculated before or during the test depends on personal preference. Some statisticians also prefer to calculate the test statistic before starting the test and to insert the calculated value in the formal hypothesis test.

The test statistic is an overall measure of the difference between the expected and observed frequencies. Each cell difference is squared so that positive and negative differences do not cancel out and are in proportion to the size of the expected cell contents. When the contributions from each cell are totalled their sum is compared with a critical value from the chi-squared table.

EXAMPLE 10.1 *continued*

Step 1 State both hypotheses

Null hypothesis (H_0): There is **no association** between gender and job category. (Remember that 'null' means none.)

Alternative hypothesis (H_1): There is an association between gender and job category.

Steps 2, 3 and 4

See Section 10.4.1

continued

EXAMPLE 10.1 *continued*

Step 5

Find the critical value from the chi-squared table

Number of degrees of freedom $(\nu) = (r-1)(c-1)$

$$= (4-1)(2-1)$$
$$= 3 \times 1 = 3$$

Level of significance $= 5\%$

χ^2 table (Table D5) is always one tailed because squares exclude the possibility of negative values.

Critical value: $\chi^2_{5\%, \nu=3} = 7.816$

Step 6

Calculate the test statistic

The test statistic is calculated from the contingency table which includes both the observed and the expected values for the frequency of staff. The data may be tabulated as in Table 10.4 or the contribution of each cell may be calculated directly and then the test statistic found as the sum of these contributions:

$$\text{Test statistic} = \sum \frac{(O-E)^2}{E}$$

The observed and expected frequencies for each cell are transferred from Table 10.3 and used to complete Table 10.4.

Table 10.4

O	E	$(O-E)$	$(O-E)^2/E$
20	11.67	8.33	5.946
15	23.33	−8.33	2.974
20	16.67	3.33	0.665
30	33.33	−3.33	0.333
10	15.00	−5.00	1.667
35	30.00	5.00	0.833
10	16.67	−6.67	2.669
40	33.33	6.67	1.335
Total			16.422

Test statistic: 16.422

Conclusion: test statistic > critical value therefore reject H_0. We conclude that there is an association between gender and job category in the supermarket chain.

Looking again at the data (Table 10.3) we can see that far more males than expected were supervisors or shelf stackers and more females were cleaners or till operators.

10.5 Chi-squared (χ^2) test for independence – 2 by 2 tables

For tables with only four cells the general method is the same as for larger tables but more error is involved unless we correct for it.

When using the χ^2 tables you may have noticed from the diagram that it represents a continuous distribution. The data we are testing is categorical. This is an obvious source of error but, fortunately it is not really serious unless we only have one degree of freedom, as in a 2 × 2 table.

For a 2 × 2 table we apply the Yates correction in which each absolute difference between observed and expected values is reduced by 0.5. This smooths out the stepped effect of the discrete data. The formula for calculating the test statistic therefore becomes:

$$\sum \frac{(|O - E| - 0.5)^2}{E}$$

Otherwise the method is the same as the one in Example 10.1.

EXAMPLE 10.2

A small firm is investigating car ownership among its workforce. Are male employees more likely to own a car than female employees? In response to a questionnaire the frequencies in Table 10.5 were observed.

Table 10.5

	Car ownership	
Gender	Own a car	Do not own a car
Male	45	16
Female	60	34

We shall carry out a chi-squared test, using a Yates correction, to see if car ownership is associated with gender.

Complete the contingency table and calculate the expected values.

Table 10.6

	Car ownership				Total
Gender	Own a car		Do not own a car		
Male	48	(41.3)	13	(19.7)	61
Female	57	(63.7)	37	(30.3)	94
Total	105		50		155

For the first cell the expected value $E = \dfrac{61 \times 105}{155} = 41.3$

The expected values add up to the same total as the observed values for each row and column, so all the other cells can be found by difference.

For the second cell $E = 61 - 41.3 = 19.7$
for the third cell $E = 105 - 41.3 = 63.7$
for the fourth cell $E = 94 - 63.7 = 30.3$ or $E = 50 - 19.7 = 30.3$

continued

EXAMPLE 10.2 *continued*

We shall first transfer the observed and expected frequencies from Table 10.6, then calculate the test statistic and use it in the formal hypothesis test.

Test statistic: $\sum \dfrac{(|O - E| - 0.5)^2}{E}$

Table 10.7

O	E	$(|O - E| - 0.5)$	$(|O - E| - 0.5)^2/E$
48	41.3	6.2	0.931
13	19.7	6.2	1.951
57	63.7	6.2	0.603
37	30.3	6.2	1.269
Total			4.754

Hypothesis test

Null hypothesis (H$_0$): There is no association between gender and car ownership.

Alternative hypothesis (H$_1$): There is an association between gender and car ownership.

Level of significance: 5% level of significance

Critical value:

Number of degrees of freedom $(\nu) = (r - 1)(c - 1) = (2 - 1)(2 - 1) = 1 \times 1 = 1$

χ^2 table (Table D5) is one tailed only for this test.

$\chi^2_{5\%, \nu=1} = 3.842$

Test statistic: 4.754 (from Table 10.7)

Conclusion: test statistic > critical value therefore reject H$_0$ Conclude that there is an association between gender and car ownership in this firm.

Looking again at the data (Table 10.6) we see that more males and fewer females than expected had a car.

10.6 Chi-squared test for goodness of fit

If a particular distribution is hypothesised for a population then a chi-squared test can be carried out to investigate whether or not the sample data could have come from a population with the hypothesised distribution. The observed values come from the sample and the expected values from the theoretical hypothesised distribution. The expected values are calculated by multiplying the sample size by the appropriate probability value from the statistical table to which the sample is being compared.

The sample data are most easily explored in a computer package, such as SPSS, which can test them against any of the main distributions. Example 10.3 illustrates the method by comparing results from a single die to the uniform distribution which the data would follow if the die was a fair one.

EXAMPLE 10.3

We wish to find out whether a die is fair or not. We throw the die 120 times and record the results. They are:

Number shown on face	1	2	3	4	5	6
Frequency	20	10	10	20	20	40

If the die is unbiased the expected frequencies would be:

Number shown on face	1	2	3	4	5	6
Frequency	20	20	20	20	20	20

H_0: The die is fair, that is, not biased. H_1: The die is not fair, that is, biased.

Critical value: chi-squared tables, 5%, $n - 1 = 5$ degrees of freedom, critical value $= 11.07$.

Test statistic: $\sum \dfrac{(O - E)^2}{E}$

Table 10.8

Value	Observed	Expected	$O - E$	$(O - E)^2/E$
1	20	20	0	0
2	10	20	−10	5
3	10	20	−10	5
4	20	20	0	0
5	20	20	0	0
6	40	20	+20	20
				30

The value of the test statistic is therefore 30.

Conclusion: The test statistic exceeds the critical value so we reject H_0 and conclude that the die is biased.

10.7 A further chi-squared test for independence

EXAMPLE 10.4

In a recent survey within a supermarket chain, a random sample of 160 employees, working as stackers, sales staff and administrators, were asked to grade their attitude towards future wage restraint on the scale:

   Very favourable; favourable; unfavourable; very unfavourable.

Of the 40 stackers interviewed, 7 gave the response 'favourable', 24 the response 'unfavourable', and 8 the response 'very unfavourable'. There were 56 sales staff and from these, 10 responded 'very unfavourable', 9 responded 'favourable' and 3 responded 'very favourable'. The rest of the sample were administrators. Of these, 16 gave the response 'very favourable' and 2 gave the response 'very unfavourable'. In the whole survey, exactly half the employees interviewed responded 'unfavourable'.

continued

EXAMPLE 10.4 *continued*

We first draw up a contingency table showing these results and then test whether attitude towards future wage restraint is dependent on the type of employment.

Setting up the table

There are three types of employee giving four different responses, that is, we have a 3×4 (or a 4×3) table.

Adding extra rows and columns for the subtotals and titles we need 5×6 cells.

Cover Table 10.9 and have a go at compiling it for yourself. As you come to each number in the frequency of response insert it into the appropriate cell. Find the missing figures by difference. There is sufficient information here to enable you to complete your table. Check it against Table 10.9.

Table 10.9

	Very favourable	Favourable	Unfavourable	Very unfavourable	Total
Stackers	1	7	24	8	40
Sales staff	3	9	34	10	56
Administrators	16	24	22	2	64
Total	20	40	80	20	160

The expected values are calculated next: (Row total $\times$ column total/Overall total) and inserted into the table.

Table 10.10

	Very favourable		Favourable		Unfavourable		Very unfavourable		Total
Stackers	1	(5)	7	(10)	24	(20)	8	(5)	40
Sales staff	3	(7)	9	(14)	34	(28)	10	(7)	56
Administrators	16	(8)	24	(16)	22	(32)	2	(8)	64
Total	20		40		80		20		160

Hypothesis test

Null hypothesis (H_0): There is no association between job category and attitude towards wage restraint.

Alternative hypothesis (H_1): There is an association between job category and attitude towards wage restraint.

Level of significance: 5% level of significance

Critical value:

Number of degrees of freedom $(\nu) = (r - 1)(c - 1) = (3 - 1)(4 - 1) = 2 \times 3 = 6$

Level of significance = 5%

χ^2 table (Table D5), 5%, 6 degrees of freedom, critical value $= 12.59$

Test statistic $\quad \sum \dfrac{(O - E)^2}{E}$

continued

EXAMPLE 10.4 *continued*

Table 10.11

O	E	$(O - E)$	$(O - E)^2/E$
1	5	−4	3.200
7	10	−3	0.900
24	20	+4	0.800
8	5	+3	1.800
3	7	−4	2.286
9	14	−5	1.786
34	28	+6	1.286
10	7	+3	1.286
16	8	+8	8.000
24	16	+8	4.000
22	32	−10	3.125
2	8	−6	4.500
Total			32.969

Test statistic: 32.969

Conclusion: test statistic > critical value therefore reject H_0

We conclude that there is an association between job category and attitude towards future wage restraint. The administrators were in favour but the other groups were against it.

10.8 Further analysis of categorical data

If a chi-squared test shows the presence of significant association between two variables, the researcher will probably wish to investigate further and find out more precisely which groups within the variables are the main source of the association.

One easy way of doing this is to look at the contribution each cell makes to the test statistic. The higher the contribution the stronger the association. A more formal method of testing sections of the table is partitioning. This involves the construction of a series of 2 × 2 subtables – one for each degree of freedom. Each subtable is tested for significance. If only a limited amount of data are available, it may be found that some of the expected values are too small for the chi-squared test to be valid. Remember that no expected frequency should be less than 1 and the number of expected frequencies below 5 should not exceed 20% of the total frequencies. If these conditions are infringed it is often possible to combine rows or columns in a meaningful way to increase cell contents but this approach should only be used if the new combinations are sensible. The Fisher exact probability test is useful for small samples in 2 × 2 tables.

If the categories of each variable are ordered, concordance can be tested using Kendal's tau, or some other ordinal measure, instead of a chi-squared value as the critical value.

Cross-tabulated categorical data can be displayed graphically by means of correspondence analysis for two variables and optimal scaling for more. This is best done using a computer package, such as SPSS. The degree of association between two categories, one from each variable, is illustrated by their closeness in the correspondence diagram.

10.9 Summary

In this chapter we have considered categorical data with frequencies measured on subsets within two variables. This is the type of data which is very often collected in surveys and which cannot be analysed by many of the previous methods used in this course which require interval or ratio data.

The data were generally presented in cross-tabulated format and were then analysed by the following procedure in order to test for the independence of the two variables.

- Present the data in a cross-table
- Complete the table with row and column totals
- Calculate the frequencies expected for each cell under the null hypothesis of independence
- State the null hypothesis of independence and the alternative hypothesis of association
- Find the critical value from the chi-squared table with $(r - 1)(c - 1)$ degrees of freedom
- Calculate the test statistic from the formula $\sum \dfrac{(O - E)^2}{E}$
- Compare the two values and conclude whether the variables are independent or not
- If significant association is found, inspect the data to find its main source.

This method of testing is not only very useful but it is easy to carry out in practice. During some part of your course you are quite likely to investigate a topic of interest by carrying out a small survey. Along with the graphical presentation (Chapter 2) chi-squared tests should be your main tool for analysis (Weimer 1993, Chapter 12).

10.10 Computer output for chi-squared tests – Example 10.1

Minitab

Expected counts are printed below observed counts

	Males	Females	Total
1	20	15	35
	11.67	23.33	
2	20	30	50
	16.67	33.33	
3	10	35	45
	15.00	30.00	
4	10	40	50
	16.67	33.33	
Total	60	120	180

Expected values

Chi-Sq = 5.952 + 2.976 +
         0.667 + 0.333 +
         1.667 + 0.833 +
         2.667 + 1.333 = 16.429

Calculation of test statistic

H_0 rejected $p < 0.05$

DF = 3, P-Value = 0.001

SPSS output

SEX * JOBCAT Crosstabulation						
			JOBCAT			
		1	2	3	4	Total
SEX 1	Count	20	20	10	10	60
	Expected count	11.7	16.7	15.0	16.7	60.0
2	Count	15	30	35	40	120
	Expected count	23.3	33.3	30.0	33.3	120.0
Total	Count	35	50	45	50	180
	Expected count	35.0	50.0	45.0	50.0	180.0

Expected values

Chi-Square Tests			
	Value	df	Asymp. Sig. (2-sided)
Pearson chi-square	16.429[a]	3	.001
Likelihood ratio	16.327	3	.001
Linear-by-linear association	14.946	1	.000
N of valid cases	180		

H_0 rejected $p < 0.05$

[a] 0 cells (0%) have expected count less than 5. The minimum expected count is 11.67.

10.11 Tutorial 10 – Chi-squared test

10.1 Purchases of different strengths of lager are thought to be associated with the gender of the drinker and a brewery has commissioned a survey to find out if this is true. A summary of the results is shown below:

		Strength	
	High	Medium	Low
Male	20	50	30
Female	10	55	35

Are gender and lager preference associated at 5% significance?

10.2 A firm is testing a new brand of coffee in three regions and wishes to see if the demand is regionalised. The demand at a random sample of 200 shops in each of the regions can be classified as high, medium or low and the results are summarised opposite. Test at 1% level whether or not there is a relationship between demand and region.

Region	High	Demand Medium	Low
North	105	55	40
South	120	47	33
Midlands	125	38	37

10.3   The respondents of a survey were classified by magazine read and income as follows:

	Annual income (£)		
Magazine read	under 10,000	10,000 and under 15,000	15,000 and over
A	21	36	30
B	48	26	19

Test the hypothesis that the magazine read is independent of level of income using a 5% level of significance.

10.4   The management at head office wants to know how employees feel about working conditions, particularly whether there are differences of opinion between various departments.

	Department			
Conditions	A	B	C	D
Good	65	112	85	80
Average	27	67	60	44
Poor	8	21	15	16

Random samples are taken from each of the four departments with the above results. Do these data indicate that such differences of opinion exist at 5% significance?

10.5   During times of business decline many groups offer suggestions for spurring the economy into a turnaround. A survey was conducted among 100 business executives, 100 economists and 100 government officials to find the opinion of each regarding the best way of reversing the trend of business decline. Their responses are tabulated below. Do these data represent sufficient evidence to assume that opinions differ among business executives, economists and government officials? Test at a 1% significance level.

Opinion	Business executives	Economists	Government officials
Increase government spending	10	15	39
Cut personal income taxes	37	37	33
Decrease interest rates	24	34	15
Offer tax incentives to business	29	14	13
Total	100	100	100

10.12 Supplementary exercise 10

10.6 A brand manager is concerned that her brand's share may be unevenly distributed throughout the country. In a study, in which the country was divided into four geographic regions, random samples were taken from each region and surveyed with the following results.

	Region			
	A	B	C	D
Purchase the brand	47	52	43	49
Do not purchase the brand	53	48	57	51

Test, at 5% significance, whether the brand's share is regional or not.

10.7 A market research company wished to find out whether the value placed on its work varied among the marketing managers of different industries. A survey of marketing managers in four different industries provided the data in the table. Does this provide sufficient evidence to show that the perceived value differs among the four industries involved in the study? Use a 1% level of significance.

	Industry type			
Perceived value	Consumer firms	Industrial organisations	Retail and wholesale	Finance and insurance
Little value	9	22	13	9
Moderate value	29	41	6	17
Great value	26	28	6	27

10.8 Sixty workers were randomly selected and asked to give an opinion on a new pension scheme which their employer was considering. All replied. Of 10 workers with high income, 8 were in favour of the new scheme, 1 was undecided and 1 was against the new scheme. Of 25 workers with average income the numbers for and against were 7 and 15, respectively, the rest being undecided. Of the remaining workers with a low income 2 were for and 13 against.

Are the opinions of the workers independent of their income as tested at 5% significance?

10.9 A sample survey was carried out recently to discover the opinions of professionals in various fields about their prospects for the coming year. A sample of 500 was taken with the following results.

	Profession		
	Bankers	Industrialists	Teachers
Poor prospects	40	50	30
Average prospects	80	120	60
Good prospects	30	80	10

Does this data indicate that there are differences of opinion about the future by professionals in different fields of activity?

10.10   A survey was carried out in order to investigate the spending habits on drink of customers who travelled to a supermarket by different means. The results are shown in the table below. Is there any association between the mode of travel and the amount spent on drink, at 1% significance?

| | | Expenditure on drink | |
Mode of travel	None	1p and under £10	At least £10
On foot	40	20	10
By bus	30	35	15
By car	25	33	42

10.11   A group of 200 office workers, of whom 80 are male, were questioned about their driving capabilities. Three quarters of the females were qualified drivers and one fifth of them were non-drivers. Four of the males were learners and six were non-drivers. Is there any difference between the driving capabilities of the two sexes at 1% significance?

10.12   The table below describes the distribution of defective tubes found in boxes of 100 from three suppliers A, B and C. Is there any evidence that any supplier is producing more defective tubes than the others at 1% significance?

| | | No. of defective tubes | | |
Firm	0	1	2	3 or more
Supplier A	560	200	140	100
Supplier B	370	110	80	40
Supplier C	490	150	110	50

10.13   A magazine subscription service conducted a survey to study the relationship between the number of magazine subscriptions per household and family income. The survey, based on 1000 interviews, produced the results shown in the table. Is the number of subscriptions per household independent of family income? Use 5% significance.

| | | | Family income | | |
Number of subscriptions per household	Less than £10 000	£10 000 to £14 999	£15 000 to £19 999	At least £20 000	Total
0	20	54	78	31	183
1	29	151	281	93	554
2	15	31	89	37	172
>2	8	19	40	24	91
Total	72	255	488	185	1000

10.14   You are working for a local authority and are looking into the types of housing in each of its housing areas. Consider the table overleaf which shows the number (to the nearest hundred) of various kinds of dwellings found in the suburban area of Bradfield. Is there any evidence of association between the ownership of a dwelling and its size?

	Private dwellings	Council dwellings	Total
One bedroom	950	650	1600
Two bedrooms	3000	1700	4700
Three bedrooms	4050	2150	6200
Total	8000	4500	12 500

10.15 Use a chi-squared test with the Yates correction to see whether the number of defective articles is independent of the machine producing them at 5% significance.

	Machine output	
	Defective articles	Perfect articles
Machine A	25	375
Machine B	42	558

11 Index Numbers

11.1 Objectives of this chapter

Chapters 1 to 5 were concerned with describing data – descriptive statistics. Chapters 6 to 10 have involved the use of the analytical results from a sample, with a variety of techniques, to infer the value for some unknown information about the population – inferential statistics.

In this chapter we start the final section of the course which deals with changes over time – time series. We know that most values change with time and so we need some method of quantifying this change. We also need some method of comparing values at different times and comparing changes of two or more different items at different times. In order to compare relative changes over time we make use of **index numbers**. Your company may know that its sales are growing but how does this growth compare with that of its competitors, the industry as a whole or the Retail Price Index?

Having completed this chapter you should understand the relative importance of changes over time. You should be able to compute indexes to measure these changes and to use an index to compare the changing values of different goods in different industries over time. The main index we shall use for comparison will be the Retail Price Index (RPI) so you should also gain some understanding of how it is computed and its general importance in business and economics.

11.2 Introduction: measuring changes over time

In business, managers and other decision makers may be concerned with the way in which the values of variables change over time: prices paid for raw materials, numbers of employees and customers, annual income and profits, and so on. **Index numbers** are one way of describing such changes.

Index numbers were originally developed by economists for monitoring and comparing different groups of goods. It is necessary in business to understand and manipulate the different published index series, and to construct index series of your own. Having constructed your own index, it can then be compared to a national one, such as the RPI, a similar index for your industry as a whole and also to indexes for your competitors. These comparisons are a very useful tool for decision making in business.

For example, an accountant of a supermarket chain could construct an index of the company's own sales and compare it to the index of the volume of sales for the general supermarket industry. A graph of the two indexes will illustrate the company's performance within the sector.

Figure 11.1

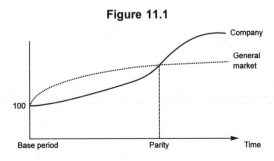

197

It is immediately clear from Figure 11.1 that, after initially lagging behind the general market, the supermarket company caught up and then overtook it. In the later stages, the company was having better results than the general market but that, as with the whole industry, these had levelled out.

11.3 Index numbers

Index numbers can be used to describe the changes in any quantity over time. The measurements may be of industrial production, commodity prices, share prices, employment figures, and so on. They may refer to the whole world, the UK, or just your own company. Think of them as a mathematical tool for applying to any changes over time which may describe absolutely anything. In this course we will be mainly concerned with either prices or quantities or a combination of both.

An essential requirement is that index numbers measure the changing value of a variable over time in relation to its value at some fixed point in time, the base period, when the index is given the value of 100. They have no units because they are ratios and are always expressed as percentages.

Indexes may be based at any convenient period, which is occasionally adjusted, and they are published with any convenient frequency:

Yearly   Gross National Product (GNP)
Monthly   Unemployment figures
Daily   Stock market prices

11.3.1   Price indexes

One of the most important uses of indexes is to show how the price of a product **changes over time** due to changing costs of raw materials, variable supply and demand, changes in production processes, general inflation, and so on. It is often of interest to compare an index to the RPI or to indexes of the competitors' prices.

Quantification of these changes, which are beyond the control of the producing company, may need some type of response and so form an essential part of the decision making process. An increase in the price of raw materials may require a decision about selling prices; a change in supply may mean contracting an additional source with a corresponding price adjustment; a change in demand may necessitate price adjustments so that the company remains competitive, and so on.

11.3.2   The Retail Price Index (RPI)

Each month the government publishes a variety of indexes that are designed to help us understand prevailing business and economic conditions. The most widely known of these is the **Retail Price Index (RPI)**. This is the measure of inflation which is reported in the media and which influences all our lives. It is the measure used to revise social security and pension payments, which are 'index linked', and forms the basis of many wage claims.

The RPI is based on the amount spent by a typical household on a range of goods and services. It gives an aggregate value based upon the price of a representative selection of 83 subgroups of 14 different major categories of goods, about 350 in total, ranging from food to leisure services. In total about 15 000 prices are collected monthly and their prices recorded. The relative importance of these goods and services is updated annually using weightings produced by the Central Statistical Office, mainly from the 'Family Expenditure Survey', which collects information on the spending habits of approximately 10 000 households.

11.3.3 Quantity indexes

Quantity indexes are treated in exactly the same way as price indexes but, as the name suggests, they are concerned with quantities and assume that prices remain the same or are of no relevance. We are used to seeing the index of unemployment figures regularly in the media, whether seasonally adjusted or not. A company, or industry, will be interested in changes in the quantity of goods produced from year to year. A country is concerned with its Gross National Product (GNP) which describes the annual total value of goods and services produced.

11.4 Simple indexes

We first have to decide on the base period and then find the ratio of the value at any subsequent period to the value in that base period, the **price relative**. This ratio is then finally converted to a percentage.

$$\textbf{Index for any time period } n = \frac{\text{value in period } n}{\text{value in base period}} \times 100$$

EXAMPLE 11.1

The retail price of a particular model of car for the previous five years has been:

Year	1	2	3	4	5
Price (£)	12 380	12 490	12 730	13 145	13 750

Using **Year 1** as the **base year** we can compare all the other prices to the value of £12 380 in that year.

Year 2: $\dfrac{12490}{12380} \times 100 = 100.9$ Year 3: $\dfrac{12730}{12380} \times 100 = 102.8$ and so on.

Year	1	2	3	4	5
Price (£)	12 380	12 490	12 730	13 145	13 750
Index	100.0	100.9	102.8	106.2	111.1

If we used Year 5 as the **base year** we would compare all the other prices to the value of £13 750 in that year.

Year 1: $\dfrac{12380}{13750} \times 100 = 90.0$ Year 2: $\dfrac{12490}{13750} \times 100 = 90.8$ and so on.

Year	1	2	3	4	5
Price (£)	12 380	12 490	12 730	13 145	13 750
Index	90.0	90.8	92.6	95.6	100.0

Alternatively if a series of index numbers is known and we know the price or quantity described by one of them the complete series of prices can be calculated. The price or quantity for an unknown period is found by just scaling up, or down, in the same ratio as the relevant index numbers.

EXAMPLE 11.2

Table 11.1 shows the monthly price index for an item:

Table 11.1

Month	1	2	3	4	5	6	7	8	9	10	11	12
Index	121	112	98	81	63	57	89	109	131	147	132	126

If the price in month 3 is £240, what is the price in month 8?

The index numbers for months 8 and 3 are 109 and 98 respectively so the value of £240 for month 3 needs scaling up by the ratio of 109:98 for month 8.

Price in month 3 is £240 $\Rightarrow$ Price in month 8 is £240 $\times \dfrac{109}{98} = £266.94$

If the price in month 7 is £218, what is the price in month 2?

Price in month 7 is £218 $\Rightarrow$ Price in month 2 is £218 $\times \dfrac{112}{89} = £274.34$

Filling in the table and giving the results to the nearest pound gives:

Table 11.2

Month	1	2	3	4	5	6	7	8	9	10	11	12
Index	121	112	98	81	63	57	89	109	131	147	132	126
Price (£)	296	274	240	198	154	140	218	267	321	360	323	309

11.5 Calculating changes

One essential use to which index numbers are put is that of monitoring changes over time. These changes may be calculated in **percentage point change**, which can be misleading as the value depends on whether the two periods of measurement are near to the base year or not, or as a **percentage change** in which the change does not depend on the choice of base year.

11.5.1 Percentage point change

The percentage point change is simply the difference between the index values for consecutive time periods. If the series is near the base period, when the index numbers are in the low hundreds, the changes will be small. If, on the other hand, the index is high and nearly due for rebasing, the numbers may be approaching 400 or 500 and the changes will appear comparatively large. These percentage point changes are therefore not comparable over time.

EXAMPLE 11.3

Using the figures from Example 11.2, what are the percentage point changes between the consecutive months?

Table 11.1

Month	1	2	3	4	5	6	7	8	9	10	11	12
Index	121	112	98	81	63	57	89	109	131	147	132	126

A simple subtraction provides these figures, negative for decrease, positive for increase.

Table 11.3

Month	1	2	3	4	5	6	7	8	9	10	11	12
Index	121	112	98	81	63	57	89	109	131	147	132	126
% point change		−9	−14	−17	−18	−6	+32	+20	+22	+16	−15	−6

11.5.2 *Percentage change*

Percentage changes are calculated by the usual method of finding the ratio of the change to the previous value and multiplying by 100.

EXAMPLE 11.4

Using the figures from Example 11.2 again, what are the percentage changes between the consecutive months?

Table 11.1

Month	1	2	3	4	5	6	7	8	9	10	11	12
Index	121	112	98	81	63	57	89	109	131	147	132	126

The percentage points change is divided by the index it has come from and multiplied by 100 in same method as used for finding any percentage change.

$$\text{For month 2: } \frac{112 - 121}{121} \times 100 = -7.4 \qquad \text{For month 3: } \frac{98 - 112}{112} \times 100 = -12.5$$

Table 11.4

Month	1	2	3	4	5	6	7	8	9	10	11	12
Index	121	112	98	81	63	57	89	109	131	147	132	126
% change		−7.4	−12.5	−17.3	−22.2	−9.5	56.1	22.5	20.2	12.2	−10.2	−4.5

These values will be the same whether the index is near the base year or not, that is, they will not be affected by a change in the base period.

11.6 Changing the base period

The base period can be chosen as any convenient time. It is usual to update the base period fairly regularly to avoid:

- Any significant change which makes comparison with earlier figures meaningless.
- The numbers growing so large that a points change is many times a percentage change.

At one time, for political reasons, the method of measuring employment kept changing so a series across changes would not compare like with like. Just after rebasing, a change of 5 index points would equal a 5% change. If the index was around the 250 level it would only equal 2% and if round the 500 level only 1%. An employment increase of 5% sounds much better than the 1%! Economic figures appear more stable after rebasing. The Retail Price Index was last rebased at the end of 1986 when its value was 385.9.

We need therefore to know how to change a base period. Published index numbers may include a sudden change such as a series 470, 478, 485 becoming series 100, 103, 105, etc. We need to convert both sets of numbers to a common base year so that they can be analysed as a whole, continuous series. This is sometimes known as 'splicing' the two indexes.

In order to change from one index series to another we need the value in the first series for the same period as that in which the rebasing to 100 for the second takes place. The ratio of these two values forms the basis of any conversion between them.

EXAMPLE 11.5

The amount spent on advertising by a supermarket is index linked and is described by the indexes in Table 11.5.

Table 11.5

Year	1	2	3	4	5	6	7	8
Index 1	100	138	162	196	220			
Index 2					100	125	140	165

Typically each index series is completed and then, if we have, say, the advertising expenditure for any one year, we can use the figure to calculate that for any of the other years.

First identify the base year for each series. Remember that in its base year the value of an index is 100.

Base year for each index: Index 1 = Year 1   Index 2 = Year 5

Both values are known for year 5

From year 5: ratio of old:new = 220:100 (**Note:** All new values will be smaller)

From year 5: ratio of new:old = 100:220 (**Note:** All old values will be bigger)

These ratios will be applied when converting from old to new and vice versa.

continued

EXAMPLE 11.5 *continued*

Complete the table for index 1 and index 2:

Index 1

Old index = New index $\times \dfrac{220}{100}$

Year 6:   Old index = $125 \times \dfrac{220}{100} = 275.0$ Year 7:   Old index = $140 \times \dfrac{220}{100} = 308.0$

Index 2

New index = Old index $\times \dfrac{100}{220}$

Year 1:   New index = $100 \times \dfrac{100}{220} = 45.5$ Year 2:   New index = $138 \times \dfrac{100}{220} = 62.7$

Complete both index series and checking that each is adjusted in the right direction.

Table 11.6

Year	1	2	3	4	5	6	7	8
Index 1	100	138	162	196	220	275.0	308.0	363.0
Index 2	45.5	62.7	73.6	89.1	100	125	140	165

Advertising expenditure can be calculated for all years if the expenditure for any one year is known by multiplying its value by the ratio of the relevant index numbers from **either** series.

Given that advertising expenditure was known to be £4860 in year 3, that for:

$$\text{Year } 1 = 4860 \times \frac{100}{162} = 3000 \quad \text{or} \quad 4860 \times \frac{45.5}{73.6} = 3000$$

$$\text{Year } 2 = 4860 \times \frac{138}{162} = 4140 \quad \text{or} \quad 4860 \times \frac{62.7}{73.6} = 4140 \text{ etc.}$$

Table 11.7

Year	1	2	3	4	5	6	7	8
Index 1	100	138	162	196	220	275.0	308.0	363.0
Index 2	45.5	62.7	73.6	89.1	100	125	140	165
Sales (£)	3000	4140	4860	5880	6600	8250	9240	10890

11.7 Comparing time series

A company knows that its sales are rising year by year but so are those of its main competitor which is smaller. How can the progress of the two companies be compared? An index for each company is produced with the same base year and the two indexes compared.

EXAMPLE 11.6

The sales, in £000 000, of two companies over 8 years are given in Table 11.8. Company B is smaller than Company A.

Table 11.8

Year	1	2	3	4	5	6	7	8
Company A	123.2	134.8	145.2	153.4	162.9	169.3	171.2	187.1
Company B	5.7	6.2	6.9	7.3	8.9	9.5	9.9	10.6

It is obvious that both companies are increasing their sales, but which one is doing better?

A comparison can be made by calculating an index series for both companies with the same base year, in this example Year 1.

Year 2   Company A: $100 \times \dfrac{134.8}{123.2} = 109.4$ Company B: $100 \times \dfrac{6.2}{5.7} = 108.8$

Table 11.9

Year	1	2	3	4	5	6	7	8
Company A	123.2	134.8	145.2	153.4	162.9	169.3	171.2	187.1
Index A	100	109.4	117.9	124.5	132.2	137.4	139.0	151.9
Company B	5.7	6.2	6.9	7.3	8.9	9.5	9.9	10.6
Index B	100	108.8	121.1	128.1	156.1	166.7	173.7	186.0

Figure 11.2   Comparison of two companies' sales indexes with the same base year used

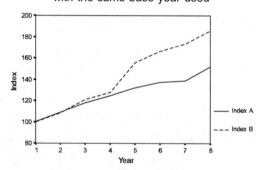

The smaller company, B, is doing comparatively better than the larger company, A.

11.8 Deflating an index

An index may be deflated to remove the effect of inflation over the long term. Any worker expects his earnings to increase over his working lifetime due to promotions, annual increments, cost of living rises. Does the purchasing power of his salary also increase? The employer would like to keep the overall salary bill from rising in real terms, even though individuals are earning more. This should be possible since, in general, high earners are retiring and lower earners are joining the workforce.

The Retail Price Index is often used to compute real changes in earnings or expenditure as it compares the purchasing power of money at different points in time. It is generally accepted as a standard measure of inflation even though calculated from a restricted 'basket of goods'.

EXAMPLE 11.7

Table 11.10 shows Tom's earnings between 1992 and 1998, in £000; the total wages bill for his company, in £000 000, and the published RPI figures for the same years.

Table 11.10

Years	1992	1993	1994	1995	1996	1997	1998
Tom's earnings	15.3	16.1	16.9	18.0	20.9	21.4	21.9
Total wages bill	5.41	5.62	5.83	6.04	6.25	6.46	6.67
RPI	138.5	140.7	144.1	149.1	152.7	157.4	162.9

In order to deflate a figure for 1993 and make it equivalent to the corresponding figure for 1992 it must be multiplied by the ratio of the 1992 to 1993 figures for the RPI.

The purchasing power of Tom's earnings in 1993, in 1992 terms, is:

$$16.1 \times \frac{138.5}{140.7} = 15.85, \text{ that is, £15\,850}$$

The total salary bill for the company, in 1992 terms, is:

$$5.62 \times \frac{138.5}{140.7} = 5.53, \text{ that is, £5530\,000}$$

Both these values are more in real terms than the actual 1992 values so real increases have taken place. If all the subsequent values are similarly deflated we get Table 11.11.

Table 11.10

Years	1992	1993	1994	1995	1996	1997	1998
Tom's earnings	15.30	15.85	16.24	16.72	18.96	18.83	18.62
Total wages bill	5.41	5.53	5.60	5.61	5.67	5.68	5.67

The comparisons are clearer if the indexes are plotted (Figure 11.3).

Figure 11.3

(a) Tom's actual and deflated earnings

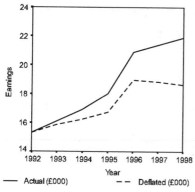

(b) Company's actual and deflated wages bill

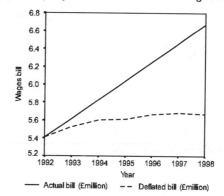

continued

EXAMPLE 11.7 *continued*

Tom's earnings rose steadily, in real terms, until 1996 when he got a substantial rise. Had he been promoted? After that the purchasing power of his earnings declined. The total wages bill also rose steadily but in decreasing amounts until it levelled out. In recent years Tom's earnings in real terms have actually been decreasing but the company's total wage bill has indeed levelled out as they hoped.

11.9 Simple aggregate indexes

A simple aggregate is not a realistic approach to including more than one item in an index. For example, you would get some idea of the total price of a shopping basket by adding up all the unit costs of the items, but this assumes that you purchase exactly one of each. This is an unrealistic assumption for a household's weekly shopping outlay. If, however, the aim of the exercise is to compare prices from year to year then the use of a simple aggregate index is quite justified.

11.9.1 *Aggregate price index*

The relevant prices are summed year by year and the resulting sums treated as price relatives. Any variations in corresponding quantities (1 kg or 10 kg) and units (cost per g or cost per kg) are ignored.

EXAMPLE 11.8

A company buys four items at the prices in Table 11.12.

Table 11.12

| | Price paid per unit | | |
Items	Year 1	Year 2	Year 3
A	10	11	13
B	23	25	26
C	17	17	18
D	19	20	23

Find the simple aggregate price index number for year 2 using year 1 as the base year:

$$\frac{\text{Sum of prices in year 2}}{\text{Sum of prices in base year}} = \frac{11 + 25 + 17 + 20}{10 + 23 + 17 + 19}$$

$$= \frac{73}{69} \times 100 = 105.8$$

Find the simple aggregate price index number for year 3 using year 1 as the base year:

$$\frac{\text{Sum of prices in year 3}}{\text{Sum of prices in base year}} = \frac{13 + 26 + 18 + 23}{10 + 23 + 17 + 19}$$

$$= \frac{80}{69} \times 100 = 115.9$$

11.9.2 Aggregate quantity index

The relevant quantities are summed year by year and the resulting sums are treated as a single index. Any variations in corresponding price (£ or p) are ignored.

EXAMPLE 11.9

A company buys the following quantities of four items.

Table 11.13

Items	Price paid per unit		
	Year 1	Year 2	Year 3
A	20	24	26
B	55	51	53
C	63	84	86
D	28	34	37

Find the simple aggregate quantity index number for year 2 using year 1 as the base year:

$$\frac{\text{Sum of quantities in year 2}}{\text{Sum of quantities in base year}} = \frac{24+51+84+34}{20+55+63+28} = \frac{193}{166} \times 100 = 116.3$$

Find the simple aggregate quantity index number for year 3 using year 1 as the base year:

$$\frac{\text{Sum of quantities in year 3}}{\text{Sum of quantities in base year}} = \frac{26+53+86+37}{20+55+63+23} = \frac{202}{166} \times 100 = 121.7$$

11.10 Weighted aggregate indexes

Neither the simple aggregate price index nor the simple aggregate quantity index is completely realistic as both prices and quantities will vary. Some combination of both price and quantity variation is therefore needed. This is achieved by weighting the prices by their corresponding quantities. But which weights are to be used? Three variations will be described:

- **Laspeyre index** which uses weights from the base year
- **Paasche index** which uses weights from the current year
- **Fisher index** is the geometric mean of Laspeyre's and Paasche's indexes.

Because quantities as well as prices tend to rise in our consumer-based society, the base weights tend to underestimate reality and the current weights tend to overestimate it. Hence the Laspeyre index tends to overestimate changes and the Paasche index tends to underestimate them. It seems reasonable to suggest that reality lies somewhere between the two indexes. Fisher has suggested that this is best described by the geometric mean of the other two:

$$\text{Fisher's index} = \sqrt{\text{Laspeyre's index} \times \text{Paasche's index}}$$

We shall look at all three indexes combining the simple prices and quantities used in Examples 11.8 and 11.9.

11.10.1 The Laspeyre base weighted index

This index compares prices from a current year to those of a base year with both being weighted by the quantities bought in the base year.

EXAMPLE 11.10

A company buys four products with the characteristics shown in Table 11.14.

Table 11.14

Items	Number of units bought			Price paid per unit		
	Year 1	Year 2	Year 3	Year 1	Year 2	Year 3
A	20	24	26	10	11	13
B	55	51	53	23	25	26
C	63	84	86	17	17	18
D	28	34	37	19	20	23

Find the base-weighted aggregate index, Laspeyre's index, for year 2 using year 1 as the base year.

$$\text{Index for year 2} = \frac{\sum(\text{prices in year 2} \times \text{weights in base year})}{\sum(\text{prices in base year} \times \text{weights in base year})}$$

$$= \frac{11 \times 20 + 25 \times 55 + 17 \times 63 + 20 \times 28}{10 \times 20 + 23 \times 55 + 17 \times 63 + 19 \times 28} = \frac{3226}{3068} \times 100 = 105.1$$

Find the base-weighted aggregate index, Laspeyre's index, for year 3 using year 1 as the base year.

$$\text{Index for year 3} = \frac{\sum(\text{prices in year 3} \times \text{weights in base year})}{\sum(\text{prices in base year} \times \text{weights in base year})}$$

$$= \frac{13 \times 20 + 26 \times 55 + 18 \times 63 + 23 \times 28}{10 \times 20 + 23 \times 55 + 17 \times 63 + 19 \times 28} = \frac{3468}{3068} \times 100 = 113.0$$

11.10.2 The Paasche current weighted index

This index compares prices from a current year to those of a base year with both being weighted by the quantities bought in the current year.

EXAMPLE 11.11

A company buys four products with the characteristics shown in Table 11.14.
    Find the current period-weighted aggregate index, Paasche index, for year 2 as current year using year 1 as the base year.

$$\text{Index for year 2} = \frac{\sum(\text{prices in current year} \times \text{weights in current year})}{\sum(\text{prices in year 1} \times \text{weights in current year})}$$

$$= \frac{11 \times 24 + 25 \times 51 + 17 \times 84 + 20 \times 34}{10 \times 24 + 23 \times 51 + 17 \times 84 + 19 \times 34} = \frac{3647}{3487} \times 100 = 104.6$$

continued

EXAMPLE 11.11 *continued*

Find the current period-weighted aggregate index, Paasche index, for year 3 as current year using year 1 as the base year.

$$\text{Index for year 3} = \frac{\sum \text{prices in current year} \times \text{weights in current year})}{\sum \text{prices in year 1} \times \text{weights in current year})}$$

$$= \frac{13 \times 26 + 26 \times 53 + 18 \times 86 + 23 \times 37}{10 \times 26 + 23 \times 53 + 17 \times 86 + 19 \times 37} = \frac{4115}{3644} \times 100 = 112.9$$

11.10.3 *The Fisher index*

The Laspeyre and the Paasche indexes for these data are fairly close with the former being higher than the latter, as expected. The Fisher index will now combine them.

EXAMPLE 11.12

Using the data and results from Examples 11.10 and 11.11.

$$\text{Fisher's index for Year 2} = \sqrt{\text{Laspeyre's index} \times \text{Paasche's index}}$$

$$= \sqrt{105.1 \times 104.6}$$

$$= 104.8$$

$$\text{Fisher's index for Year 3} = \sqrt{\text{Laspeyre's index} \times \text{Paasche's index}}$$

$$= \sqrt{113.0 \times 112.9}$$

$$= 112.9 \text{ (4 sig figs)}$$

The type of aggregate index chosen is decided by the relative importance placed on the weightings by economic experts.

11.11 Further example of index number calculations

In this example we will consider some data describing the salaries in a company, working through the different types of index number manipulations.

EXAMPLE 11.13

The data in Table 11.15 describe the average salaries, (£000), for the workers in your company over eight consecutive years:

Table 11.15

Year	1	2	3	4	5	6	7	8	9	10
Average salary	10.9	11.4	12.0	12.7	13.6	14.4	15.0	15.5	16.3	17.6

continued

EXAMPLE 11.13 *continued*

(a) Calculate an index for these average salaries using year 5, when the RPI was rebased, as the base year

Year 1: $\dfrac{10.9}{13.6} \times 100 = 80.1$ Year 2: $\dfrac{11.4}{13.6} \times 100 = 83.8$ etc.

Table 11.16

Year	1	2	3	4	5	6	7	8	9	10
Index number	80.1	83.8	88.2	93.4	100	105.9	110.3	114.0	119.9	129.4

(b) Calculate the percentage points change between consecutive years

This is found as the change in the index numbers themselves.

Table 11.17

Year	1	2	3	4	5	6	7	8	9	10
Index number	80.1	83.8	88.2	93.4	100	105.9	110.3	114.0	119.9	129.4
Percentage point change		3.7	4.4	5.2	6.6	5.9	4.4	3.7	5.9	9.5

(c) Calculate the percentage change between consecutive years

This is calculated as the change divided over the earlier value as a percentage.

Table 11.18

Year	1	2	3	4	5	6	7	8	9	10
Index number	80.1	83.8	88.2	93.4	100	105.9	110.3	114.0	119.9	129.4
Percentage change		4.6	5.3	5.9	7.1	5.9	4.2	3.4	5.2	7.9

The RPI was rebased in January 1987 giving an average index for the year of 101.9. This is equivalent to year 5 in the salary index so we need to rebase the RPI figures for the earlier years in order to compare our whole range of salaries with the RPI.

(d) Complete both indexes and plot on the same diagram

Table 11.19

Year	1982	1983	1984	1985	1986	1987	1988	1989	1990	1991
Old index	320.4	335.1	351.8	373.2	385.9	394.5				
New index						101.9	106.9	115.2	126.1	133.5

Old index for 1988 = $106.9 \times \dfrac{394.5}{101.9} = 413.8$;   for 1989 = $115.2 \times \dfrac{394.5}{101.9} = 446.0$

New index for 1986 = $385.9 \times \dfrac{101.9}{394.5} = 99.7$;   for 1985 = $373.2 \times \dfrac{101.9}{394.5} = 96.4$

continued

EXAMPLE 11.13 *continued*

Table 11.20

Year	1982	1983	1984	1985	1986	1987	1988	1989	1990	1991
Old index	320.4	335.1	351.8	373.2	385.9	394.5	413.8	446.0	488.2	516.9
New index	82.8	86.6	90.9	96.4	99.7	101.9	106.9	115.2	126.1	133.5

Figure 11.4   Comparison and old and new RPI values

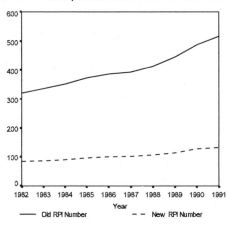

You can see why the old index number was rebased. The new one gives a better impression of economic stability, even though they both describe the same situation.

(e) How has the average salary faired compared to the RPI?

The indexed average salary is taken from Table 11.16 and the RPI from Table 11.20. Note that both are rebased at the same time, 1986. The RPI approximately.

Table 11.21

Year	1982	1983	1984	1985	1986	1987	1988	1989	1990	1991
Average salary	10.9	11.4	12.0	12.7	13.6	14.4	15.0	15.5	16.3	17.6
New index	82.8	86.6	90.9	96.4	99.7	101.9	106.9	115.2	126.1	133.5

Figure 11.5   Comparison of average salaries and RPI

The average salaries have generally kept step with the RPI, using 1986 as the base year. If we next look at the percentage increases, a clearer picture may emerge.

continued

EXAMPLE 11.13 *continued*

Figure 11.6 Comparison of salary and RPI increases

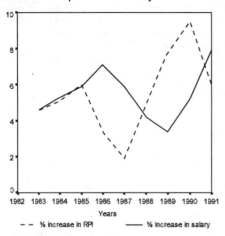

Years

– – % increase in RPI ——— % increase in salary

It becomes clearer from Figure 11.6 that salary increases were keeping step with the RPI but were lagging one year behind, as might be expected if the management were responding to union claims following the publishing figures.

(f) Deflate the salaries index by the RPI to see how the workers were faring in real terms, starting from 1982

$$1983: \quad 11.4 \times \frac{82.8}{86.6} = 10.9; \qquad 1984: \quad 12.0 \times \frac{82.8}{90.9} = 10.9$$

Table 11.22

Year	1	2	3	4	5	6	7	8	9	10
Average salary	80.1	83.8	88.2	93.4	100	105.9	110.3	114.0	119.9	129.4
RPI	82.8	86.6	90.9	96.4	99.7	101.9	106.9	115.2	126.1	133.5
Deflated average salary	10.9	10.9	10.9	10.9	11.3	11.7	11.6	11.2	10.7	10.9

In real terms the average salaries had remained the same for the first few years, then they had risen over two years and finally settled back to their original purchasing value.

Table 11.23 gives the average salaries of different types of employees in your company and the numbers of each employed.

Table 11.23

	Average salary (£000) Years				Number of employees Years			
	1	2	3	4	1	2	3	4
Administrative	27.2	28.9	31.8	33.0	35	42	53	63
Clerical	12.9	13.7	14.6	15.2	25	19	16	14
Manual	18.9	19.6	20.1	21.0	123	130	127	125
Security	15.0	16.0	17.1	17.9	5	4	6	7
Maintenance	11.5	12.3	13.1	14.0	23	26	24	21

continued

EXAMPLE 11.13 *continued*

(g) Calculate the simple aggregate indexes for both average salaries and number of employees, using year 1 as the base year

Sum up the totals for each year and then rebase them to year 1

Table 11.24

	Average salary (£000) Years				Number of employees Years			
	1	2	3	4	1	2	3	4
Administrative	27.2	28.9	31.8	33.0	35	42	53	63
Clerical	12.9	13.7	14.6	15.2	25	19	16	14
Manual	18.9	19.6	20.1	21.0	123	130	127	125
Security	15.0	16.0	17.1	17.9	5	4	6	7
Maintenance	11.5	12.3	13.1	14.0	23	26	24	21
Totals	85.5	90.5	96.7	101.1	211	221	226	230
Rebased	100	105.8	113.1	118.2	100	104.7	107.1	109.0

Index for average salaries is:

Table 11.25

Year	1	2	3	4
Index	100.0	105.8	113.1	118.2

Index for number of employees is:

Table 11.26

Year	1	2	3	4
Index	100.0	104.7	107.1	109.0

(h) Calculate the Laspeyre index for the average salaries for years 2, 3 and 4

Remember the base year is the same, year 1, giving the weights for each.

Table 11.23

	Average salary (£000) Years				Number of employees Years			
	1	2	3	4	1	2	3	4
Administrative	27.2	28.9	31.8	33.0	35	42	53	63
Clerical	12.9	13.7	14.6	15.2	25	19	16	14
Manual	18.9	19.6	20.1	21.0	123	130	127	125
Security	15.0	16.0	17.1	17.9	5	4	6	7
Maintenance	11.5	12.3	13.1	14.0	23	26	24	21

continued

EXAMPLE 11.13 *continued*

Year 2:

$$\frac{28.9 \times 35 + 13.7 \times 25 + 19.6 \times 123 + 16.0 \times 5 + 12.3 \times 23}{27.2 \times 35 + 12.9 \times 25 + 18.9 \times 123 + 15.0 \times 5 + 11.5 \times 23} = \frac{4127.7}{3938.7} = 104.8$$

Year 3:

$$\frac{31.8 \times 35 + 14.6 \times 25 + 20.1 \times 123 + 17.1 \times 5 + 13.1 \times 23}{27.2 \times 35 + 12.9 \times 25 + 18.9 \times 123 + 15.0 \times 5 + 11.5 \times 23} = \frac{4337.1}{3938.7} = 110.1$$

Year 4:

$$\frac{33.0 \times 35 + 15.2 \times 25 + 21.0 \times 123 + 17.9 \times 5 + 14.0 \times 23}{27.2 \times 35 + 12.9 \times 25 + 18.9 \times 123 + 15.0 \times 5 + 11.5 \times 23} = \frac{4529.5}{3938.7} = 115.0$$

Year	2	3	4
Laspeyre index	104.8	110.1	115.0

(i) Calculate the Paasche index for the average salaries for Years 2, 3 and 4. Remember the current year changes for each calculation.

Year 2:

$$\frac{28.9 \times 42 + 13.7 \times 19 + 19.6 \times 130 + 16.0 \times 4 + 12.3 \times 26}{27.2 \times 42 + 12.9 \times 19 + 18.9 \times 130 + 15.0 \times 4 + 11.5 \times 26} = \frac{4405.9}{4203.5} = 104.8$$

Year 3:

$$\frac{31.8 \times 53 + 14.6 \times 16 + 20.1 \times 127 + 17.1 \times 6 + 13.1 \times 24}{27.2 \times 53 + 12.9 \times 16 + 18.9 \times 127 + 15.0 \times 6 + 11.5 \times 24} = \frac{4888.7}{4414.3} = 110.7$$

Year 3:

$$\frac{33.0 \times 63 + 15.2 \times 14 + 21.0 \times 125 + 17.9 \times 7 + 14.0 \times 21}{27.2 \times 63 + 12.9 \times 14 + 18.9 \times 125 + 15.0 \times 7 + 11.5 \times 21} = \frac{5336.1}{4603.2} = 115.9$$

Year	2	3	4
Paasche index	104.8	110.7	115.9

(j) Calculate the Fisher index for years 2, 3 and 4

Year 2:

$$\sqrt{104.8 \times 104.8} = 104.8$$

Year 3:

$$\sqrt{110.1 \times 110.7} = 110.4$$

Year	2	3	4
Fischer index	104.8	110.4	115.4

11.12 Summary

In this chapter we have used index numbers to describe how the price, or quantity, of items varies over time. We have seen that the numbers generally rise with time and are periodically rebased to 100 so that they remain reasonably stable. We looked in some detail at the Retail Price Index (RPI), its construction and use.

From the index numbers themselves we have calculated and monitored changes. We compared changes in salaries with standard indexes, such as the RPI, to see how they varied in real terms.

We calculated simple aggregate and weighted aggregate indexes, which are used more often in the of the world of business.

After studying Chapter 11 you should have the confidence to use the many tables of time-related data in government and other publication.

11.13 Tutorial 11 – Index numbers

11.1 The retail price of a typical undergraduate textbook over a period of 4 years is listed below:

Year	1997	1998	1999	2000
Price	£14.50	£15.25	£15.95	£16.40

(a) Find the price index based on 1997 prices.

(b) Find the percentage points change between consecutive years. (base year = 1997)

(c) Find the percentage increase between consecutive years.

11.2 A car showroom is giving a special offer on one type of car. The advertised price of this car in four consecutive quarters was £10 450, £10 800, £11 450 and £9999.

(a) Find the price index based on the price in the first quarter

(b) Find the price index based on the price in the final quarter

(c) What are the quarterly changes in (b) in terms of percentage points based on the last quarter?

(d) What are the quarterly changes in terms of percentages?

11.3 The annual output of a company is described by the following indexes:

Year	1	2	3	4	5	6	7	8
Index 1	100	125	153	167				
Index 2				100	109	125	140	165

(a) Complete index 1 and index 2 for years 1 to 8.

(b) If the factory made 23 850 units in year 1, how many did it make in each of the other years?

(c) What was the percentage increase in output each year?

11.4 The following are two sets of retail prices of a typical student's shopping basket. The items were on sale in a London supermarket during the autumn of 1998 and 2000:

Item	1998 price	2000 price
1 pizza	£2.09	£2.59
1 loaf	£0.69	£1.00
1 pint of milk	£0.35	£0.48
Can of baked beans	£0.32	£0.34
4-pack of lager	£2.65	£2.40
500g apples	£0.45	£0.67

Calculate the simple aggregate price index for 2000 using 1998 as the base year.

11.5 A company buys four products with the following characteristics:
(Year 1 = base year)

Items	Number of units bought		Price per unit	
	Year 1	Year 2	Year 1	Year 2
A	121	141	9	10
B	149	163	21	23
C	173	182	26	23
D	194	203	31	33

(a) Calculate the simple price aggregate for year 2 based on year 1.
(b) Calculate the base-weighted price aggregate for year 2.
(c) Calculate the current-weighted price aggregate for year 2.

11.6 Six companies from within the UK were selected at random from a directory of graduate employers. The following table shows the graduate and non-graduate earnings in 1999 from these companies. Each employee has been in the company between two and three years.

Location	Graduate earning	Non-graduate earning
Company 1	£18 000	£13 500
Company 2	£24 000	£15 000
Company 3	£14 500	£18 800
Company 4	£46 000	£30 000
Company 5	£19 000	£14 000
Company 6	£22 000	£16 000

(a) Find the simple aggregate index to compare graduate and non-graduate salaries in 1999.
(b) What percentage more did the graduates get over the non-graduates?
(c) What percentage less did the non-graduates get than the graduates?

11.14 Supplementary exercise

11.7   The following index is based on year 1:

Year	1	2	3	4	5	6	7	8
Index 1	100	107	115	126	139	145	150	152

(a) Calculate a new index based on year 4.

(b) Calculate a new index based on year 8.

(c) Find the percentage point rises between subsequent years.

(d) Find the percentage rises between subsequent years.

11.8   The following table shows the values of an old index from years 1 to 5. It was rebased in year 5, so the new index is shown for subsequent years:

Year	1	2	3	4	5	6	7	8
Index 1	250	278	340	385				
Index 2				100	109	123	136	147

(a) Complete index 1 and index 2 for years 1 to 8.

(b) If an index linked pension was worth £8500 in year 1, what was it worth in the other years?

(c) What was the percentage point increase in pension each year using (i) index 1 and (ii) index 2?

(d) What was the percentage increase in pension each year?

11.9   Your company's turnover, in £ million, has been as shown below:

Year	1991	1992	1993	1994	1995	1996	1997	1998
Turnover	72.5	74.6	77.0	80.2	82.0	84.7	86.0	88.4

In the corresponding years the value of the RPI has been:

Year	1991	1992	1993	1994	1995	1996	1997	1998
RPI	133.5	138.5	140.7	144.1	149.1	152.7	157.4	162.9

Find the deflated turnover, taking the RPI into consideration, using 1991 as the base year.

11.10 The following information was recorded about sales of gardening items from a local nursery:

Item	Number of items sold			Price per item (£)		
	Year 1	Year 2	Year 3	Year 1	Year 2	Year 3
Forks	50	62	59	12.50	13.20	14.00
Spades	86	78	73	10.75	10.75	11.00
Trowels	120	142	135	4.25	4.95	5.50
Hoes	35	42	45	7.73	8.40	9.20
Shears	19	22	27	22.50	23.00	24.00

(a) Calculate the simple aggregate price index for years 2 and 3. Year 1 = 100.

(b) Calculate the simple aggregate quantity index for years 2 and 3. Year 1 = 100

(c) Calculate Laspeyre's index for years 2 and 3 with year 1 as the base year.

(d) Calculate Paasche's index for years 2 and 3.

(e) Calculate Fisher's index for years 2 and 3.

11.11 A businessman has a portfolio of shares from six companies A, B, C, D, E and F. He increases his holding of these from time to time and keeps a record of the share prices at the end of each month. The table below records his holdings and the share prices at the end of 4 consecutive months:

Co.	Share price (£)				Number held (000)			
	April	May	June	July	April	May	June	July
A	58.2	54.5	57.5	60.2	4.0	4.0	5.5	5.5
B	0.78	0.52	0.36	0.27	12.0	13.0	14.0	15.0
C	4.67	6.86	7.90	9.32	7.5	8.0	8.0	8.5
D	1.23	3.64	4.67	2.30	3.0	3.0	3.0	5.0
E	27.3	28.6	28.9	29.5	7.5	7.5	7.5	7.5
F	37.0	24.7	20.5	10.3	2.0	7.0	12.0	17.0

(a) Calculate Laspeyre's index for May, June and July using April as the base month.

(b) Calculate Paasche's index for comparing May, June and July with April.

(c) Calculate Fisher's index for comparing May, June and July with April

12 Time Series

12.1 Objectives of this chapter

A **time series** is simply a list of values measuring a single item such as sales, prices or quantities at regular intervals over time. In Chapter 11 we used time series in the form of index numbers to investigate changes over time. The main interest was in past time periods and the main objective was a comparison of different series.

In this chapter we again study the past but with the main purpose of identifying patterns in past events which will be used in Chapter 13, to forecast future values and events. Ideally we make use of computer packages to identify past patterns, or lack of them, and then fit the best possible model to the past data. This model will then be used in Chapter 13 to forecast values for them in the near future.

By the end of this chapter you should be able to plot a time series of data; identify the type of model likely to produce the best fit, establish its formula, if appropriate, with the help of a computer package, decompose any seasonal pattern present, and establish the goodness of fit of the model by analysing its residuals.

12.2 Introduction – inspection of a time series

There are many standard methods used in forecasting, as we shall see in Chapter 13. They all, however, depend on the principle of finding the best model to fit the past time series of data and then using the same model to forecast future values.

The best method to use in any circumstance depends on the form taken by the past data so it seems reasonable to plot the data values as the first step. The past values are plotted against the time periods as in a scatter diagram. This is often called a sequence diagram. Inspection of the plotted data should give some indication of which type of model, or models, might be the most suitable to apply. The selected models can then be fitted by a computer package such as SPSS, which will be used to illustrate the methods in this chapter. More than one model is generally produced and the best of these selected by comparing how well each fits the data. In Chapter 13 the best fitting models for each set of data will be used for forecasting purposes.

Time series of past data → Suitable method → Best fitting model → Forecast

If the plotted data appear to follow a **linear pattern** on the sequence diagram then **linear regression** is a suitable model to employ with the regular time periods, t, being used as the independent variable. The time periods should be regularly spaced but any missing values can be accommodated by adjusting the value of t in the following time periods.

Table 12.1 shows three typical patterns exhibited by time series with suggested types of suitable model. (This is, by no means, an exhaustive list of either past data time series or suitably fitting models.)

Table 12.1

Time series of past data	General description	Some suitable methods
Quarterly sales vs *Date* (Q1 1994 – Q4 1996); values ranging 26–42	Linear (?), non-linear (?), non-seasonal	Linear regression (?), non-linear regression (?), exponential smoothing
Monthly sales vs *Date* (Jan 1993 – Jul 1996); values ranging 80–200	Non-linear, non-seasonal	Non-linear regression, exponential smoothing
Quarterly sales (£0000) vs *Date* (Q1 1991 – Q3 1996); values ranging 40–80	Linear, seasonal	Seasonal decomposition, additive or multiplicative, exponential smoothing (Decomposition methods are generally better)

We shall consider each type of series in turn. For each we will produce two models by different methods; select the better of each pair and then use this model in Chapter 13 to produce short-term forecasts for each.

The decision regarding the best model for each series will be based visually on graphical assessment of closeness and, also, numerically on the size of the errors as a measure of 'misfit'.

Generally, if a model reasonably fits past chronological data it can be used to predict values in the near future under the same prevailing conditions.

12.3 Non-seasonal time series

We shall try to model the first time series in Table 12.1 by using both linear and non-linear regression. We have previously found regression equations to describe the linear relationship between an independent and a dependent variable. The same method applies to time series analysis in which time is the independent variable. Using SPSS, linear and non-linear models can be produced together and immediately compared. From the shape of the data it is evident that any smooth model, whether a straight line or a curve, is unlikely to fit it well. Never expect miracles – all we aim for is the best possible fit. We judge this by comparing the 'misfit' of the models and selecting that with the lowest value. Finally we will fit exponential smoothing models to the same data and compare the results.

12.3.1 Time series plot

We shall first produce the time series plot and decide on suitable models to try.

The data in the first series describe the quarterly sales (£000) of a particular item for 12 consecutive quarters:

| 39 | 41 | 36 | 39 | 38 | 38 | 36 | 33 | 34 | 35 | 33 | 28 |

Figure 12.1 Time series of quarterly sales

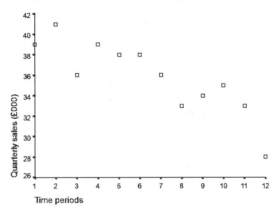

The general shape appears to be slightly convex upwards but a straight line might fit equally well, especially to the first eleven points. It is definitely not seasonal as this would be expected to show a repeated pattern of fours for quarterly data. We shall try fitting linear, quadratic and cubic models to this data.

12.3.2 Regression models

The calculation of the linear regression model is the same as in Chapter 9. In this example the independent variable is the time period and the dependent variable is the sales.

There are many models available in SPSS. We shall apply the simplest:

- The linear model: $y = a + x$ (12.1)

- The quadratic model: $y = a + bx + cx^2$ (12.2)

- The cubic model: $y = a + bx + cx^2 + dx^3$ (12.3)

Often it is not easy to judge which model is the best fit from a diagram. From SPSS we can produce coefficients for the formula for each model and also a numerical measure of how well each fits the data. This measure is the same R-squared value as we used, in percentage form, to judge the goodness of fit of a linear regression model in Chapter 9.

EXAMPLE 12.1 *continued*

Fit the linear, quadratic and cubic models to these data:

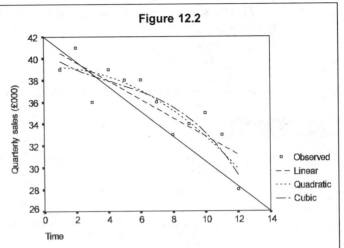

Figure 12.2

It is not easy to judge which model gives the best fit so we need the regression analysis.

Independent: TIMES

Dependent	Mth	Rsq	df	F	Sigf	b0	b1	b2	b3
SALES	LIN	.744	10	29.02	.000	41.3333	-.8462		
SALES	QUA	.792	9	17.19	.001	39.1818	.0759	-.0709	
SALES	CUB	.802	8	10.83	.003	40.6667	-1.0717	.1412	-.0109

For the linear model b0 gives the value of the constant, *a*, and b1 the value of the slope, *b*. Similarly for the other models the coefficient of x^2 is under b2 and that of x^3 under b3.

These three models are described by linear, quadratic and cubic equations which are respectively:

$$y = 41.33 - 0.846x \tag{12.1}$$

$$y = 39.18 + 0.076x - 0.071x^2 \tag{12.2}$$

$$y = 40.67 - 1.072x + 0.141x^2 - 0.011x^3 \tag{12.3}$$

where y = sales and x = time period which takes the values 1 to 12 for this data.

Which of these models gives the best fit? The Rsq value, which has not been adjusted for the differing degrees of freedom, suggests that it is the cubic model. With adjustment this may not be the case.

We will check further by analysing the residuals as a measure of misfit. We are looking for the set of residuals with a mean of zero and the smallest spread about that mean. As a rule of thumb, this can be assessed by a comparison of standard deviations, box plots, etc.

The preference for the cubic model is borne out by a simple analysis of the residuals.

Variable	Mean	Std Dev	Minimum	Maximum	N	Label
ERR_1 (lin)	.00	1.79	-3.17949	2.12821	12	Residuals from Linear model
ERR_2 (quad)	.00	1.61	-2.77123	2.15185	12	Residuals from Quadratic model
ERR_3 (cubic)	.00	1.57	-2.55977	1.99900	12	Residuals from Cubic model

All have a mean of zero as required so we choose the model with the smallest standard deviation; the cubic model. We shall use this model in Chapter 13 to produce a forecast for the sales for each of the following two months.

12.3.3 *Exponential smoothing models*

Exponential smoothing is a technique for averaging out the random components in a series. It is particularly useful for short term forecasting. A variety of models are available allowing for different combinations of trend and seasonality. The type of trend and/or seasonality determines how many parameters are included in the exponential smoothing model.

The general idea is that the estimate for the next value in time will be the same as the present estimated value adjusted for how far the present estimate is out, that is, some proportion of the error at this stage is used to correct for the next stage. The proportional adjustment varies between models. Do we adjust by 10% of the error or 50% of the error?

Trial and error is used to produce the best model. The initial values for the level and trend can also be selected rather than accepting the automatic values produced by SPSS.

The best model is that which produces the smallest errors, as measured by the SSE. This is the sum of the squares of the errors already met in analysis of variance (Chapter 8).

Steady model

This **model** assumes that the data have no general trend, either up or down, and that there is no seasonal variation, that is, variations are random around some steady mean value.

The proportion of the error by which the next estimate is adjusted is described by the symbol α (alpha) which is usually between 0.1 and 0.5. The value of α is always between 0 and 1. The closer the value of α is to zero the less influence the current observation has in determining the forecast. Low values are suitable for fairly smooth data with few fluctuations because a smooth model is produced.

$$\text{New forecast} = \text{old forecast} + \text{alpha} \times \text{error in previous forecast} \tag{12.4}$$

Growth model (Holt's model)

The method for the growth model is similar to the steady model but it also includes a second smoothing constant, β (beta), which is generally smaller than alpha and adjusts for error in forecast trend. The trend may be positive or negative but the model is still referred to as a 'growth' model. The use of β corrects for a portion of the most recent error in the slope. (Some textbooks and SPSS use γ (gamma) rather than β as the second smoothing constant.)

$$\text{New forecast} = \text{previous forecast} + \alpha \times \text{error in previous forecast}$$
$$+ \text{previous trend} + \beta \times \text{error in previous forecast trend} \tag{12.5}$$
$$\text{New trend} = \text{previous trend} + \beta \times \text{error in previous trend}$$

Seasonal model

Exponential smoothing can also be used for seasonal data by using a third smoothing constant for the seasonality. It does not seem to give nearly as good a model as the method of seasonal decomposition (Section 12.5).

Although the data in Example 12.1 appear to follow a downward trend we shall first demonstrate a few steady models before finding the best fitting growth model.

EXAMPLE 12.1 *continued*

Steady models

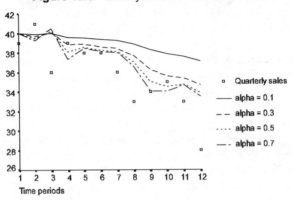

Figure 12.3 Steady models fitted to sales

Even with an alpha figure of 0.7 the model lags behind the actual data.

Initial values:	Series	Trend
	40.00000	Not used
The SSE is:	Alpha	SSE
	.1000000	201.0
	.3000000	105.2
	.5000000	82.6
	.7000000	78.6

The value for the smoothing constant of 0.7 gives the best model but a trend is clearly needed. A growth model seems likely to improve the fit considerably.

Growth models

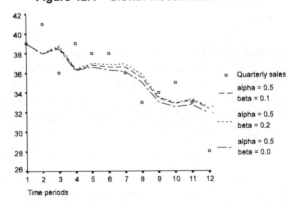

Figure 12.4 Growth models fitted to sales

It is difficult to tell which is the best model, but the use of a trend has certainly improved the general fit.

Initial values:	Series	Trend	
	40.00000	−1.00000	
The SSE is:	Alpha	Gamma	SSE
	.5000000	.1000000	57.1
	.5000000	.2000000	59.7
	.5000000	.0000000	54.1

continued

EXAMPLE 12.1 *continued*

The best model of these is alpha $= 0.5$; beta (gamma) $= 0.0$ This has a lower SSE than any of the steady models. (Note that this is not the same model as the previous one for alpha $= 0.5$ as an initial trend of 1 has been applied.)

The best regression and best exponential smoothing models will be compared in Section 12.6. We shall use this model for forecasting sales for each of the following two months in Chapter 13.

12.4 A further example of non-seasonal modelling

EXAMPLE 12.2

Figure 12.5 describes the monthly sales of an item produced by your company during four years.

Figure 12.5 Time series of monthly sales

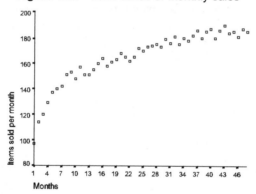

Considering the shape of the graph, it is evident that the data are not seasonal, that the plot rises fairly steadily and although a straight line might fit it reasonably well for the second half, the overall fit would probably require a curve. We shall again use SPSS to produce the best exponential smoothing model and the best fitting regression curve.

SPSS has a useful weapon known as a 'grid search'. Instead of the analyst using trial and error to produce innumerable models and then comparing their respective SSEs to select the best, a general, fairly coarse, trawl through all possible parameters will produce an approximation to the best model quickly. This model can then be finely tuned to find an improved version giving the lowest SSE.

Just showing part of the output indicates that the best model is a growth (Holt's) model with $\alpha = 0.4$ and $\beta\ (\gamma) = 0.7$ giving a SSE of 931

```
Initial values:     Series        Trend
                   95.00000      10.00000
The 5 smallest SSEs are:    Alpha         Gamma        SSE
                            .400          .700        931.12
                            .400          .600        933.84
                            .400          .800        939.41
                            .300         1.000        947.76
                            .500          .500        948.43
```

How well does this model appear to fit the data?

continued

EXAMPLE 12.2 *continued*

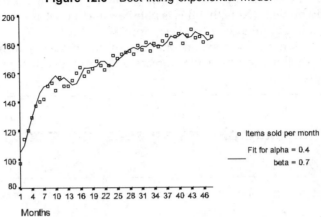

Figure 12.6   Best-fitting exponential model

This model fits the data reasonably well but a smoother model might be preferable. We shall next look for a smooth fitting curve using regression.

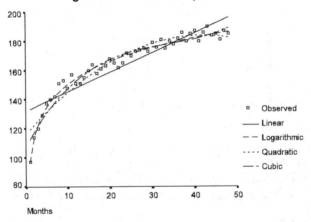

Figure 12.7   Items sold per month

The smoother models look better. Clearly the linear model is not the best but we need some numerical comparison of the curves. (Using the right mouse button in SPSS gives the formula of each model so unfamiliar ones can be tried.)

Independent: MONTHS

Dependent	Mth	Rsq	df	F	Sigf	b0	b1	b2	b3
SALES	LIN	.825	46	216.88	.000	131.892	1.3471		
SALES	LOG	.977	46	1991.96	.000	97.0253	23.1584		
SALES	QUA	.930	45	299.88	.000	116.030	3.2505	−.0388	
SALES	CUB	.950	44	278.31	.000	107.376	5.2666	−.1407	.0014

Judged by the Rsq value the logarithmic model is very good.

This model is of the form $y = a + b \times \ln(t)$ where ln is the natural logarithm.

In this case using the coefficients produced: sales $= 97.0 + 23.2\ln(\text{month})$

Plotting the two models selected by the different methods gives Figure 12.8.

continued

EXAMPLE 12.2 *continued*

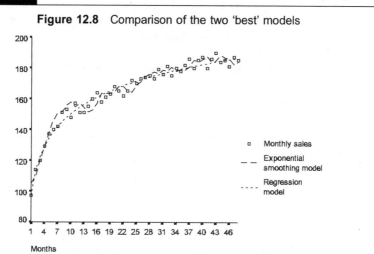

Figure 12.8 Comparison of the two 'best' models

These are obviously very different types of models. One follows the general curve, the other tries to follow the individual items on it. Which one fits the data better and is, therefore, likely to give the better forecast?

In Section 12.6 we shall look for the preferable set of residuals and in Chapter 13 we shall consider the forecasts made by each model for the following two months.

12.5 Decomposition of seasonal time series

12.5.1 *Additive model – by calculation and graph*

In a time series diagram you may find a repeated pattern demonstrating periodicity. If this is the case then this periodicity, which is caused by some seasonal factor, must form part of the model.

The additive model for a seasonal time series is:

$$\text{value} = \text{trend} + \text{seasonal component} + \text{a random amount} \tag{12.6}$$

The trend is the line of best fit, usually non-linear, through the data and the seasonal component is the amount by which the trend is adjusted in that particular time period, for example, a particular quarter of the year. The trend and the seasonal component both need to be identified from the past data.

The trend is found as the running average of the appropriate number of periods. If the data is monthly groups of twelve would be averaged; if quarterly, the groups would contain four consecutive time periods.

We shall analyse a seasonal time series describing the sales of ice cream by a particular company over a period of four years. We then use the results to estimate sales for the four quarters of the following year accompanied by the maximum likely errors to be found in the estimates. We shall first assume that the best model to use is an additive one and tackle the analysis by hand. For comparison, the same data will be analysed using SPSS for an additive model. Finally we shall consider, from SPSS output only, whether a multiplicative model might give a better fit to the data.

EXAMPLE 12.3

A small ice-cream manufacturer who supplies your company's supermarket chain reports sales figures of £50 000 for the last quarter. Can this be used to estimate his sales in the following quarter?

A single figure is never sufficient to provide the answer unless the sales are constant. We also need the figures for many earlier quarters so that we can identify any past pattern and use it for future sales predictions.

Table 12.2

Year	Sales (£000)			
	Quarter 1	Quarter 2	Quarter 3	Quarter 4
1997	40	60	80	35
1998	30	50	60	30
1999	35	60	80	40
2000	50	70	100	50

This time series should be plotted accurately on a full sheet of graph paper, leaving room for the forecasts for the four quarters of the following year (to save drawing the graph again). The graph in Figure 12.9 has been produced in SPSS.

If consecutive points are connected the periodicity of four is more evident.

Figure 12.9   Quarterly sales

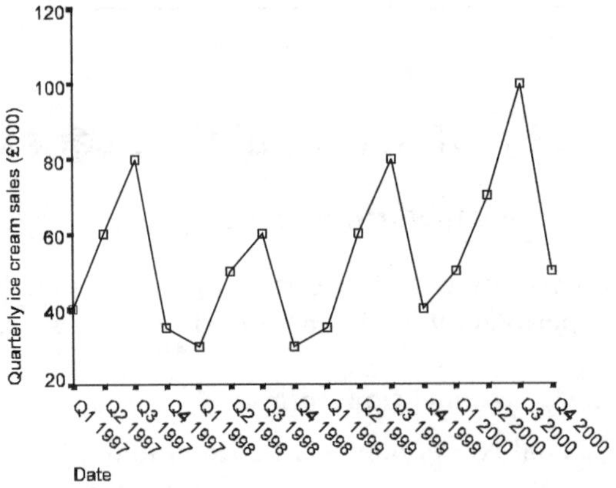

The next step is to calculate the values for the trend by finding a cycle average for each cycle of four values. The first value is calculated from quarters 1 to 4 of year 1997; the second from quarter 2 of 1997 to quarter 1 of 1998; the third from quarter 3 1997 to quarter 2 of 1998; and so on.

Unfortunately, because there are an even number of time points in each cycle, the first cycle average is centred half way between quarters 2 and 3; the second between quarters 3 and 4; etc. We cannot therefore compare them directly with the sales in order to find the difference between them. The next stage is to find the moving average of each two consecutive cycle averages to give the trend values which will then be against a quarter.

These figures are plotted on the graph, taking care that the series starts at quarter 3. By this method the trend values for either the first two or the last two quarters are unfortunately lost.

continued

EXAMPLE 12.3 *continued*

Observed	=	Trend	+	Seasonal	+	Random
sales value		value		variation		amount
A	=	T	+	S	+	R

The **trend value, T**, is the value of the sales if the seasonal effect had been 'averaged out'

The **seasonal variation, S**, is the average effect of a particular quarter

The **random amount, R**, is the random variation due to neither of the previous variables

The table is built up in columns from the left to the right.

After the dates, the sales figures are entered in chronological order.

The first cycle average: $\dfrac{40 + 60 + 80 + 35}{4} = \dfrac{215}{4} = 53.75$

The second cycle average: $\dfrac{60 + 80 + 35 + 30}{4} = \dfrac{205}{4} = 51.25$

The first moving average trend figure: $\dfrac{53.75 + 51.25}{2} = 52.50$

The second moving average trend figure: $\dfrac{51.25 + 48.75}{2} = 50.00$

Table 12.3

Date		Sales (A) (£000)	Cycle average	Trend (T) Moving average	First residual $R_1 = A - T$	Fitted value $F = T + S$
1997	Q$_1$	40				
1997	Q$_2$	60				
			53.75			
1997	Q$_3$	80		52.50	+27.50	75.42
			51.25			
1997	Q$_4$	35		50.00	−15.00	33.75
			48.75			
1998	Q$_1$	30		46.25	−16.25	32.08
			43.75			
1998	Q$_2$	50		43.13	+6.87	49.17
			42.50			
1998	Q$_3$	60		43.13	+16.87	66.04
			43.75			
1998	Q$_4$	30		45.00	−15.00	28.75
			46.25			
1999	Q$_1$	35		48.75	−13.75	34.58
			51.25			
1999	Q$_2$	60		52.50	+7.50	58.54
			53.75			
1999	Q$_3$	80		55.63	+24.37	78.54
			57.50			
1999	Q$_4$	40		58.75	−18.75	42.50
			60.00			
2000	Q$_1$	50		62.50	−12.50	48.33
			65.00			
2000	Q$_2$	70		66.25	+3.75	72.29
			67.50			
2000	Q$_3$	100				
2000	Q$_4$	50				

continued

EXAMPLE 12.3 *continued*

Plotting the trend with the data we can see that it is a smoothed average through the quarterly sales.

Figure 12.10 Quarterly sales and trend

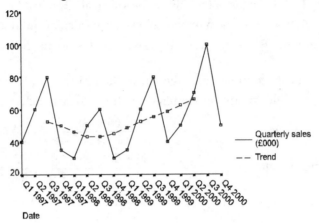

Later the smoothed trend line needs to be extended into the near future and then adjusted by the appropriate seasonal factor to give the forecasts. Figure 12.10 could, in theory, be used to extend the trend but it would be difficult to read values from it accurately. A large hand drawn graph is therefore preferable.

We next need the 'seasonal factors'. For this data we can see that the sales are always high in quarter 3 but what value do we put on the seasonal factor for quarter 3? It seems reasonable that it should be the average of the differences from the trend, the first residuals, for that particular quarter. Check the values in the table of the first residuals.

Seasonal Factor (S) is the average seasonal deviation from the trend

Table 12.4

	Quarter 1	Quarter 2	Quarter 3	Quarter 4
	—	—	+27.50	−15.00
	−16.25	+ 6.87	+16.87	−15.00
	−13.75	+ 7.50	+24.37	−18.74
	−12.50	+ 3.75		
Total	−42.50	+18.12	68.74	−48.74
Average	−14.17	+6.04	+22.91	−16.25

The additive model to which we shall fit the data is:

$$\text{Fitted sales value} = \text{Trend value} + \text{Seasonal factor}$$
$$A = T + S \tag{12.7}$$

If the fitted, model values are calculated by adding together the smoothed trend and the seasonal factors, this data can also be added to the graph to see how well our model would have performed in the past.

continued

EXAMPLE 12.3 *continued*

Check in the table that the fitted values are the sums of the trend values and the appropriate seasonal factors. Plotting the fitted values with the data gives an idea of how well the model fitted the past data.

The differences between the observed values and the model values are referred to as the 'second residuals'. These will be analysed in Section 12.6 and in Chapter 13, we shall use them to estimate how good any forecasts made from this model are likely to be.

If we add the fitted graph values to our sales graph data we can compare the theoretical model with the observed sales data.

Figure 12.11   Sales and fitted additive model

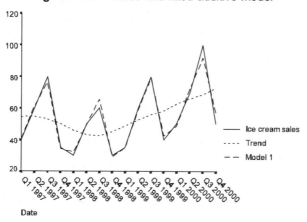

It is evident that this model is a good fit for the past sales of ice cream. The 'differences' between the observed values and the model values are obviously small. We shall analyse them in Section 12.6.

12.5.2 *Additive model by computer package*

Figures 12.1 to 12.11 have all been produced from SPSS. Here we will take a look at the SPSS analysis which is an extension of our hand calculated method and a little more sophisticated.

EXAMPLE 12.3 *continued*

SPSS output

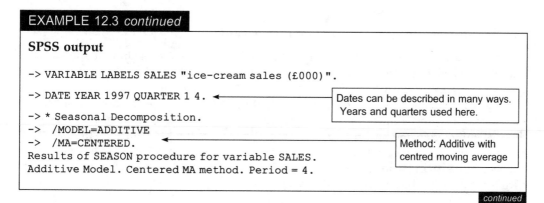

```
-> VARIABLE LABELS SALES "ice-cream sales (£000)".

-> DATE YEAR 1997 QUARTER 1 4.  ◄
```
Dates can be described in many ways. Years and quarters used here.
```
-> * Seasonal Decomposition.
-> /MODEL=ADDITIVE
-> /MA=CENTERED.  ◄
```
Method: Additive with centred moving average
```
Results of SEASON procedure for variable SALES.
Additive Model. Centered MA method. Period = 4.
```

continued

EXAMPLE 12.3 *continued*

DATE	SALES	Moving averages	Ratios	Seasonal factors	Seasonally adjusted series	Smoothed trend-cycle	Irregular component
Q1 1997	40.000	.	.	−13.802	53.802	55.573	−1.771
Q2 1997	60.000	.	.	6.406	53.594	54.705	−1.111
Q3 1997	80.000	52.500	27.500	23.281	56.719	52.969	3.750
Q4 1997	35.000	50.000	−15.000	−15.885	50.885	50.098	.787
Q1 1998	30.000	46.250	−16.250	−13.802	43.802	45.978	−2.176
Q2 1998	50.000	43.125	6.875	6.406	43.594	43.177	.417
Q3 1998	60.000	43.125	16.875	23.281	36.719	42.413	−5.694
Q4 1998	30.000	45.000	−15.000	−15.885	45.885	45.098	.787
Q1 1999	35.000	48.750	−13.750	−13.802	48.802	48.756	.046
Q2 1999	60.000	52.500	7.500	6.406	53.594	52.622	.972
Q3 1999	80.000	55.625	24.375	23.281	56.719	55.747	.972
Q4 1999	40.000	58.750	−18.750	−15.885	55.885	58.432	−2.546
Q1 2000	50.000	62.500	−12.500	−13.802	63.802	62.645	1.157
Q2 2000	70.000	66.250	3.750	6.406	63.594	65.955	−2.361
Q3 2000	100.000	.	.	23.281	76.719	68.733	7.986
Q4 2000	50.000	.	.	−15.885	65.885	70.122	−4.236

The following new variables are being created:

Name	Label
ERR_1	Error for SALES from SEASON, MOD_1 ADD CEN 4
SAS_1	Seas adj ser for SALES from SEASON, MOD_1 ADD CEN 4
SAF_1	Seas factors for SALES from SEASON, MOD_1 ADD CEN 4
STC_1	Trend-cycle for SALES from SEASON, MOD_1 ADD CEN 4

The moving averages are the trend figures calculated by hand previously and the 'ratios' (a description more suited to the following multiplicative model) are the same first residuals. The seasonal factors and the smoothed trend cycle describe the average effect due to a particular quarter and the sales level without that effect. These differ slightly from our calculated figures as they have been further smoothed and also extended to cover the first and last two time periods. We shall look at seasonally adjusted series later.

No fitted values from the model have been produced by default but can easily be obtained as the sum of smoothed trend cycle and seasonal factors which have automatically been produced and saved by SPSS as STC_1 and SAF_1. The errors, ERR_1, and deseasonalised sales, SAL_1, have also been saved.

Minitab produces similar analysis using a moving average model.

12.5.3 *Multiplicative model by computer package*

In order to have a second seasonal model of these ice-cream sales for comparison with the additive one, we shall produce a multiplicative model in SPSS, analyse its residuals to see which is preferable and use it also to make short term forecasts.

If the seasonal adjustment is proportional to the level of the series then a multiplicative model may be more appropriate. The processes of division and multiplication replace those of subtraction and addition at each stage. Otherwise the procedure is similar to that for the additive model. Using SPSS, the multiplicative model is selected as the method of analysis rather than an additive one, otherwise the method is the same. Could this model give a better fit to the ice-cream sales data?

EXAMPLE 12.3 continued

SPSS output

Results of SEASON procedure for variable SALES.
Multiplicative Model. Centered MA method. Period = 4.

DATE	SALES	Moving averages	Ratios (*100)	Seasonal factors (*100)	Seasonally adjusted series	Smoothed trend-cycle	Irregular component
Q1 1997	40.000	.	.	72.158	55.434	54.903	1.010
Q2 1997	60.000	.	.	114.864	52.236	54.338	.961
Q3 1997	80.000	52.500	152.381	144.548	55.345	52.201	1.060
Q4 1997	35.000	50.000	70.000	68.430	51.147	49.228	1.039
Q1 1998	30.000	46.250	64.865	72.158	41.575	45.659	.911
Q2 1998	50.000	43.125	115.942	114.864	43.530	43.527	1.000
Q3 1998	60.000	43.125	139.130	144.548	41.509	43.261	.960
Q4 1998	30.000	45.000	66.667	68.430	43.841	45.257	.969
Q1 1999	35.000	48.750	71.795	72.158	48.505	48.280	1.005
Q2 1999	60.000	52.500	114.286	114.864	52.236	51.856	1.007
Q3 1999	80.000	55.625	143.820	144.548	55.345	56.135	.986
Q4 1999	40.000	58.750	68.085	68.430	58.454	59.757	.978
Q1 2000	50.000	62.500	80.000	72.158	69.292	63.466	1.092
Q2 2000	70.000	66.250	105.660	114.864	60.942	65.699	.928
Q3 2000	100.000	.	.	144.548	69.181	67.730	1.021
Q4 2000	50.000	.	.	68.430	73.068	72.140	1.013

The following new variables are being created:

Name	Label
ERR_2	Error for SALES from SEASON, MOD_2 MUL CEN 4
SAS_2	Seas adj ser for SALES from SEASON, MOD_2 MUL CEN 4
SAF_2	Seas factors for SALES from SEASON, MOD_2 MUL CEN 4
STC_2	Trend-cycle for SALES from SEASON, MOD_2 MUL CEN 4

The moving average is the same as previously but the rest of the figures are quite different as multiplication and division have replaced addition and subtraction. Do not worry if you cannot reproduce the figures, just trust SPSS! As previously the errors, deseasonalised values, seasonal factors and trend values have been saved.

Figure 12.12   Sales and fitted multiplicative model

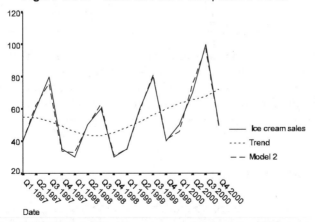

Comparing this graph with Figure 12.11 it is not easy to see which model fits the 'ice-cream sales' data better. In Section, 12.6, we will compare them by analysing each set of residuals.

12.5.4 *Seasonal effects and deseasonalised values*

In order to find fitted model values in the additive model we added the seasonal factor to the smoothed trend cycle values. In the multiplicative model the seasonal factor is multiplied by the corresponding smoothed trend cycle value.

The same seasonal factors are also used for deseasonalising data. We may hear in the media that unemployment has gone down but that the deseasonalised value has gone up. What does this mean? For some items, such as unemployment and ice-cream sales for which there is obviously a seasonal component it is reasonable to remove that component before comparing different quarters.

For the additive model the seasonal factor is subtracted from the observed data in order to deseasonalise it. For the multiplicative model it is divided by it.

These are the values in the columns of seasonally adjusted series in the SPSS output. Consecutive quarters can be compared using this series to see whether sales have improved without the effect of, say, the amount of sales due to the higher summer temperatures coming into the equation.

It now makes sense to calculate percentages changes, to compare with appropriate published indexes, and so on. The deseasonalised values can be compared to the trend value at any point in time to see whether, for example, sales were better or worse than the general trend at that time.

EXAMPLE 12.3 *continued*

How can we compare the ice-cream sales in summer with those in winter?

We shall 'deseasonalise' the observed sales figures.

Table 12.5

Date	Observed sales	−	Seasonal factor	=	Deseasonalised sales	Trend (from SPSS output)
2000 Q_1	50	−	−14.17	=	64.17	62.65
2000 Q_2	70	−	+6.04	=	63.96	66.00
2000 Q_3	100	−	+22.91	=	77.09	68.73
2000 Q_4	50	−	−16.25	=	66.25	70.12

Having removed the amount due to each quarter we can see that quarters 1 and 2 were very similar but that quarter 3 showed an increase, in real terms, of £13 130 over quarter 2. This was followed by a decrease in sales of £10 840 between quarters 3 and 4. Compared to the trend quarters 1 and 3 performed well but quarters 2 and 4 did not.

12.6 Residual analysis

The main requirement of a model, no matter which method has been used to produce it, is that it should fit the observed data well. The differences between the model values and the observed values should therefore be as small as possible. Ideally they should be normally distributed with a mean of zero and a small standard deviation. They should be randomly distributed against time, for example, not positive for the early data and negative for the later times, or there is some factor missing from the model. Normality can be judged graphically by histograms or boxplots and numerically by Kolmogorov–Smirnov (K–S) tests for normality. Each of these methods will be demonstrated in the following examples.

Graphically we can examine the plots of the observed and model values to see how closely they fit. The vertical differences between the pairs of values indicate the magnitude of the separate residuals. These residuals can be saved and analysed to see which set best fulfils the conditions above.

In this chapter we have analysed three sets of data and produced two models for each. We have considered each graphically and we are satisfied that good models have been produced. Some measure of the goodness of fit has been produced for each model but these have not been immediately comparable as were the Rsq and SSE values for the regression and exponential smoothing models respectively and irregular components for the two seasonal decomposition models. Even the seasonal decomposition models cannot be directly compared as one measures differences with a mean of zero, and the other ratios with a mean of 1.

For each model we shall find the differences between the observed and model values, residuals or errors, and analyse them to see which set best fulfils the required conditions for residuals.

Two measures often used to compare residuals are mean absolute deviation (**MAD**) and mean square error (**MSE**) (see Appendix C for formulae). We shall use their **standard deviation** which is equivalent to $\sqrt{\text{MSE}}$.

We return to Examples 12.1 to 12.3 for residual analysis.

The sizes of the mean and standard deviation are found as descriptive statistics. The normality is judged graphically by histograms, box plots or numerically using the Kolmogorov–Smirnov normality test. The chronological randomness is judged by sequence plots.

EXAMPLE 12.4

Residual analysis of Example 12.1

Our two preferred models for this data were the cubic regression model and the growth exponential smoothing model with alpha = 0.5, beta = 0.0, and with initial conditions of 40 for the starting value and 1.0 for the trend.

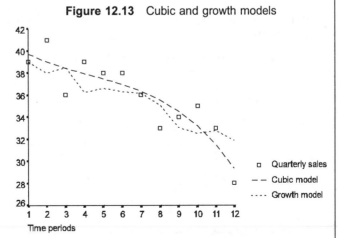

Figure 12.13   Cubic and growth models

It is still not easy to decide which is best. The residuals are calculated and analysed to produce the results in Figure 12.14.

continued

EXAMPLE 12.4 *continued*

Figure 12.14

Descriptive statistics					
	N	Minimum	Maximum	Mean	Std. deviation
Quarterly sales	12	28	41	35.83	3.54
Errors from cubic model	12	−2.55977	1.99900	−5.3E-15	1.5723984
Errors from growth model	12	−3.87988	3.00000	−3.233236	2.1914435

As judged by the descriptive statistics of the errors the cubic model was preferable with the smaller mean and smaller standard deviation.

As this is only a small sample, graphical judgements of normality will be poor. A Kolmogorov–Smirnov test is more appropriate.

Figure 12.15

One-sample Kolmogorov–Smirnov test			
		Errors from cubic model	Errors from growth model
N		12	12
Normal Parameters[a,b]	Mean	0000000	.3233236
	Std Deviation	1.5723983	2.1914434
Most Extreme	Absolute	.161	.163
Differences	Positive	.105	.113
	Negative	−.161	−.163
Kolmogorov–Smirnov Z		.556	.566
Asymp. Sig. (2-tailed)		.917	.906

a. Test distribution is normal.
b. Calculated from data.

Both sets of residuals are normal with significance values > 0.05. The cubic significance is slightly higher.

Figure 12.16 Errors of both models plotted against time

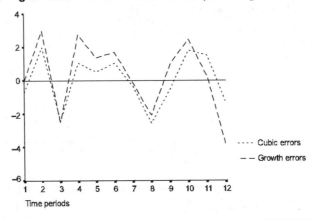

continued

EXAMPLE 12.4 *continued*

Both graphs in Figure 12.16 appear to be random against time. For most of the sequence the cubic errors are smaller as they appear to be nearer the zero line.

Cubic model: $y = 40.67 - 1.072x + 0.141x^2 - 0.011x^3$ is judged to be the better one.

Although the cubic model has been judged to give the better fit, the cubic and growth models will be used to demonstrate forecasting in Chapter 13.

EXAMPLE 12.5

Residual analysis of Example 12.2

The two best fitting models for this data were a logarithmic model with coefficients 97.0 and 23.2 and a growth exponential model with alpha $= 0.4$, beta $= 0.7$ and initial conditions of 95 for the position and 10 for the trend.

Figure 12.17   Comparison of the two best models

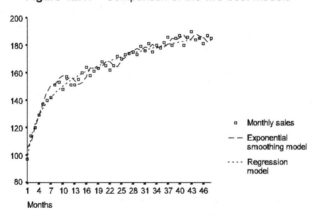

In Figure 12.17, one model is smooth and the other undulating so they are not easy to compare graphically. It is better to use residual analysis (Figure 12.18).

Figure 12.18

Descriptive statistics					
	N	Minimum	Maximum	Mean	Std Deviation
Items sold per month	48	97	190	164.90	20.76
Errors from growth model	48	−10.15796	7.40862	−.7421744	4.3873240
Errors from logarithmic model	48	−6.60895	5.87125	5.67E.15	3.1194525

The logarithmic model is better and the errors from that model appear normal (Figure 12.19).

continued

EXAMPLE 12.5 *continued*

Figure 12.19 Errors from logarithmic model

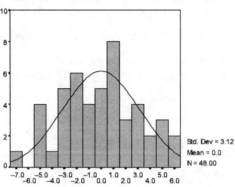

Std. Dev = 3.12
Mean = 0.0
N = 48.00

Figure 12.20

One-sample Kolmogorov–Smirnov test

		Errors from growth model	Errors from logarithmic model
Normal Parameters[a,b]	Mean	−.7421744	−1.61E-08
	Std. Deviation	4.3873239	3.1194525
Most Extreme	Absolute	.064	.053
Differences	Positive	.064	.053
	Negative	−.061	−.048
Kolmogorov–Smirnov Z		.443	.370
Asymp. Sig. (2-tailed)		.989	.999

a. Test distribution is normal.
b. Calculated from data.

Both models produce normal residuals as checked by the K–S test for normality (Figure 12.20).

From Figure 12.21, the errors from both models are random against time, although the logarithmic errors are generally smaller.

Figure 12.21 Errors from both models against time

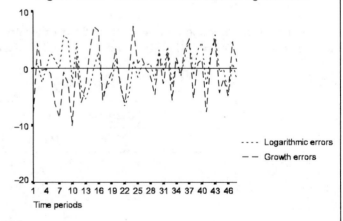

- - - - Logarithmic errors
— — Growth errors

Time periods

This gives the selected model:

Number of items sold $= 97.0 + 23.2 \ln(t)$

The growth and logarithmic models will be used in Chapter 13 for forecasting

EXAMPLE 12.6

Residual analysis of Example 12.3

For this seasonal data we produced additive and a multiplicative models (Figure 12.22).

Figure 12.22 Both seasonal models fitted to sales

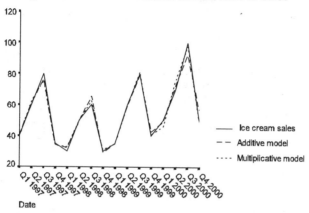

Both models give a good fit to the observed data. Residual analysis produces output presented as Figure 12.23.

Figure 12.23

Descriptive statistics					
	N	Minimum	Maximum	Mean	Std. Deviation
Ice cream sales	16	30	100	54.38	20.24
Additive model	16	−6.81	7.99	−.2865	3.4499
Multiplicative model	16	−5.46	4.54	−.1614	2.5643

The residuals from the multiplicative model look better. Box plots are generated for both sets of residuals (Figure 12.24).

Figure 12.24 Box plots of both sets of residuals

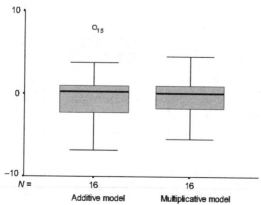

Both box plots are symmetrical. Multiplicative errors have a smaller spread about zero.

continued

EXAMPLE 12.8 *continued*

The results of the Kolmogorov–Smirnov test are shown in Figure 12.26.

Figure 12.26

One-sample Kolmogorov–Smirnov test		Additive	Multiplicative
N		16	16
Normal Parameters[a,b]	Mean	−.2865	−.1614
	Std. Deviation	3.4499	2.5643
Most Extreme	Absolute	.213	.128
Difference	Positive	.213	.128
	Negative	−.131	−.101
Kolmogorov–Smirnov Z		.851	.512
Asymp. Sig. (2-tailed)		.464	.956

a. Test distribution is normal
b. Calculated from data

Both sets of errors are judged to be normal, with those from the multiplicative model being better.

Figure 12.27   Both sets of errors against time

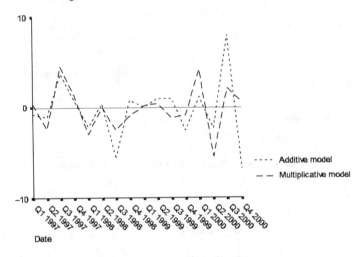

Both sets of errors in Figure 12.27 appear random against time. With a quarterly seasonal model it is important that the pattern of four in a repeat is no longer evident.

The multiplicative model is judged to be the better model but both will be used for forecasting in Chapter 13.

12.7 Further analysis of time series

There are many other procedures for the analysis of a time series. You may come across autoregression models which take into account the correlation between successive observations; Box-Jenkins methods which use autoregression, differencing and moving average combined; or spectral analysis which analyses the periodic components of the series as a whole. You may find that it often makes sense to add time-delay to a time series as the next term may not depend on the previous one but on the one before that.

Further details of all these more advanced methods can be found in Groebner and Shannon, 1993, Chapters 17 and 18. They are more difficult to understand than the methods we have studied but can all be automated by computer packages such as SPSS and Minitab, so they are not a problem to carry out. The results are, however, more difficult to interpret.

12.8 Summary

In this chapter you have met three of the main methods of time series analysis so you should have a suitable tool for most of the data you will meet on your course.

The most appropriate method is generally dictated by the data itself, so the first step is always to plot the observed data in chronological order. The graph can then be considered to see whether the data might be described by a linear or non-linear function; have an upward or downward trend or generally have a steady level; whether they show any seasonality and, if so, to identify its periodicity. The best modelling method can then be identified.

If more than one model is produced comparison is usually made by the sum of the squared errors, SSE. Eventually the real test of any model is how well its predictions match actual events in the future, so the true verdict has to await the judgement of time!

More specifically, we have studied three methods of forecasting in this chapter with variations of each. For regression we considered both linear and curved; for exponential smoothing we used both steady and growth models; and for seasonal decomposition we tried additive and multiplicative models.

Summary of the methods

Any data

1 First plot the data **in chronological order** on a graph against time. Study the result to see which type of model might be appropriate.

Non-seasonal data

2 If the time series plot indicates no seasonality type the data into SPSS or Minitab so that both curve fitting and exponential smoothing can be tried in order to find the best model.

3 Use curve fitting regression, which includes linear regression, to identify the best model; save the predicted values and residuals; plot the predicted with the observed values to see how close the fit is and finally analyse the residuals to see that they satisfy the required conditions.

4   Use the exponential smoothing method with a grid search in the first instance to get a suitable model. Try to improve on this model by altering the initial conditions and the parameters slightly using the SSE as the criterion for improvement. Plot the saved fitted values regularly to see how well the model fits the observed data. Finally analyse the residuals to see that they satisfy the required conditions.

5   Compare the two models both graphically and by residual analysis in order to select the better model.

Seasonal data may be analysed by hand or by using SPSS or Minitab.

Computer analysis

2   Type in the data in chronological order, produce a time series plot and identify its periodicity.

3   Select an additive model and analyse the time series saving the fitted values and the errors.

4   Select a multiplicative model and analyse the same time series saving the fitted values and the errors.

5   Compare both models graphically and by means of residual analysis, and, hence, select the model which fits the data better.

Non-computer analysis

2   Calculate and tabulate the moving cycle of four averages $(Q_1 + Q_2 + Q_3 + Q_4)/4$, $(Q_2 + Q_3 + Q_4 + Q_1)/4$, and so on. Hence calculate the centred trend values (T) and plot them on the same graph as your data, A. The first value is plotted against the third time slot, as the extreme values have been lost in the averaging.

3   Calculate values for the first residuals (R_1): $(R_1 = A - T)$ for each separate quarter and from them calculate the average seasonal factor, S, for each of the four quarters. Check that the average of these averages is not very far from zero.

4   Calculate the fitted values (F): $F = T + S$.
    If the model is a 'perfect fit' the fitted values will be the same as the observed sales. We expect them to be close, indicating that we have a 'good' model.

5   Calculate the second residuals (R_2): $R_2 = A - F$
    These are the random amounts by which the model has 'mismatched' the observed data in the past and give an indication of how good forecasts are going to be. They should be small and randomly distributed about a value of zero.

For all methods

6   Assess your model
    The fitted and observed values should be similar. The discrepancy between them should be very small and randomly distributed about zero.

In the next chapter we shall produce forecasts for the next time cycle for all these methods using the work done in this chapter and assess how precise the forecasts are likely to be. Only time will tell how accurate they are!

12.9 Tutorial 12 – Time series analysis

In Tutorial 12 you will construct and draw a graph of a time series in each question for a set of data and in Tutorial 13 you will use the same series in order to produce short term forecasts using the same graphs.

12.1 The quarterly sales, (£0 000s) of a departmental store have been monitored for the past five years with the following results:

	Total quarterly sales (£0 000s)			
Year	Q_1	Q_2	Q_3	Q_4
1996	48	58	57	65
1997	50	61	59	68
1998	52	62	59	69
1999	52	64	60	73
2000	53	65	60	75

(a) Plot the given data as a time series leaving room for the four forecasts for 2001.
(b) Calculate the three values missing from the table (p. 244) which are indicated by question marks.
(c) Plot the trend line on the same graph as your observed values.
(d) Calculate the seasonal averages for each of the four quarters.
(e) Find the deseasonalised data for the first quarter of 2000

12.2 A group of hotels has returned the following figures for their quarterly turnover.

	Turnover (£0 000)			
Year	Q_1	Q_2	Q_3	Q_4
1997	337	410	438	374
1998	321	416	462	414
1999	335	428	447	369
2000	311	399	422	

(a) Calculate the three values missing from the table on p. 245, produced from the above data, which are indicated by **question marks**.
(b) Plot the turnover figures and the trend figures on one graph leaving room for four forecasts.
(c) Calculate the seasonal average for each of the four seasons.

Table for Question 12.1

Date		Sales (£0 000s)	Cycle average	Trend	First residual	Second residual
1996	Q_1	48				
	Q_2	58				
			57.00			
	Q_3	57		57.250	−0.250	+0.969
			57.50			
	Q_4	65		57.875	+7.125	−1.281
			58.25			
1997	Q_1	50		58.500	−8.500	+0.406
			58.75			
	Q_2	61		59.125	+1.875	−0.063
			59.50			
	Q_3	59		59.750	−0.750	+0.469
			60.00			
	Q_4	68		60.125	+7.875	−0.531
			60.25			
1998	Q_1	52		60.250	−8.250	+0.656
			60.25			
	Q_2	62		60.375	+1.625	−0.313
			60.50			
	Q_3	59		60.500	−1.500	−0.281
			60.50			
	Q_4	69		60.750	+8.250	−0.156
			61.00			
1999	Q_1	52		61.125	−9.125	−0.219
			61.25			
	Q_2	64		?	?	0.312
			?			
	Q_3	60		62.375	−2.375	−1.156
			62.50			
	Q_4	73		62.625	+10.375	+1.969
			62.75			
2000	Q_1	53		62.750	−9.750	−0.844
			62.75			
	Q_2	65		63.000	+2.000	+0.062
			63.25			
	Q_3	60				
	Q_4	75				

Table for Question 12.2

Date		Sales (£0 000)	Cycle average	Trend	First residual	Second residual
1997	Q_1	337				
	Q_2	410				
			389.75			
	Q_3	438		387.750	50.250	−3.917
			385.75			
	Q_4	374		386.500	−12.500	−4.875
			387.25			
1998	Q_1	321		390.250	−69.250	0.583
			393.25			
	Q_2	416		398.250	17.750	−4.938
			403.25			
	Q_3	462		405.000	57.000	2.833
			406.75			
	Q_4	414		408.250	5.750	13.375
			409.75			
1999	Q_1	335		407.875	−72.875	−3.042
			406.00			
	Q_2	428		400.375	27.625	4.938
			394.75			
	Q_3	447		?	?	1.083
			?			
	Q_4	369		385.125	−16.125	−8.500
			381.50			
2000	Q_1	311		378.375	−67.375	2.458
			375.25			
	Q_2	399				
	Q_3	422				

12.3 The following figures represent the quarterly number of cars sold by a group of car distributors.

	Cars sold			
Year	Q_1	Q_2	Q_3	Q_4
·1997	727	767	779	811
1998	777	811	818	838
1999	816	853	847	872
2000	851	881		

(a) Plot the number of cars sold and the trend figures on a graph leaving room for the forecast for the next four quarters. Make use of the Minitab output overleaf.

Minitab output

Row	Cars	Trend	1st.resid	Seasonal	Fitted	2nd.resid
1	727	*	*	*	*	*
2	767	*	*	*	*	*
3	779	777.250	1.750	−0.1670	777.083	1.91669
4	811	789.000	22.000	15.5830	804.583	6.41669
5	777	799.375	−22.375	−20.6250	778.750	−1.75000
6	811	807.625	3.375	6.8130	814.437	−3.43750
7	818	815.875	2.125	−0.1670	815.708	2.29169
8	838	826.000	12.000	15.5830	841.583	−3.58331
9	816	834.875	−18.875	−20.6250	814.250	1.75000
10	853	842.750	10.250	6.8130	849.563	3.43750
11	847	851.375	−4.375	−0.1670	851.208	−4.20831
12	872	859.250	12.750	15.5830	874.833	−2.83331
13	851	*	*			
14	881	*	*			

Summary statistics

Variable	N	Mean	StDev
Turnover	14	817.7	43.5
1st.resi	10	1.86	13.97
2nd.resi	10	0.00	3.63

12.10 Supplementary exercise 12

12.4 · The following data describe the number of holiday bookings made through a travel firm over the past four years. You are asked to interpret the Minitab output below from the analysis of this data using an additive model.

		Holiday bookings		
Year	Q_1	Q_2	Q_3	Q_4
1997	5455	9645	13 297	6633
1998	5548	9748	13 838	7024
1999	5700	10 718	14 121	7321
2000	6103	10 581	14 483	7848

Minitab output for Question 12.4

Time		Bookings	Trend
1997	Q_1	5455	
	Q_2	9645	
	Q_3	13297	8769.13
	Q_4	6633	8793.63
1998	Q_1	5548	8874.13
	Q_2	9748	8990.63
	Q_3	13838	9058.50
	Q_4	7024	9198.75
1999	Q_1	5700	9355.38
	Q_2	10718	9427.88
	Q_3	14121	9515.38
	Q_4	7321	9548.63
2000	Q_1	6103	9576.75
	Q_2	10581	9687.88
	Q_3	14483	
	Q_4	7848	

(a) Plot the given data as a time series leaving room for the four forecasts for 2001.

(b) Demonstrate the calculation of the first trend figure.

(c) Plot the trend line on the same graph as your observed values.

(d) Calculate the first residuals and all four seasonal averages.

12.5   A long-established retail store had kept records of its quarterly sales for the previous seven years. You have been asked to provide a seasonal decomposition of this time series and have produced the analysis from SPSS. You now need to interpret this output.

	Quarterly sales (£000)			
Year	Q_1	Q_2	Q_3	Q_4
1994	81.2	92.4	91.3	99.7
1995	88.9	103.2	102.5	114.2
1996	97.8	112.3	112.5	125.8
1997	112.1	127.5	125.7	138.1
1998	117.3	136.8	138.3	145.4
1999	126.1	146.2	148.9	163.2
2000	143.2	161.0	160.9	177.4

SPSS output for question 12.5 (see Section 12.5.1 for explanation of column headings)

DATE	SALES	Moving averages	Ratios	Seasonal factors	Seasonally adjusted series	Smoothed trend-cycle	Irregular component
Q_1 1994	81.200	.	.	−11.203	92.403	90.629	1.773
Q_2 1994	92.400	.	.	2.662	89.738	91.137	−1.399
Q_3 1994	91.300	92.113	−.813	.031	91.269	92.019	−.750
Q_4 1994	99.700	94.425	5.275	8.510	91.190	94.066	−2.875
Q_1 1995	88.900	97.175	−8.275	−11.203	100.103	97.500	2.602
Q_2 1995	103.200	100.388	2.813	2.662	100.538	100.404	.134
Q_3 1995	102.500	103.313	−.813	.031	102.469	103.219	−.750
Q_4 1995	114.200	105.563	8.638	8.510	105.690	105.577	.113
Q_1 1996	97.800	107.950	−10.150	−11.203	109.003	108.067	.936
Q_2 1996	112.300	110.650	1.650	2.662	109.638	110.538	−.900
Q_3 1996	112.500	113.888	−1.388	.031	112.469	113.730	−1.261
Q_4 1996	125.800	117.575	8.225	8.510	117.290	117.543	−.253
Q_1 1997	112.100	121.125	−9.025	−11.203	123.303	121.367	1.936
Q_2 1997	127.500	124.312	3.188	2.662	124.838	124.371	.467
Q_3 1997	125.700	126.500	−.800	.031	125.669	126.408	−.738
Q_4 1997	138.100	128.313	9.787	8.510	129.590	128.454	1.136
Q_1 1998	117.300	131.050	−13.750	−11.203	128.503	130.767	−2.264
Q_2 1998	136.800	133.538	3.262	2.662	134.138	133.604	.534
Q_3 1998	138.300	135.550	2.750	.031	138.269	135.852	2.417
Q_4 1998	145.400	137.825	7.575	8.510	136.890	137.721	−.831
Q_1 1999	126.100	140.325	−14.225	−11.203	137.303	139.989	−2.687
Q_2 1999	146.200	143.875	2.325	2.662	143.538	143.838	−.300
Q_3 1999	148.900	148.238	.662	.031	148.869	148.308	.562
Q_4 1999	163.200	152.225	10.975	8.510	154.690	152.499	2.191
Q_1 2000	143.200	155.575	−12.375	−11.203	154.403	155.445	−1.042
Q_2 2000	161.000	158.850	2.150	2.662	158.338	158.793	−.455
Q_3 2000	160.900	.	.	.031	160.869	162.699	−1.830
Q_4 2000	177.400	.	.	8.510	168.890	166.833	2.057

(a) Plot the time series and its smoothed trend cycle on the same graph.

(b) Calculate the summary statistics for the irregular components and comment on the
suitability of the additive model given that the sales have a mean of 124.6 and standard deviation of 25.5 (£000).

12.6 The following data describes the sales of sun tan lotion made by a pharmaceutical company over the past four years. Make use the SPSS analysis, using a multiplicative model, which follows.

Year	Sales of sun tan lotion (£000)			
	Q_1	Q_2	Q_3	Q_4
1996	72.0	113.0	139.7	85.6
1997	70.2	118.8	150.0	92.0
1998	77.9	126.9	160.5	100.0
1999	85.3	141.0	174.2	103.3
2000	89.5	147.7		

(a) Plot the given data as a time series leaving room for the four forecasts for the next four quarters.

(b) Demonstrate the calculation of the first two ratios.

(c) Plot the smoothed trend cycle on the same graph as your observed values.

SPSS output for question 12.6 (see Section 12.5.1 for explanation of column headings)

Results of SEASON procedure for variable SALES.
Multiplicative Model. Centered MA method. Period = 4.

DATE	SALES	Moving averages	Ratios (* 100)	Seasonal factors (* 100)	Seasonally adjusted series	Smoothed trend– cycle	Irregular component
Q_1 1996	72.000	.	.	68.845	104.582	103.382	1.012
Q_2 1996	113.000	.	.	110.943	101.854	102.767	.991
Q_3 1996	139.700	102.350	136.492	137.142	101.866	102.438	.994
Q_4 1996	85.600	102.850	83.228	83.070	103.046	102.860	1.002
Q_1 1997	70.200	104.863	66.945	68.845	101.968	104.155	.979
Q_2 1997	118.800	106.950	111.080	110.943	107.082	106.414	1.006
Q_3 1997	150.000	108.713	137.979	137.142	109.376	108.768	1.006
Q_4 1997	92.000	110.688	83.117	83.070	110.750	110.975	.998
Q_1 1998	77.900	113.012	68.930	68.845	113.152	112.903	1.002
Q_2 1998	126.900	115.325	110.037	110.943	114.383	114.961	.995
Q_3 1998	160.500	117.250	136.887	137.142	117.032	117.520	.996
Q_4 1998	100.000	119.938	83.377	83.070	120.381	120.498	.999
Q_1 1999	85.300	123.413	69.118	68.845	123.901	123.411	1.004
Q_2 1999	141.000	125.538	112.317	110.943	127.092	125.317	1.014
Q_3 1999	174.200	126.475	137.735	137.142	127.022	126.429	1.005
Q_4 1999	103.300	127.837	80.806	83.070	124.353	127.481	.975
Q_1 2000	89.500	.	.	68.845	130.001	129.162	1.006
Q_2 2000	147.700	.	.	110.943	133.131	132.407	1.005

13 Forecasting

13.1 Objectives of this chapter

In the previous chapter we modelled different types of time series with the objective of producing the model that best fitted the observed data. This chapter continues the same theme with the preferred models selected in Chapter 12 being used to predict the values to be taken in the near future by these same models. As this is the last topic on the course it has deliberately been kept short to allow time for organising and starting revision (Chapter 15) before the final examination.

Having completed this chapter and already knowing how to select the best model, you should be capable of making reasonable predictions and also of assessing how good they are likely to be.

13.2 Introduction – The importance of forecasting

The role of forecasting is extremely important in the forward planning of any company. Unfortunately it is never an exact science as too many unknown quantities, over which the forecaster has no control, are inevitably involved. It is obvious that any company which knew exactly the demands on its future production would have a tremendous advantage over its competitors who might be over- or under-producing.

Forecasts covering the whole economic environment enable the company's corporate planners to make decisions regarding the future development of the company. Product and market forecasts will enable them to take advantage of potential growth areas. These predictions combined with good sales forecasts should give them the edge over competitors in producing appropriate quantities of goods. Financial forecasts should enable a company to manage its finances smoothly taking advantage of good times while avoiding problems in the leaner years.

13.3 Forecasts

The forecasts we make from identified models all make the same basic assumption that the conditions prevailing for the time periods over which the modelling data was collected will continue into the future. In other words, any trends or patterns identified in building up the model will still apply when the model is being used to make forecasts. This is common sense but should always be checked by plotting the modelling data. You may find that the pattern changed part way through data collection and only the later part of the data is suitable for projection into the future. If that is the case then only the later part should contribute to the forecasting process.

No forecast can claim to be exact, so it should always be quoted with a margin of error. The size of the errors will reflect how well the model fitted the past data from which it was constructed. Hopefully it was a good fit and will produce a precise forecast. Unfortunately this may not be the case and, at the other extreme, this month's figure may still be the best bet for next month's!

Be careful not to confuse precision with accuracy. Precision can be measured from past errors but only the future will measure accuracy by revealing whether your forecast was on target or not.

13.4 Forecasting from a non-seasonal time series model

Whether using regression or exponential smoothing the best model is identified by the estimation of its parameters. These are the coefficients for regression and the smoothing constants for exponential smoothing.

The two best models estimated in Chapter 12 will be used for each series and their forecasts, with expected precision, will be estimated. We can use the expected precision to compare the models but it is also useful to plot the estimated forecast along with the previous data to check that it seems reasonable. If the forecasts from both models are close it might seem reasonable to take their average as the reported forecast.

EXAMPLE 13.1

We analysed the following time series in Example 12.1:

39 41 36 39 38 38

36 33 34 35 33 28

The data described the quarterly sales (£000) of a particular item made by your company for 12 consecutive quarters. The plotted series looked like the graph in Figure 13.1.

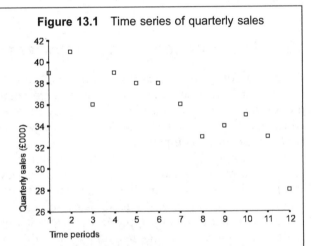

Figure 13.1 Time series of quarterly sales

These data were rather scattered and obviously not close to any recognisable model and so they are unlikely to provide a 'good' forecast. They were definitely not seasonal so regression and exponential smoothing models were fitted. The best of each type was found to be the cubic regression model with coefficients 40.67, −1.07, 0.141 and −0.011, and the growth model with smoothing constants $\alpha = 0.5$, $\beta = 0.0$ and initial conditions 40 and −1.0.

Regression model

The best model was identified as

$$y = 40.67 - 1.07x + 0.141x^2 - 0.011x^3 \tag{13.1}$$

where x is the time period which took the values of 1 to 12 in the time series model.

The next time period would be period 13 so substituting $x = 13$ we calculate the forecast to be:

$$\text{Sales} = 40.67 - 1.07 \times 13 + 0.141 \times 13^2 - 0.011 \times 13^3 = 26.4$$

So the forecast would be £26 400 if we think three significant figures are suitable.

continued

EXAMPLE 13.1 continued

Exponential smoothing model

The model which best fitted this data was found to be a growth model with initial value 40 and initial trend -1.0. The smoothing constants were $\alpha = 0.5$, $\beta = 0.0$. (SPSS used gamma (G) instead of beta (β) for the second smoothing constant.)

SPSS analysis produced the output in Figure 13.2 for the fitted values and errors.

Figure 13.2

	Quarterly sales	Fit for SALES from EXSMOOTH, MOD_1 HO A .50 G .00	Error for SALES from EXSMOOTH, MOD_1 HO A .50 G .00
1	39	39.00000	.00000
2	41	38.00000	3.00000
3	36	38.50000	−2.50000
4	39	36.25000	2.75000
5	38	36.62500	1.37500
6	38	36.31250	1.68750
7	36	36.15625	−.15625
8	33	35.07813	−2.07813
9	34	33.03906	.96094
10	35	32.51953	2.48047
11	33	32.75977	.24023
12	28	31.87988	−3.87988
Total N	12	12	12

Case summaries[a]

a Limited to first 100 cases.

Remember the growth model:

New forecast = previous forecast + $\alpha \times$ error in previous forecast
+ previous trend + $\beta \times$ error in previous forecast trend

New trend = previous trend + $\beta \times$ error in previous trend   (12.5)

Because the value of beta in this case is zero the model simplifies to:

New forecast = previous forecast + $0.5 \times$ error in previous forecast − 1.0   (13.2)

as the initial value for the trend will remain unchanged at -1.0 for the whole series.

It can be seen that for period 12 the forecast was 31.88 and its error -3.88.

The new forecast is therefore

$$31.88 + 0.5 \times (-3.88) + (-1) = 28.94$$

giving £28 900 (3 sf).

Summary

The regression model and exponential smoothing model have produced forecasts of £26 400 and £28 900 respectively from a poorly fitting model.

Looking back at Figure 13.1, the second forecast is probably the more likely but only time will tell which is actually nearer the true figure.

13.5 A further non-seasonal time series forecast

EXAMPLE 13.2

Four years of monthly sales were analysed in Example 12.2. The plotted series looked like Figure 13.3.

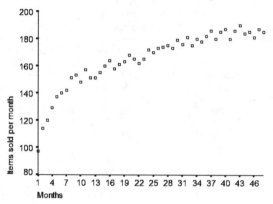

Figure 13.3 Time series of monthly sales

These data were less scattered than in Example 13.1 and follow a fairly smooth curve so they are likely to provide a 'better' forecast. They were definitely not seasonal so regression and exponential smoothing models were fitted. The best of each type was found to be the logarithmic regression model with coefficients 97.03 and 23.16 and the growth model with smoothing constants $\alpha = 0.4$, $\beta = 0.7$ with initial conditions 95 and 10.0 for the series and trend respectively.

Regression model

The best model was identified as

$$y = 97.03 + 23.16 \times \ln(t)$$ (13.3)

where t is the time period and $\ln(t)$ is its natural logarithm.

The model was constructed from periods 1 to 48 so the next time period would be period 49. Substituting 49 for t we calculate the forecast to be:

Sales $= 97.03 + 23.16 \times \ln(49) = 187.16$

So the forecast would be 187 items.

In Section 12.6 we saw that the standard deviation of the errors from the logarithmic model was 3.12, giving an interval of $2 \times 3.12 \pm 6.2$ on either side of this forecast.

Exponential smoothing model

The model which best fitted this data was found to be a growth model with initial value of 95 and initial trend of 10. The smoothing constants were $\alpha = 0.4$, $\beta = 0.7$.

SPSS analysis produced the output in Figure 13.4 for fitted values and errors, the last part of which is shown below. This output also includes the forecast for period 49.

continued

EXAMPLE 13.2 *continued*

Figure 13.4

Case summaries[a]

	Items sold per month	Fit for SALES from EXSMOOTH, MOD_6 HO A .40 G .70	Error for SALES from EXSMOOTH MOD_6 HO A .40 G .70
40	187	185.53669	1.46331
41	180	187.66264	−7.66264
42	186	183.99266	2.00734
43	190	184.75273	5.24727
44	184	188.27801	−4.27801
45	185	186.79533	−1.79533
46	181	185.80303	−4.80303
47	187	182.26280	4.73720
48	185	183.86508	1.13492
49		184.34423	
Total N	48	49	48

a Limited to first 100 cases.

The forecast by the best exponential smoothing model is 184 items

Summary

Both methods have come up with similar forecasts: 187 and 184. Looking back at Figure 13.3, or the latter part of Figure 13.4 there is no reason to discard either forecast so perhaps their arithmetic mean is as good a figure as any. Again only time will tell the value of the true figure.

13.6 Forecasting with a seasonal model

When analysing a seasonal model (Section 12.5) we identified a moving average trend and also a set of four seasonal factors. The trend was only defined in the past and, if the model was analysed by hand, it was missing for the first two and the last two periods. The seasonal factors were calculated from the past but can also be applied in the near future.

The first model used was the **additive model**:

$$\text{Fitted value} = \text{Trend value} + \text{Seasonal factor}$$
$$A = T + S \tag{12.7}$$

The future fitted values become the **forecasts** so the process of forecasting by this method is to extend the trend into the future and apply the seasonal factors to it to complete the model:

$$\text{Forecast value} = \text{Trend value} + \text{Seasonal factor}$$
$$F = T + S \tag{13.4}$$

The trend could be extended by eye using your own best judgement because it is a smooth line. An alternative is to produce an 'optimistic' line and a 'pessimistic' line and from them produce a range for the forecasts.

In Example 13.3 we shall use the decomposition of the time series as analysed in Example 12.3. We shall first make use of the hand calculated additive model, then the SPSS analysis of the additive model and finally the SPSS analysis of the multiplicative model.

EXAMPLE 13.3

Figure 13.5 reproduces Figure 12.10 with extra space for forecasts.

Figure 13.5 Quarterly sales and trend

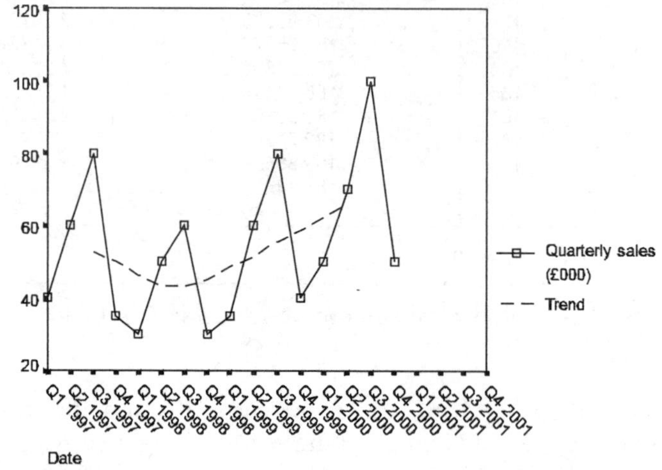

You should have a hand drawn graph from Example 12.3 which is a larger version of Figure 13.5. Extend the trend line by hand to cover the four quarters of 2001, read off and record the value at each of the quarters. One suggestion is shown below but your judgement is just as good as anyone else's and you may have chosen a different route. Stick with yours, then read off and record your trend values for the four quarters of 2001 from your large scale graph.

Figure 13.6 Trend extended into the near future

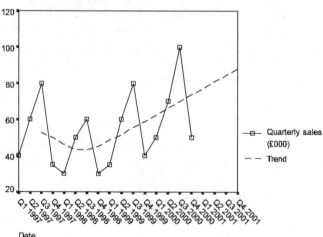

Suggested values are: Q_1 77.2; Q_2 80.8; Q_3 84.4; Q_4 88.0

continued

EXAMPLE 13.3 *continued*

Additive model

Forecast value $=$ Trend value $+$ Seasonal factor

$$F \quad = \quad T \quad + \quad S \tag{13.4}$$

Table 13.1

		Trend	+	Seasonal factor	=	Forecast	
2001	Q_1	77.2	+	-14.17	=	63.03	£63 000
	Q_2	80.8	+	$+6.04$	=	86.84	£86 800
	Q_3	84.4	+	$+22.91$	=	107.31	£107 300
	Q_4	88.0	+	-16.25	=	71.75	£71 800

Remember your forecasts are just as good as these since you have calculated them from your chosen trend line extension.

Alternatively, the trend may be modelled using the SPSS output from the additive model and finding the best fitting curve for the trend. Using non-linear regression produced reasonable fits with a quadratic or cubic model.

```
Independent:  Time
Dependent  Mth   Rsq  d.f.      F  Sigf       b0       b1      b2       b3
STC_1      QUA  .933   13   89.95  .000 59.5863  -4.0527  .3158
STC_1      CUB  .951   12   77.95  .000 64.2215  -6.9021  .7224  -.0159
```

Looking at the graph in Figure 13.7 to see which fitted best towards the end of the past data suggested that the cubic model should be used:

Figure 13.7 Trend with quadratic and cubic models

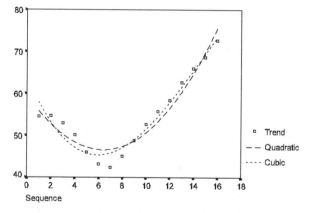

Using the cubic model to find the next four trend values:

$$\text{Trend} = 64.2 - 6.90t + 0.722t^2 - 0.016t^3$$

Q_1 $(t = 17)$ Trend $= 64.2 - 6.90 \times 17 + 0.722 \times 17^2 - 0.016 \times 17^3 = 76.95$

$Q2$ $(t = 18)$ Trend $= 64.2 - 6.90 \times 18 + 0.722 \times 18^2 - 0.016 \times 18^3 = 80.62$

Q_3 $(t = 19)$ Trend $= 64.2 - 6.90 \times 19 + 0.722 \times 19^2 - 0.016 \times 19^3 = 84.00$

Q_4 $(t = 20)$ Trend $= 64.2 - 6.90 \times 20 + 0.722 \times 20^2 - 0.016 \times 20^3 = 87.00$

continued

EXAMPLE 13.3 *continued*

Using these trend figures with the seasonal figures for the SPSS output produces Table 13.2.

Table 13.2

		Trend	+	Seasonal factor	=	Forecast	
2001	Q_1	76.95	+	−13.80	=	63.15	£63 200
	Q_2	80.62	+	+6.41	=	87.03	£87 000
	Q_3	84.00	+	+23.28	=	107.28	£107 300
	Q_4	87.00	+	−15.89	=	71.11	£71 100

These two methods of trend extrapolation have been fairly consistent with their forecasts. We shall next try the multiplicative model.

Multiplicative model

Alternatively the trend may be modelled by using the SPSS output from the multiplicative model and finding the best fitting curve for the trend. Non-linear regression produced reasonable fits with a quadratic or cubic model.

Dependent	Mth	Rsq	d.f.	F	Sigf	b0	b1	b2	b3
STC_2	QUA	.931	13	87.08	.000	58.9065	−3.8648	.3052	
STC_2	CUB	.960	12	95.67	.000	64.6602	−7.4018	.8099	−.0198

Looking at the graph in Figure 13.8 to see which fitted best towards the end of the past data suggested the cubic model might be low but the quadratic is definitely too high.

Figure 13.8 Trend with quadratic and cubic models

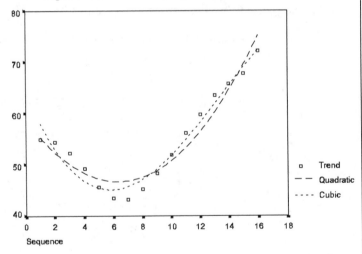

Using the cubic model with the higher Rsq value to find the next four trend values:

$$\text{Trend} = 64.7 - 7.40t + 0.810t^2 - 0.020t^3$$

Q_1 $(t = 17)$ Trend $= 64.7 - 7.40 \times 17 + 0.810 \times 17^2 - 0.020 \times 17^3 = 74.73$

Q_2 $(t = 18)$ Trend $= 64.7 - 7.40 \times 18 + 0.810 \times 18^2 - 0.020 \times 18^3 = 77.30$

Q_3 $(t = 19)$ Trend $= 64.7 - 7.40 \times 19 + 0.810 \times 19^2 - 0.020 \times 19^3 = 79.33$

Q_4 $(t = 20)$ Trend $= 64.7 - 7.40 \times 20 + 0.810 \times 20^2 - 0.020 \times 20^3 = 80.70$

continued

EXAMPLE 13.3 *continued*

Using these trend figures with the seasonal figures for the SPSS output (p. 233) produces Table 13.3.

Table 13.3

		Trend	×	Seasonal factor	=	Forecast	
2001	Q_1	74.73	×	0.7216	=	53.93	£53 900
	Q_2	77.30	×	1.1486	=	88.79	£88 800
	Q_3	79.33	×	1.4455	=	114.67	£114 700
	Q_4	80.70	×	0.6843	=	55.22	£55 200

The forecasts from this model seem different from the others but we have no reason to believe that they are any worse.

Summary

Tabulating the results from Table 13.1 to 13.3 gives Table 13.4.

Table 13.4

	Hand drawn additive	*Additive (SPSS)*	*Multiplicative (SPSS)*
Q_1	£63 000	£63 200	£53 900
Q_2	£86 800	£87 000	£88 800
Q_3	£107 300	£107 300	£114 700
Q_4	£71 800	£71 100	£55 200

It certainly looks as though the multiplicative model is out of line with the other two.

13.7 How good is a forecast?

A good forecast needs to be both precise and accurate. We judge the precision of a forecast by considering the errors (residuals) that would have been produced had that model been used to 'back forecast' in the past when we knew the true values for comparison. Assuming that the prevailing conditions continue into the near future, we check that the residuals are normally distributed and then quote a 95% confidence interval for the forecast. Its maximum likely error is 1.96 standard deviations on either side of the forecast. This is a rule of thumb which is useful for making comparisons.

We cannot judge accuracy until the future event actually happens so we can compare its true value with that which has been predicted for it. We can however check that forecast values are not unlikely to happen. We can check that past patterns are still evident in future values and that past trends have been carried through into the future.

We have forecasts for Examples 13.1 to 13.3. We shall now look to see how 'good' they are.

EXAMPLE 13.4 *Evaluation of forecasts*

Example 13.1

Our forecasts for period 13 are £26 400 for the regression model and £28 900 for the exponential smoothing model. The higher one seems more likely but we have no reason to reject either.

We now look at the maximum likely error of the two forecasts.

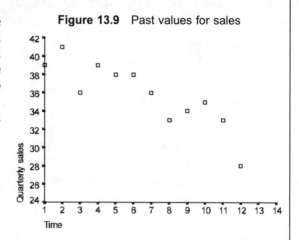

Figure 13.9 Past values for sales

Regression model

In Section 12.6 (Figure 12.14) the standard deviation of the residuals from this model was found to be 1.57 giving intervals of £3100 either side of the forecast. Our forecast therefore becomes from £23 300 to £29 500 – not very precise!

Exponential smoothing model

The errors (Section 12.6, Figure 12.14) had a standard deviation of 2.19 giving an interval of ±4.4 and a forecast estimation of from £24 500 to £33 300 – even worse!

A precise forecast was never expected from this irregular data.

Example 13.2

Our forecasts for period 49 are 187 for the regression model and 184 for the exponential smoothing model. Both seem equally likely from the diagram.

We now look at the precision of the two models.

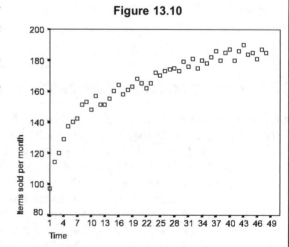

Figure 13.10

Regression model

In Section 12.6, Figure 12.14, we saw that the standard deviation of the errors from the logarithmic model was 3.12, giving a maximum likely error of ± 6.2 on either side of this forecast, or 3% which is obviously an improvement on the last model.

Our forecast is therefore between 181 and 193 items.

continued

EXAMPLE 13.4 *continued*

Exponential smoothing model

These errors (Section 12.6, Figure 12.18) had a standard deviation of 4.39 giving a maximum likely error of ± 8.8 and a forecast estimation of between 175 and 193 items.

Example 13.3

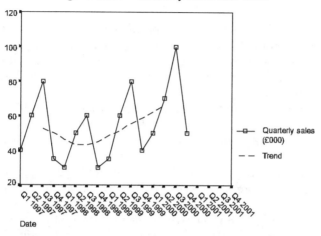

Figure 13.11 Quarterly sales and trend

The forecasts from the three models for this time series were summarised in Table 13.4 which is repeated here.

Table 13.4

	Hand drawn additive	Additive (SPSS)	Multiplicative (SPSS)
Q_1	£63 000	£63 200	£53 900
Q_2	£86 800	£87 000	£88 800
Q_3	£107 300	£107 300	£114 700
Q_4	£71 800	£71 100	£55 200

Plot these figures on your graph paper and see which set you think is most likely to produce the better forecast.

Moving average model

The summary statistics for the residuals from the three models are given in Table 13.5.

Table 13.5

Model	Mean	Standard deviation
Hand drawn additive	0.0167	2.77
Additive from SPSS	−0.265	3.45
Multiplicative from SPSS	−0.161	2.56

Forecasts from the multiplicative model will be the most precise, but time alone will tell if they are the most accurate.

Note that there is no correct answer when looking for a forecast – all we can do is produce the most likely figure given the prevailing conditions. We can never allow for unexpected changes in circumstances, such as a particularly cold and wet August which could play havoc with ice-cream sales.

13.8 Further methods of forecasting

Basically any time series can be used for producing forecasts, so any of the models described briefly in Section 12.7 can be applied when appropriate.

Alternatively autoregression models are particularly useful if it is felt that there is some time lapse before a series responds to changing conditions because they also depend on older values of the time series.

There are many forecasting models generated by Box-Jenkins techniques. These may be autoregressive models, moving average models or a combination of the two. They are effective in producing small errors but are often complicated and generally not easy to understand.

If future estimations can be found for the independent variables, multiple regression will often produce good forecasts as the influences of many factors are taken into consideration. Because these forecasts do not depend on just one variable they may be more robust to small changes and they will be better for slightly longer-term forecasting than the models used in this chapter which are essentially suitable for short-term forecasting only.

Multiple regression can also cope with seasonality if a 'dummy' variable, is assigned to each of the four seasons. The value of the dummy variable is 1 for that particular season and 0 for the other three. This may seem involved but it works well in practice.

13.9 Summary

This chapter has been a continuation of Chapter 12. We have made use of the time series identified in Chapter 12 to make forecasts for the near future.

We have used three types of model: regression with time as the independent variable, exponential smoothing models, and seasonal decomposition in which the model included a seasonal factor as well as a trend.

In every case the best fitting model was continued into the near future. The future values it produced were taken as the required forecasts. These forecasts were each quoted with a margin of error which reflected the quality of fit of the model to the data in the past on the assumption that the modelling conditions would continue unchanged into the near future.

None of these models are suitable for long-term forecasting because any change from the conditions under which the model was built up would require the use of a completely new model.

At the end of the day forecasting is still considered to be an art rather than a science and a 'gut feeling' by an experienced operative may be as justified as any statistical analysis!

13.10 Tutorial 13 – Forecasting

Note: Make use of the graphs you drew for Tutorial 12 in these questions. Question 13.1 corresponds to Question 12.1, 13.2 to 12.2, and so on.

13.1 (f) Extend the trend line and use it to forecast the sales of the departmental store for each of the quarters of 2001, describing clearly the model used. State your forecasts and add them to your graph to check that they look reasonable.

    (g) Calculate the standard deviation of the second residuals and estimate the maximum likely error in your forecasts

13.2 (c) Using an additive model forecast the turnovers for

       2000 Quarter 4,   2001 Quarter 1,   2001 Quarter 2,   2001 Quarter 3

       Add them to your graph and check the continuity of the seasonal pattern.

    (d) What is the maximum error likely in your forecasts?

    (e) Obtain deseasonalised data for

       1999 Quarter 4,   2000 Quarter 1,   2000 Quarter 2,   2000 Quarter 3

    (f) Is the model used appropriate for forecasting with this data? Explain your answer.

13.3 (b) Using an additive model forecast the turnovers for:

       2000 Quarter 3,   2000 Quarter 4,   2001 Quarter 1,   2001 Quarter 2

       Add them to your graph.

    (c) What is the maximum error likely in your forecasts?

    (d) Obtain deseasonalised data for

       1999 Quarter 3,   1999 Quarter 4,   2000 Quarter 1,   2000 Quarter 2

    (e) Assess the suitability of your model for forecasting with this data

13.11 Supplementary Exercise 13

Note: Make use of the graphs you drew for Supplementary Exercise 12 in these questions. Question 13.4 corresponds to Question 12.4, 13.5 to 12.5, and so on.

13.4 (e) Extend your trend line and produce forecasts for the four quarters of 2001, add them to your graph and check that they look reasonable.

    (f) Calculate the fitted values and the second residuals.

    (g) Calculate the standard deviation of the second residuals and estimate the maximum error expected in your forecasts.

13.5 (c) Extend your smoothed trend cycle and use it to calculate the forecasts for the four quarters of 2001 and add them to your graph.

    (d) What is the maximum likely error in these forecasts?

    (e) From the computer output for Question 12.5 identify the deseasonalised values for the four quarters of 2000.

13.6 (e) Extend your trend line and produce forecasts for the next four quarters, remembering that the output is from a multiplicative model, and add them to your graph.

14 Introduction to Operational Research

14.1 The concept

The *Oxford Dictionary* describes operational research (OR) as: 'The scientific study of business and other operations, providing a quantitative basis for management decisions'. The Operational Research Society prefers the definition: ' The application of methods of science to complex problems arising in the direction and management of large systems of men, machines, materials and money'. Both definitions point out that OR is a scientific approach designed to take the guesswork out of dealing with the problems which face the management of large operations. It is concerned with planning operations and the allocation of scarce and limited resources such as personnel, time and money.

OR is really too large a topic to be treated as one chapter of a first-year course. For a fuller description and discussion of any topics in this introduction, visit Oakshott, Littlechild and Shutler or Daellenbach.

OR developed as an interdisciplinary science during the Second World War. Its history makes fascinating reading as described in the first chapter of Littlechild and Shutler, *Operations Research in Management*.

OR attempts to deal with problems which actually arise in the operation of systems making use of interdisciplinary teams and adopting a scientific approach. Practical experimentation with any real system may be very expensive or may not even be possible so an abstract model is built to describe the system quantitatively. This model provides the basis for any experimentation – generally using a dedicated computer package.

Models will include variables which may or may not be under the control of the system management. Uncertainty about uncontrolled factors is modelled by a probability distribution identified on the basis of some previous knowledge about the system.

In practical terms, the researcher is concerned with studying the system in order to put forward implementable policies leading to better performance by a particular system. Often the 'best' policy may not be acceptable as it contravenes a given time limit or budget so real constraints concerning time, money and manpower need to be built into any realistic model.

Most problems are complex and are better analysed by specially designed computer packages, such as Microsoft Project, Xpress MP, Witness or DATA, or spreadsheets, such as Excel or Lotus with Goalseek or Solver. A limited number of straightforward problems which can be tackled by the simpler operational research methods will be illustrated in this chapter. The examples are not intended as learning material.

We shall look at stochastic techniques, which use probability to handle uncertainty in the model, and deterministic techniques which do not.

We have already covered forecasting in Chapters 12 and 13 and will now consider:

- Decision analysis – maximisation of investment based on expected profits
- Replacement of wearing or failing items – the timing of replacements
- Stock control – the optimum quantity and frequency of buying stock

- Queuing – maximising service to customers at minimum cost using simulation
- Linear programming – optimising costs and profits within practical constraints
- Allocation problems – optimising distribution of goods within given constraints
- Project management – optimising resources in planning complex projects.

14.2 Decision analysis

In Chapter 4 you were introduced to probability trees (Section 4.7). This method of combining probabilities is particularly useful when some of the probabilities are conditional. If costs and/or profits are combined with conditional probabilities then choices can be quantified and decisions optimised. All the available information is modelled by a decision tree.

EXAMPLE 14.1

The marketing manager at Merlin plc is considering the launch of a new product. He can either carry out market research in order to estimate its saleability (which has a 0.7 probability of being favourable), put it on the market immediately or, as suggested by the accountant, abandon the idea completely. If he makes either of the first two decisions the sales may be either high, medium or low with the associated estimated probabilities given in Table 14.1.

Table 14.1 Probabilities estimated for sales levels

Level of sales	If market research is carried out Favourable	If market research is carried out Unfavourable	If no market research Immediate launch
High	0.5	0.1	0.2
Medium	0.4	0.3	0.6
Low	0.1	0.6	0.2

The company estimates that high sales will gross £2 million, medium sales will gross £1 million and low sales will gross £300 000. Estimated costs for market research, purchase, installation and running of the full scale plant are estimated to be £575 000. If the project is abandoned at any stage the pilot plant will be sold at an expected price of £150 000, otherwise it will be retained.

(1) We shall first model the data by building up a probability tree which includes all the information regarding the decisions or outcomes with any costs (negative), revenues (positive) and their associated probabilities.
(2) We then work backwards through the model from right to left bringing together information from the appropriate branches: the expected returns associated with each decision and represented by ☐ and the associated probabilities by ◯.
(3) These data are then evaluated quantitatively by the management and provide the basis for their decision.

In this instance the aim is to maximise potential profit so the highest expected return is selected. An alternative scenario might be to minimise costs. Any selection must be made within the context of the question.

This method gives a quantitative guide, but of course it is not the whole story. For example, the management might wish to provide full employment for their workers, irrespective of profit. The results of any analysis by the researcher are passed up the line to provide the basis for a management decision.

Figure 14.1

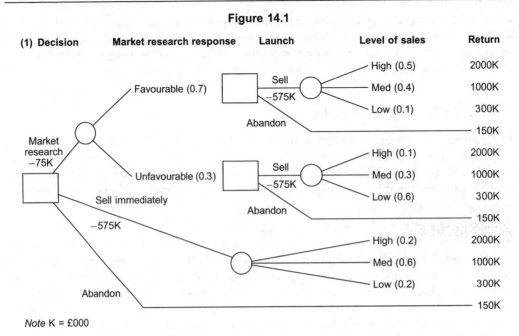

Note K = £000

Figure 14.1 contains all the given information in the form of a decision (probability) tree as in Section 4.7. Probabilities branch away from the circles and decisions are identified by rectangles. The first decision needed is to carry out market research at a cost of 75K, launch the product immediately at a cost of 575K or abandon the whole project. Whether the market research is found to be favourable or not the decision can be taken at that time to sell the product or to abandon the project. The probability of selling successfully is dependent on previous events but the return expected depends only upon the level of the sales (high, medium or low). At any stage abandoning the project gives a return of 150K. Make sure you understand the source of all the figures before moving on to the next diagram.

Figure 14.2

(2) Decision	Market research response	Launch	Level of sales	Return

Market research −75K

568.5 / 485.0 / 150.0

643.5K

Favourable (0.7)
855K / 150K
1430K Sell −575K
Abandon
High (0.5) 2000K
Med (0.4) 1000K
Low (0.1) 300K
150K

Unfavourable (0.3)
105K / 150K
680K Sell −575K
Abandon
High (0.1) 2000K
Med (0.3) 1000K
Low (0.6) 300K
150K

Sell −575K
1060K
High (0.2) 2000K
Med (0.6) 1000K
Low (0.2) 300K
150K

Abandon

Figure 14.2 builds up from right to left, combining each return with the probability of getting it to produce the expected return for a particular branch. At each probability circle the branches are combined to give the expected value at that point. The figure of 1430K above the top probability circle was calculated from:

$$2000 \times 0.5 + 1000 \times 0.4 + 300 \times 0.1 = 1430K$$

Working from right to left, we subtract the costs of 575K to give the return for deciding to sell after a high response from the market research. This return is 855K, which is clearly preferable to the 150K available for abandoning the project. Check that the return in the decision box for deciding to sell in spite of a low response from market research (the box in the middle of Figure 14.2) is 105K. A return of 105K is not preferable to 150K.

The higher returns expected from favourable and non-favourable research responses are multiplied by their probabilities and combined to give the returns from the decision to go for market research:

$$855 \times 0.7 + 150 \times 0.3 = 643.5K$$

Market research cost 75K so the final return from this decision is 568.5K.

If the product is to be sold immediately the expected return would be 1060K less the cost of manufacturing (575K), which would give 485K as the expected return. If the project were abandoned without research the return would be 150K.

We now have comparative figures on which to base any decisions. The best economic decisions at each stage are:

- first, to carry out market research and then base the second decision on its outcome
- second, if the result is favourable then sell the product at that stage, but if it is unfavourable then the whole project should be abandoned. Having identified the best economic decision the researcher's task is complete, the actual decision is up to the management.

This type of problem can be tackled numerically without the aid of a decision tree but a decision tree is recommended because it is easier to trace all the options on a diagrammatic model. A larger problem should be tackled using specially designed computer software such as DATA (data analysis by tree age).

14.3 Replacement of wearing or failing items

No machinery or equipment lasts for ever so the problem in this section is the identification of the best time to replace it. Should your new car be changed when it is two years old and costs comparably little to exchange for another new one or do you run it for many years and then change it when its replacement value will be much lower? Here we compare the option to make many small exchange payments as opposed to a few much larger ones.

Sometimes we do not have this option because equipment, such as headlight bulbs, does not wear but fails completely. If we have a rough idea how long bulbs are expected to last, should we change them at a regular service time before they fail or wait until they do fail and waste time and money on a separate trip to the garage?

Wear and failure are two different types of problem needing different models for their solution. We shall consider the model for items which gradually wear out first.

14.3.1 *The replacement of items which wear out*

EXAMPLE 14.2

Wearing is a gradual process. An item should be replaced when total costs are minimised. As any car ages annual depreciation decreases but annual maintenance costs increase. If a small car is to be changed on purely economic grounds based on these measures, when should this be? In this example we shall assume that the old car is to be replaced by an identical model which will have the same new and resale price at the different ages. The price of the car when new is £11200 and its resale value at different ages is:

(1)

Year (end)	1	2	3	4	5	6
Selling price (£)	8000	5600	3800	2300	1200	500

The corresponding maintenance costs are expected, from past experience, to be:

(2)

Year (end)	1	2	3	4	5	6
Maintenance (£)	600	700	900	1200	2000	3000

Depreciation and the cumulative maintenance costs are calculated from tables (1) and (2), then total and average annual costs are found. The minimum average annual cost can then be read from table (3).

(3)

Age at replacement	Depreciation (£) from (1)	Cumulative maintenance costs (£)	Cumulative total cost (£)	Average annual cost (£)
1	3200	600	3800	3800
2	5600	1300	6900	3450
3	7400	2200	9600	3200
4	8900	3400	12300	*3075*
5	10000	5400	15400	3080
6	10700	8400	19100	3183

On this basis the car should be changed at the end of its fourth year and will have cost £3075 pa.

It might be cheaper to replace the old car with a second-hand version of the same car, even though it would cost more to maintain. If so, when should this purchase take place and at what age should the car be bought?

The same model can be extended to take this situation into consideration.

We build up the same tables as last time but we also have to include the ages of the cars in the model. (The new price in year 0 is included for comparative purposes.)

We already know the selling price of used cars:

(1)

Year (end)	0	1	2	3	4	5	6
Selling price (£)	(11200)	8000	5600	3800	2300	1200	500

The cost of buying second hand cars is:

(4)

Year (end)	0	1	2	3	4	5	6
Purchase price (£)	(11 200)	8900	6200	4200	2600	1400	700

We need the depreciation ((buying price − selling price) from tables (1) and (4))

(5)

		Age at sale (years)					
		1	2	3	4	5	6
Age at	0	3 200	5 600	7 400	8 900	10 000	10 700
purchase	1		3 300	5 100	6 600	7 700	8 400
(years)	2			2 400	3 900	5 000	5 700
	3				1 900	3 000	3 700
	4					1 400	2 100
	5						900

The annual expected maintenance costs are:

(2)

Year (end)	1	2	3	4	5	6
Maintenance (£)	600	700	900	1200	2000	3000

Total expected maintenance costs (£) (from table (2)) accumulate as follows:

(6)

		Age at sale (years)					
		1	2	3	4	5	6
Age at	0	600	1300	2200	3400	5400	8400
purchase	1		700	1600	2800	4800	7800
(years)	2			900	2100	4100	7100
	3				1200	3200	6200
	4					2000	5000
	5						3000

The next stage is to find the total costs for each combination and then the average costs per year.
Total costs (£) (Depreciation + expected maintenance costs):

(7)

		Age at sale (years)					
		1	2	3	4	5	6
Age at	0	3800	6 900	9 600	12 300	15 400	19 100
purchase	1		4 000	6 700	9 400	12 500	16 200
(years)	2			3 300	6 000	9 100	12 800
	3				3 100	6 200	9 900
	4					3 400	7 100
	5						3 900

To find the average cost per year the figures above need to be divided, as before, by the number of years since the car was bought (age at sale – age at purchase):

(8)

		Age at sale (years)					
		1	2	3	4	5	6
Age at	0	3800	3450	3200	3075	3080	3183
purchase	1		4000	3350	3133	3125	3240
(years)	2			3300	*3000*	3033	3200
	3				3100	3100	3300
	4					3400	3550
	5						3900

The best option now seems to be to buy a two-year-old car, keep it for two years and sell it when it is four years old. We have made this decision purely on economic grounds. Who can put a price on seeing a brand new car sitting on your driveway? That may well be worth the extra £75 a year to some drivers.

Note that probability played no part in this model as all the information required could be determined from motoring magazines. It was, in general, a deterministic model even though it included expected maintenance costs.

14.3.2 *The replacement of items which fail completely*

In modelling items which fail completely probability will play a part as the time of failing is always uncertain. These are referred to as stochastic models.

We are all familiar with items in the home such as light bulbs or fuses which fail suddenly with no warning. In a college or place of work where hundreds of strip lights may be in constant use, should these be replaced in large batches as part of regular building maintenance or should each be replaced separately when it has actually failed? The first method enables items to be bought and replaced more cheaply but wastes some of their useful life; the second will make use of their full life but they will cost more to buy and their replacement will have a higher cost to the maintenance department.

Assume that each strip light will fail suddenly after a variable period of full efficiency. Individual failures are unpredictable but the distribution of the failures over a period of time will often be stable. The past history of failures enables us to predict the expected life of the lights and, hence, the optimum time for their replacement. This information in conjunction with any relevant costs will enable the identification of the best replacement policy.

EXAMPLE 14.3

The present light replacement policy in Merlin plc is to replace strip lights as and when they fail. The maintenance department buys the lights in batches of 10 at a cost of £12 each and always has an adequate number in stock for this ad hoc replacement. It is estimated that it takes two electricians, earning £12 an hour each, 20 minutes to replace a strip after it has failed, that is, £8 per light.

A new replacement policy is proposed whereby the lights would be bought in batches of 500, costing £6 each, and would be replaced at the time of annual maintenance. It has been estimated that the average replacement time would then be only 10 minutes for the same electricians. Some individual lights would obviously still need to be replaced during the course of the year if they failed. Merlin use 1000 strip lights which are burning constantly.

Records kept for the previous five years show that for a batch of 500 lights purchased, 25 were changed during the first year, 125 during the second, 200 during the third, and the remaining 150 during the fourth year after purchase.

Using these figures we can draw up the probability distribution for the failing strip lights and calculate their average life expectancy assuming average time of failure to be mid year.

Age (x) (years)	Number failing	Probability (p)	px
0.5	25	0.05	0.025
1.5	125	0.25	0.375
2.5	200	0.40	1.000
3.5	150	0.30	1.050
Total	500	1.00	2.450

The expected value for the life of the lights is 2.45 years.

Expected cost of individual replacement policy

With a life expectancy of 2.45 years and a replacement cost of £20 (purchase at £12 and an electrician's time at £8.00), we can calculate the annual replacement cost:

Average number of lights expected to be replaced each year = $1000/2.45 \cong 408$

Expected cost of replacement = $408 \times £20.00 = £8160$

Expected cost of group replacement policy

We shall first calculate the number of individual lights which fail and need to be replaced each year from the 1000 in use. This is not straightforward because, after some have been replaced, there are lights of varying ages in use. From the probabilities above:

Year after replacement	1	2	3	4
Proportion which fail	5%	25%	40%	30%

The numbers of individuals failing can be calculated using a failure tree but if the probability data is for many years the diagram becomes rather cumbersome. We shall calculate and then tabulate the expected average failures for each year from a batch of 1000 new lights and then calculate the cost of replacing them.

The table of failures is:

Year	1	2	3	4
1000 new lights	50	250	400	300
Replace 50 after year 1				
Failures expected from this 50		2.5	12.5	20
Total expected failures	50	252.5	412.5	320
Replace 253 after 2 years				
Failures expected from this 253			12.7	63.3
Total expected failures	50	252.5	425.2	383.3
Replace 425 after 3 years				
Failures expected from this 425				21.3
Total expected failures	50	252.5	425.2	404.6
Cumulative expected failures	50	302.5	727.7	1132.3

Note: These are average values so part lights are kept in the calculations.

1 At £20 for each individual replacement we first calculate the expected cumulative costs.
2 The cost of changing all the lights at maintenance time would be 1000 × £6.00 (for each light and £4.00 for the electrician's time) totalling £10 000. How often should they be changed?
3 If we decide to change them all at maintenance time we can first add this cost on and then
4 Find the average cost per year to identify the optimum changing frequency.

No. of years between regular replacements	1	2	3	4
1 Cumulative expected costs (£)	1 000	6 050	14 554	22 646
2 Cost of changing 1000 (£)	10 000	10 000	10 000	10 000
3 Total expected cumulative cost	11 000	16 050	24 554	32 646
4 Expected average cost per year	11 000	8 025	8 185	8 162

How does the best of these figures compare with the old system? The individual replacement policy was expected to cost an average of £8160 pa so group replacement can be more economical.

The optimum policy is therefore to replace all the lights during routine maintenance every two years, with any failures being replaced in between.

This has been a fairly simplistic demonstration of replacement strategies. The same principle can be applied to more complex situations.

14.4 Stock control

Stock control is a balancing act: holding too much stock ties up money which could otherwise be earning interest and holding too little stock risks having to disappoint potential customers if, for example, car manufacture has to cease for lack of parts. We need a stock control policy which minimises the total costs of procuring stock and looking after it, and also provides a reasonable service to customers. We need to know how much stock to order and how often to order it.

The advantages and disadvantages of holding large stocks are:

Advantages
- Bulk discounts from suppliers for purchasing large quantities
- Less frequent order and delivery costs which are often 'per order'.

Disadvantages
- Capital, which could be earning interest, is tied up in the stock
- Useful space is taken up by storage
- Higher insurance cost which is usually proportional to average stock value
- Higher labour cost for looking after the stock
- Stock may become obsolete if kept too long.

We need a compromise which will minimise the **total** costs.

We first need to estimate order and delivery costs and stock holding costs before we can formulate a stock holding policy. Larger orders mean lower ordering costs but higher holding costs. Smaller orders mean higher ordering costs but lower holding costs. In order to demonstrate the method the real-life situation will be simplified by making certain assumptions:

- The demand for stock is steady
- All deliveries shall be the same size
- Delivery will be immediate, that is, there is no lag between order and delivery time
- Stock is not allowed to run out, that is, no stockouts.

Economic order (or batch) quantity

Total stock holding cost is a combination of capital cost, warehousing, handling costs, insurance, and so on and is dependent on the value of stock held. The average stock held is the mean of the highest stock level (order quantity) and zero (stock level when an order is placed) since demand is assumed to be steady. The average stock holding costs are proportional to the average stock value.

We shall make further use of the data on the strip lights used by Merlin plc in Example 14.3 and produce a stock holding policy which will minimise their total costs.

EXAMPLE 14.4

From Example 14.3 we know that the strip lights used by Merlin plc have an average lifetime of 2.45 years and that 1000 of them are in continuous use. We also know that they cost £12 each unless bought in very large quantities (500).

Ordering and delivery costs are £20 per order irrespective of its size. Stock holding costs per annum are 10% of the average value of the strip lights held in stock.

On the basis of this information, how frequently should orders be placed and how large should they be?

With an average lifetime of 2.45 years the annual turnover of lights is $1000/2.45 = 408$. We shall use 400 pa to ease the arithmetic!

Order and delivery costs are £20 × number of orders per year.

Stockholding costs are 10% of £12 = £1.2 per light = £1.2 × average stock level pa

We shall first tabulate and graph the results to find the best policy and then calculate it mathematically.

No of orders pa	Order size (q)	Annual ordering cost (£)	Average stock	Annual stock holding costs (£)	Total annual costs (£)
10	40	200	20	24	224
8	50	160	25	30	190
5	80	100	40	48	148
4	100	80	50	60	140
3	130	60	67	80	140
2	200	40	100	120	160
1	400	20	200	240	260

We can see that the ordering costs decrease as the order size increases but the stock holding costs increase. We need the order size which minimises the total costs. This order size, obviously in the region of 100–130, can be found by graphing the separate and total costs or mathematically.

The graph for total costs is reasonably level in the region of the minimum so a convenient scheduling of orders can be set with the order number somewhere in the region of the minimum. Merlin's best policy is to place an order for, say, 100 strip lights 4 times a year, that is, every three months.

Figure 14.3 Annual costs versus order size

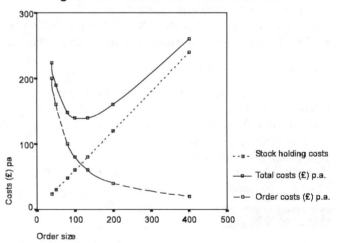

It can be shown that total costs are at a minimum when ordering costs equal holding costs, so we can check this figure mathematically. Let the size of order placed be q, then:

$$\text{order costs} = \frac{400}{q} \times £20$$

and stock holding costs $= \frac{q}{2} \times £12 \times 10\%$

Equating costs:

$$\frac{8000}{q} = \frac{1.2q}{2} \Rightarrow q^2 = \frac{8000 \times 2}{1.2} = 13333 \Rightarrow q = \sqrt{13333} = 115.5$$

This is not a convenient quantity because 116 would need to be ordered every 400/116 = 3.4 months! But, as we saw from Figure 14.3, the total costs do not differ much between 100 and 116. For four batches of 100, the total annual costs, including the purchase price of 400 strip lights would be:

cost of ordering and holding stock + purchase price of strip lights

=   £140 (from table)   +   400 × £12   = £4940

The stock profile is, therefore, as in Figure 14.4.

Figure 14.4 Stock levels for this policy

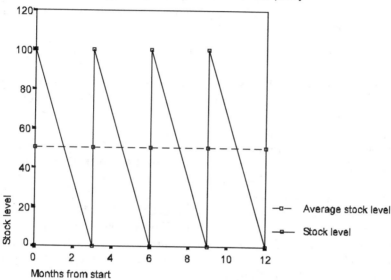

To become more realistic, the model we have used can be modified to take into consideration any deviation from the rather false assumptions we made in drawing it up. If delivery is not immediate or demand is not steady the stock should not be run down to zero but reordered at some calculated order level. This would raise the average stock figure.

Any discount allowed for quantity is built into the table of calculations. In the case of Merlin, where the lights are half price (£6) if 500 are ordered, there will be a break in the graph of ordering and total costs at 500. The total annual costs of buying 400 pa with an order level of 500 are: £20 × 400/500 = £16 for ordering costs; 0.1 × £6 × 500/2 = £150 for annual stockholding costs; and 400 × £6 for purchasing costs, totalling £2566. This is a considerable saving so the policy of buying in batches of 500 should be adopted.

A stock control system can be simulated in a spreadsheet using previous demands with ordering and holding costs in a similar manner to simulation of queuing problems.

14.5 Queuing – the use of simulation

Most people dislike having to queue for a service. It is a waste of time for the person in the queue and the service provider knows it is bad for public relations. Queuing theory is concerned with such problems as people queuing for public telephones or rail tickets or machines queuing for repair. It can be used to design the appointments system in a doctor's surgery or to decide how many checkouts should be open in a supermarket.

Essentially, a queue occurs when there is some mismatch between the demand for and the supply of a particular service. One problem may be that, though the service is continuously available, demand is uncertain and irregular. For example, customers arrive randomly to join supermarket checkout queues. If too few tills are open then customers may have to queue for a long time and may take their future custom elsewhere. If too many tills are open, the assistants may be idle but will still have to be paid. Either situation will cost the supermarket money.

The problems addressed by the theory of queuing can be tackled mathematically using algebraic formulae so long as the situation is fairly simple and well established. Alternatively a model can set up on the basis of past data and the passage of each individual through the service can be simulated, preferably using computer software.

Simulation of a queue

The two main problems to be addressed in queuing situations are that there is no definite knowledge of either the timing for the next customer joining the queue or the length of the service he will need before leaving the system. Although both are random variables, past observations enable us to find the distribution of their values.

If you find this difficult to appreciate think of a fair 6-sided die. You do not know what value the next throw will produce but you do know that, in the long term, each of the numbers will occur more or less the same number of times, that is, the distribution will be uniform with a long term mean of 3.5.

Simulation is generally a 'What if . . .?' approach to a problem and is particularly appropriate for studying queues. The model based on a previous period of observation is set up and then manipulated to see what happens if a particular event occurs. For example, it is much cheaper for a supermarket to simulate than to actually open a till and, maybe, find the operator has nothing to do!

What past observations do we need? Obviously we need knowledge of how the existing system works:

- Number of servers – any number of checkouts may be open in a supermarket
- Service mechanism – presumably the next customer will be served immediately if the server is free
- Pattern of service times – the distribution of the times taken to serve customers in the period of observation
- Queue discipline – first in first out (FIFO) is the discipline usually used for human customers
- Pattern of arrivals – distribution of the times between customer arrivals during the previous period of observation

We shall simulate a queue with one server, FIFO discipline, and immediate service starts.

EXAMPLE 14.5

The service provided by Merlin's staff restaurant is under investigation after complaints from many of its customers. Employees felt they were wasting far too much of their lunch break queuing for their food which was served by only one person at the serving hatch. On one day the situation was monitored with the time at which each customer joined the queue, started to be served and left the serving hatch being recorded.

From these recordings the time between successive arrivals at the end of the queue was found to have the following distribution:

Time between arrivals (minutes)	1	2	3	4	5	Total
Number of customers	75	39	21	12	3	150
Percentage of customers	50	26	14	8	2	100

For the simulation customers can be represented by random numbers. These range from 0.000 to 0.999 and can be produced from any statistical calculator. Using the first two digits only with no decimal point, a random number indicates for any given customer the time lapse since the previous customer joined the queue. Because the random numbers range from 00 to 99 rather than from 01 to 100 the 50th number will be 49 and not 50. These are tabulated to produce a look-up table, that is, a random number is produced and its equivalent time lapse is looked up. For example, 78 would give 3 minutes between customers.

Time between arrivals (minutes)	1	2	3	4	5
Percentage of customers	50	26	14	8	2
Cumulative percentage	50	76	90	98	100
Random number range	00–49	50–75	76–89	90–97	98–99

The time taken for each customer to be served once he/she had actually reached the service hatch was also recorded, to the nearest minute. These were tabulated and the cumulative percentage up to each time was found. Each service time had a range of random numbers allotted to produce a look up table.

Service time (minutes)	2	3	4	5	6	7	Total
Customers	42	60	21	15	9	3	150
Percentage of customers	28	40	14	10	6	2	100
Cumulative percentage	28	68	82	92	98	100	
Random number range	00–27	28–67	68–81	82–91	92–97	98–99	

The situation will be simulated for the first 30 minutes of arrivals. A longer simulation is preferable but we would need a spreadsheet. First the random numbers are generated and the corresponding inter-arrival times, actual arrival times and service times are found.

Customer	Arrivals			Services	
	Random number	Inter-arrival time	Arrival time	Random number	Service time
1			0	58	3
2	93	4	4	45	3
3	20	1	5	10	2
4	46	1	6	37	3
5	32	1	7	18	2
6	14	1	8	59	3
7	20	1	9	90	5
8	58	2	11	80	4
9	42	1	12	26	2
10	52	2	14	43	3
11	77	3	17	12	2
12	06	1	18	95	6
13	34	1	19	59	3
14	78	3	22	12	2
15	19	1	23	30	3
16	69	2	25	45	3
17	99	5	30	03	2

Transferring these arrival and service times to the next table allows the service start and finish times to be calculated, taking care that only one customer is being served at any one time. Each customer can then be timed through the system and his actual queuing time calculated. The average queuing time may be calculated. Also the length of the queue and any time the server was idle can be monitored. The average queuing time and queue length for this system are measures which allow other systems to be compared with it in order to identify the improvement produced by any alterations.

Customer	Arrival time	Queuing time	Service start	Service time	Service end	Number in queue	Server idle time
1	0		0	3	3		
2	4		4	3	7		1
3	5	2	7	2	9	1	
4	6	3	9	3	12	2	
5	7	5	12	2	14	2	
6	8	6	14	3	17	3	
7	9	8	17	5	22	3	
8	11	11	22	4	26	4	
9	12	14	26	2	28	4	
10	14	14	28	3	31	4	
11	17	14	31	2	33	4	
12	18	15	33	6	39	5	
13	19	20	39	3	42	6	
14	22	20	42	2	44	6	
15	23	21	44	3	47	7	
16	25	22	47	3	50	8	
17	30	20	50	2	52	7	

The simulated queue is obviously building up as the waiting time increases. Validation of the simulation model is provided if this was observed to happen in practice.

The average service time is $51/17 = 3$ minutes, which is not unreasonable

The average queuing time is $195/17 \approx 11\frac{1}{2}$ minutes which is not so reasonable especially in view of the steadily increasing length of the queue.

This server is working all the time, so the obvious solution would be to increase the service provision. What would happen if a second server were employed? This situation will be investigated using exactly the same arrival and service times.

Assume that a customer will go to whichever server is free, if only one is free, but will go to server 1 if both are free.

Cust.	Arr. time	Service time	Server 1 Service start	Server 1 Service end	Server 2 Service start	Server 2 Service end	Queuing time	Number in queue	Servers Idle time 1	Idle time 2
1	0	3	0	3			0	0		
2	4	3	4	7			0	0	1	3
3	5	2			5	7	0	0		2
4	6	3	7	10			1	1		
5	7	2			7	9	0	0		
6	8	3			9	12	1	1		
7	9	5	10	15			1	1		
8	11	4			12	16	1	1		
9	12	2	15	17			3	1		
10	14	3			16	19	2	2		
11	17	2	17	19			0	0		
12	18	6	19	25			1	1		
13	19	3			19	22	0	0		
14	22	2			22	24	0	0		
15	23	3			24	27	1	1		
16	25	3	25	28			0	0		
17	30	2	30	32			0	0	2	3

The average queuing time is reduced to 11/17, less than a minute; the queue has virtually disappeared and the servers are not often idle. This is a much improved situation for the employees. However, the management would have to balance customer satisfaction against an extra wage!

This is a relatively straightforward situation and many variations on the queuing theme can be investigated by simulation, preferably using a specialist package such as Witness. The stock control of Merlin's strip lights could be modelled using information on the electrician's demands from the stock. Simulation can be used to set up an appointment scheme for a doctor's surgery. The problem surgery would be monitored for a reasonable length of time so that the arrival and consultancy times of each patient could be recorded. An improved scheme could then be produced identifying reasonable surgery hours, number of doctors in attendance, lengths of consultancy, and so on.

14.6 Linear programming

Linear programming is concerned with the utilisation of limited resources to the manufacturer's greatest advantage. In theory a firm can manufacture an unlimited number of products but in practice they are limited by their production capacity, workforce, availability of raw materials, requirements of the consumer market, and so on. Linear programming is the technique most widely used to maximise a producer's profits (or minimise his costs) subject to various constraints imposed upon him.

The problem can be solved graphically if the number of products is limited to two. This helps in understanding the method which can later be extended to more variables. The Simplex method on a computer can solve problems involving thousands of variables very quickly. This method will be demonstrated by solving a fairly simple problem. At the start unlimited production is assumed possible but, as the constraints are considered one by one, the feasible production becomes more limited. Once the range of actual possibilities has been defined the production scheme which maximises profit can be identified.

EXAMPLE 14.6

Merlin plc produce two models of scientific calculator: a statistical model S48 and a graphics model G48 which cost £12 and £25 to make and produce profits of £3 and £5 respectively. The times needed for their production are 10 and 15 minutes respectively. All the calculators go to the same warehouse which requires at least 100 of each type and can take up to 500 calculators per week in total. Both calculators are built by three workers who work a 35-hour week and who can assemble either type. All the components are in plentiful supply. How many of each calculator should Merlin make each week in order to maximise their profits?

There are rather a lot of numbers to build into the model so they need to be worked through logically. The production costs are not relevant as the profit for each type of calculator is known, but all the information on demands and manpower needs to be in the model.

Let the number of S48 calculators produced be S and the number of G48 calculators produced be G.

Profits

Each S produces £3 profit totalling £3S. Each G produces £5 profit totalling £5G.

So the total profit can be represented by £$(3S + 5G)$. The function whose value needs to be maximised, the objective function, is therefore $3S + 5G$.

Constraints

The warehouse:	Can take up to 500 in total	$S + G \leq 500$
	Require at least 100 of each	$S \geq 100$ and $G \geq 100$
The workforce time:	3 men work 35 hours $= 105$ hours $= 6300$ minutes available	
	Each S and each G need 10 and 15 minutes, respectively	$10S + 15G \leq 6300$

S and G must both be positive, as it is not possible to produce a negative number of calculators $S \geq 0$ and $G \geq 0$

When the lines of equality are drawn on a graph the feasible region can be identified. For each line a '$\leq$' sign identifies the area nearer to the origin and a '$\geq$' sign that further away from it.

Figure 14.5 Identification of feasible region

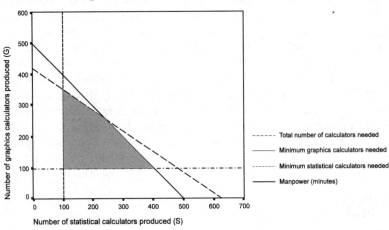

Having identified the feasible region as the shaded area, the next stage is to find the position within it that will maximise Merlin's profits. The profit function is $3S + 5G$ and the maximum profit will always be found at one of the vertexes, so if the co-ordinates of each are identified the profit for that production can be quantified.

The co-ordinates of each vertex can be identified by solving the simultaneous equations for the intersecting lines. From the co-ordinates the profit for that combination of calculators can be calculated. Working anticlockwise from the vertex nearest to the origin:

- $S = 100$ and $G = 100$

  $\Rightarrow £(3S + 5G) = £(300 + 500) = £800$

- $G = 100$ and $S + G = 500 \Rightarrow S = 400$

  $\Rightarrow £(3S + 5G) = £(3 \times 400 + 5 \times 100) = £1700$

- $10S + 15G = 6300 \Rightarrow 10S + 15G = 6300 \Rightarrow 5G = 1300 \Rightarrow G = 260$ and $S = 240$
  $1S + 1G = 500 10S + 10G = 5000$

  $\Rightarrow £(3S + 5G) = £(3 \times 240 + 5 \times 260) = £2020$

- $S = 100$ and $10S + 15G = 6300 \Rightarrow 15G = 5300 \Rightarrow G = 353.3$

  $\Rightarrow £(3S + 5G) = £(3 \times 100 + 5 \times 353) = £2065$

Maximum profits

Profits are maximised from these calculators by Merlin making 100 statistical and 353 graphics calculators weekly giving them a weekly profit of £2065

The optimum production for Merlin, under the existing conditions, is to produce 100 statistical and 353 graphics calculators per week. This uses all their manpower but leaves the total production $500 - 453 = 47$ short of the number that the warehouse could accept.

Would it be worth paying the assemblers overtime in order to make these 47? If they were all graphics calculators the extra time needed would be 47×15 minutes $\approx 11\frac{3}{4}$ hours. No information is available on hourly, or overtime, pay rates but it is likely to be less than the extra revenue produced so this is a reasonable opportunity which should not be missed. On the graph in Figure 14.5 the maximum profits vertex would then be positioned at the vertex (100, 400) which is above that previously identified.

Simplex method

By using a computer many more than two variables can be investigated. The algorithm is referred to as the Simplex method. It has been demonstrated graphically that the position of optimisation is always found on a vertex of the feasible region. The Simplex method starts at one vertex and calculates the profit there. It then moves through the adjoining vertexes one at a time calculating the profits at each. The highest profit is retained and the algorithm moves in the direction of increasing profit until the maximum is reached.

Because the power of computers is continually increasing thousands of variables can be explored together and optimal production schemes identified. The value of lost opportunity can also be assessed quickly and appropriate changes made. Sensitivity analysis allows a 'What if . . .?' approach to explore the effect of potential alterations in production.

Solver in Excel can be used for small to medium sized problems. A specialist package such as Xpress MP is needed for large problems.

14.7 Transportation (allocation)

Many companies produce goods in just a few factories and distribute them to a small number of warehouses throughout the country. Transportation methods are designed to help identify the best distribution patterns, based on availability and needs, to minimise transportation costs.

As in the section on linear programming an initial feasible solution is produced which fulfils the transportation requirements and bears the costs of the individual routes in mind but is not expected to minimise them. This model is then improved, moving as many goods as possible by any cheaper routes available while still fulfilling the requirements of the receivers. This process is repeated until the final solution, which minimises the total transportation costs, is achieved. A simple example is used to demonstrate the method.

EXAMPLE 14.7

Merlin use a fleet of hire cars at each of their three factories in Newcastle, Leeds and Sheffield. The cars are hired at the same time each year and during that time may be driven from and left at any of the factories by Merlin's staff. They may also be left at Heathrow, Manchester and East Midlands airports for later collection. At the end of each hiring year, however, each factory must have its correct complement of cars available for exchange.

At the end of one year the shortages at Newcastle, Leeds and Sheffield were 10, 8 and 7 respectively and the cars still awaiting collection from the airports were 11, 9 and 5 at Heathrow, Manchester and East Midlands respectively. A reasonable distribution policy for returning the cars to the factories is first produced by using the cheapest routes as much as possible and bearing in mind the requirements of the factories.

Obviously the transportation costs have to take into consideration the distances travelled. These costs are estimated to be (£):

Cost per car:	To		
From	Newcastle	Leeds	Sheffield
Heathrow	95	65	55
Manchester	45	15	10
East Midlands	70	40	25

It can be seen that the cheapest route is from Manchester to Sheffield so that may as well be filled first. The total number of cars in each place along with the transportation costs (*bracketed in italics*) are written into one table. Moving as many cars as possible along the cheapest route will send 7 from Manchester to Sheffield to fulfil all Sheffield's requirements. The next cheapest route is from Manchester to Leeds, so the 2 cars left at Manchester will go to Leeds. Carrying on in this manner produces the possible solution below.

Solution 1	Destinations			
Sources	Newcastle	Leeds	Sheffield	Total
Heathrow	10 (95)	1 (65)	0 (55)	11
Manchester	0 (45)	2 (15)	7 (10)	9
East Midlands	0 (70)	5 (40)	0 (25)	5
Total	10	8	7	25

This is a feasible solution and the cars end up in the correct numbers, but is it the best? The total cost of this initial solution is:

$$£(10 \times 95 + 1 \times 65 + 2 \times 15 + 7 \times 10 + 5 \times 40) = £1315$$

In order to compare the costs of the different routes the total costs for the **allocated** routes are split into despatch costs from the source airports and reception costs at the destination factories. These costs are often called shadow costs. Since the object of this exercise is comparison only, the value of zero can be allocated to any one partial cost. In this case that may as well be the despatch cost from the first source, Heathrow.

- If the shadow despatch cost from Heathrow is 0, then the shadow reception cost at Newcastle must be 95 and that at Leeds 65 since these are the total costs for the routes Heathrow to Newcastle and Heathrow to Leeds respectively
- If the shadow reception cost at Leeds is 65, then the shadow despatch costs from Manchester and East Midlands must be −50 and −25 respectively since the total costs for Manchester to Leeds and East Midlands to Leeds are 15 and 40 respectively
- If the shadow despatch cost from Manchester is −50, then the shadow reception cost at Sheffield must be 60 to make the total 10

The next table includes these shadow costs in square brackets.

Sources	Destinations Newcastle	Leeds	Sheffield	Shadow despatch costs	Total
Heathrow	10 (95)	1 (65)	0 (55)	[0]	11
Manchester	0 (45)	2 (15)	7 (10)	[−50]	9
East Midlands	0 (70)	5 (40)	0 (25)	[−25]	5
Total	10	8	7		25
Shadow reception costs	[95]	[65]	[60]		

All the partial shadow costs produce the correct total costs for the allocated routes.

Next consider the unused routes. If the cost of an unused route is less than the sum of the partial shadow costs, then an opportunity of saving money has been missed.

Opportunity cost = actual cost − (shadow despatch cost + shadow reception cost)

- Heathrow to Sheffield $\qquad$ $55 - (0 + 60) = -5$ $\qquad$ could save £5 per car
- Manchester to Newcastle $\qquad$ $45 - (-50 + 95) = 0$
- East Midlands to Newcastle $\qquad$ $70 - (-25 + 95) = 0$
- East Midlands to Sheffield $\qquad$ $25 - (-25 + 60) = -10$ $\qquad$ could save £10 per car.

So the biggest potential saving is by using the East Midlands to Sheffield route. We need therefore to relocate as many cars as possible to this route, at the same time keeping the row and column totals unchanged.

The method is to find a rectangle with this unused route in one corner and used routes at the other three corners. The maximum number of cars which can be moved around this rectangle is 5 as East Midlands has a surplus of only 5 cars. Having made those alterations, different routes are used so the calculation of the shadow costs needs repeating as some may have changed. This is done as before but since East Midlands to Sheffield is now used, and East Midlands to Leeds is not, the first route will be included in these calculations but the second will not. The shadow costs shown in the next table (see p. 284) are the recalculated values.

The total cost is now $£(10 \times 95 + 1 \times 65 + 7 \times 15 + 2 \times 10 + 5 \times 25) = £1265$

Consider again the opportunity costs for the empty routes in the table on the next page:

- Heathrow to Sheffield $\qquad$ $55 - (0 + 60) = -5$
- Manchester to Newcastle $\qquad$ $45 - (-50 + 95) = 0$
- East Midlands to Newcastle $\qquad$ $70 - (-35 + 95) = 10$
- East Midlands to Leeds $\qquad$ $40 - (-35 + 65) = 10$

Solution 2 Sources	Destinations			Shadow despatch costs	Total
	Newcastle	Leeds	Sheffield		
Heathrow	10 (95)	1 (65)	0 (55)	[0]	11
Manchester	0 (45)	7 (15)	2 (10)	[−50]	9
East Midlands	0 (70)	0 (40)	5 (25)	[−35]	5
Total	10	8	7		25
Shadow reception costs	[95]	[65]	[60]		

So using the Heathrow to Sheffield route would reduce costs further. The only possibility is that Sheffield, instead of Leeds, receives 1 car available from Heathrow and Leeds gets an extra car from Manchester. After this reallocation the table is as follows:

Solution 3 Sources	Destinations			Shadow despatch costs	Total
	Newcastle	Leeds	Sheffield		
Heathrow	10 (95)	0 (65)	1 (55)	[0]	11
Manchester	0 (45)	8 (15)	1 (10)	[−45]	9
East Midlands	0 (70)	0 (40)	5 (25)	[−30]	5
Total	10	8	7		25
Shadow reception costs	[95]	[60]	[55]		

The total cost is now $£(10 \times 95 + 1 \times 55 + 8 \times 15 + 1 \times 10 + 5 \times 25) = £1260$

Consider again the opportunity costs for the empty routes:

- Heathrow to Leeds $\quad\quad\quad\quad 65 - (0 + 60) = 5$
- Manchester to Newcastle $\quad\quad 45 - (-45 + 95) = -5$
- East Midlands to Newcastle $\quad 70 - (-30 + 95) = 5$
- East Midlands to Leeds $\quad\quad 40 - (-30 + 60) = 10$

Using the Manchester to Newcastle route would reduce costs further. The one car which Manchester previously sent to Sheffield can now be sent to Newcastle and one of those Newcastle received from Heathrow can now be received by Sheffield. After this reallocation the table is as follows:

Solution 3 Sources	Destinations			Shadow despatch costs	Total
	Newcastle	Leeds	Sheffield		
Heathrow	9 (95)	0 (65)	2 (55)	[0]	11
Manchester	1 (45)	8 (15)	0 (10)	[−50]	9
East Midlands	0 (70)	0 (40)	5 (25)	[−30]	5
Total	10	8	7		25
Shadow reception costs	[95]	[65]	[55]		

The total cost is now £$(9 \times 95 + 2 \times 55 + 1 \times 45 + 8 \times 15 + 5 \times 25) = £1255$

Consider again the opportunity costs for the empty routes:

- Heathrow to Leeds $65 - (0 + 65) = 0$
- Manchester to Sheffield $10 - (-50 + 55) = 5$
- East Midlands to Newcastle $70 - (-30 + 95) = 5$
- East Midlands to Leeds $40 - (-30 + 65) = 5$

The solution is now optimal though we could use Heathrow to Leeds at no extra cost. The final solution to this problem is therefore:

Route	Cost per car (£)	Number of cars	Total cost (£)
Heathrow to Newcastle	95	9	855
Heathrow to Sheffield	55	2	110
Manchester to Newcastle	45	1	45
Manchester to Leeds	15	8	120
East Midlands to Sheffield	25	5	125
		Total	£1255

The minimum cost of getting these cars back to their bases is £1255, a saving of £60 from the original solution of £1315. Although the first policy was drawn up by using the cheapest routes first, the final policy shows an improvement.

In this example the total number of cars in excess at the airports exactly matched the total missing from the factories. In examples on supply and demand this is not always the case. If more goods are available than are needed then a 'dummy demand' is included in the calculation as an extra demand. The optimisation method is followed in the same way to minimise transportation costs with the surplus supply ending up under the dummy demand, that is, not going anywhere but being kept in storage.

This type of problem can be solved by using Server in Excel.

As with any of the examples in this chapter a very simple situation has been investigated. In practice, transportation costs are unlikely to be the only criterion for a decision. We ignored the numbers of drivers available or whether the cars could have been moved in batches on transporters. Perhaps those at Heathrow could have been brought as far north as Sheffield on two transporters and then despatched to Leeds and Newcastle from there. This alternative could be investigated in a similar manner if the cost of hiring transporters is known and the results of the two policies compared.

14.8 Critical path (network) analysis

Networks are used to find the least time needed to complete a multi-task project in critical path analysis. They are also incorporated in project planning and PERT (project and evaluation technique) analysis, when the timing of these tasks is uncertain.

Critical path analysis is applied to the scheduling of such projects as:

- A building project – the channel tunnel, for example
- Launching a new product
- Moving personnel and equipment to new premises
- Refurbishing an office
- Expanding a factory.

All large projects are broken down into smaller discrete activities for which the duration can be reasonably estimated. Some activities can take place simultaneously while others have to run consecutively. Most of the activities will be dependent on some previous activity being completed before they can start, thus establishing an order of precedence. It is this order of precedence that provides the basis of the network.

For example, a project in Figure 14.6 consists of 8 individual activities A to H. B has to follow A and is itself followed by C and E which can take place simultaneously. D and F can follow the completion of C and E respectively. G requires that both D and F have finished before it can start. The project is finished once H, which needs G to be completed before it starts, is complete.

Figure 14.6

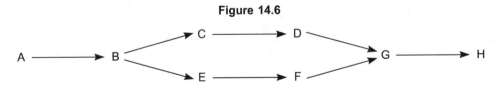

Once a network has been established the estimated duration of each activity is added and from these individual timings the total duration and the critical path for the whole project is established. Activities on the critical path are called critical activities. These are the activities for which there is no flexibility in timing unless the deadline for the whole project is to be extended. Other activities may start or finish later than planned without affecting the overall completion time. The flexibility of these timings may be explored by a Gantt chart which illustrates the start and finish time for each activity and provides an easy method of seeing which activities are taking place at any time and how much flexibility there is in timing.

Example 14.8 demonstrates how to produce the order of precedence, network, critical path and Gantt chart for a fairly simple set of data. In this example the activities are situated on the nodes of the networks, in other books they may be found on either the nodes or the arrows. There is no uniformity of presentation between textbooks but most computer packages place them on the nodes.

EXAMPLE 14.8

Merlin plc have just purchased a new site on which to have a larger factory built. The new factory will house staff and machinery from the present factory and also the extra new personnel and machinery required. The management have drawn up a list of the main tasks to be completed along with their estimated durations and have identified any preceding tasks.

Code	Activity	Preceding activity	Estimated durations (weeks)
A	Hire architect	–	2
B	Draw up plans	A	5
C	Build new premises	B	35
D	Buy new machinery	B	2
E	Install new machinery	C D	5
F	Employ new staff	C	3
G	Train new staff	E F	2
H	Move existing staff and machinery	C	4
I	Get up to full production	G H	1

Construct the network as in Figure 14.7.

Figure 14.7

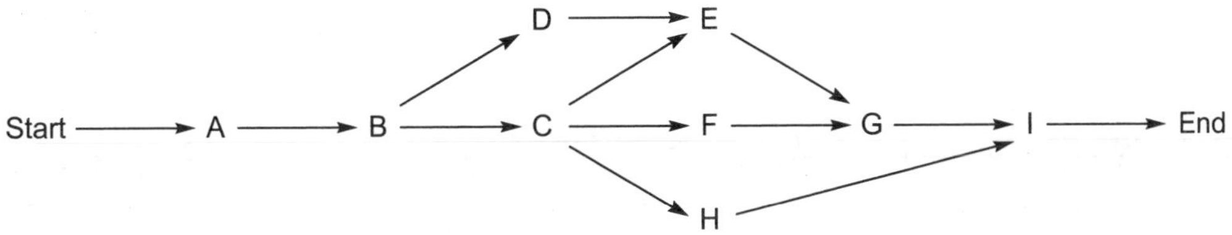

The network is then redrawn with activity code and duration on the top line of the node. Two more rows of the node are left blank for adding start and finish times (Figure 14.8).

Figure 14.8

Activity code	Duration (weeks)
Earliest starting time	Earliest finishing time
Latest starting time	Latest finishing time

Figure 14.9 Activities and durations

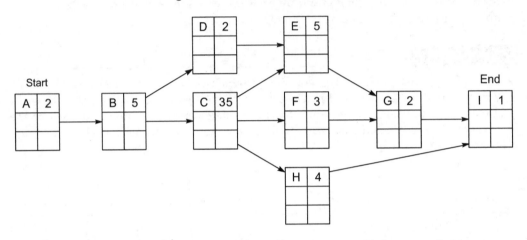

The next step is to identify the critical path. Bearing in mind that no activity can start before all activities which need to precede it are complete, the earliest starting times and finishing times are entered into the middle row of each node working from the start through to the end of the network.

Figure 14.10 Activities, durations and earliest timings

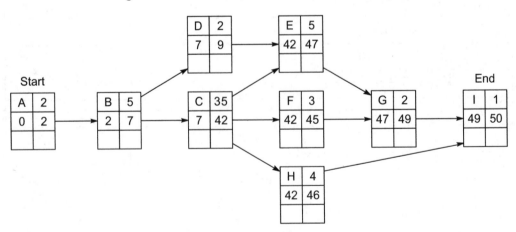

It will take a minimum of 50 weeks to complete the whole project.

Next the latest possible starting and finishing times are entered into the bottom row of the node starting from the end of the network and working backwards. Bear in mind now that the latest a preceding activity can end is the earliest any activities following it start.

Figure 14.11 Activities, durations, earliest and latest timings

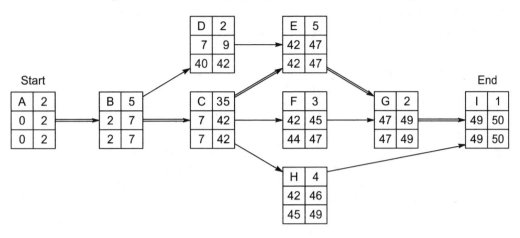

The critical activities are those with no flexibility of timing and they are joined by the critical path. This is identified in Figure 14.11 by double arrows.

The critical activities are therefore A, B, C, E, G and I. They must start as scheduled if the whole project is not to be delayed. D can start any time between weeks 7 and 40. F and H have 2 and 3 weeks flexibility respectively.

This flexibility is best illustrated by a Gantt chart which also highlights activities which are taking place at the same time. The blocks (durations) can be moved along the dotted lines (floating times) without the total duration of the whole project being affected.

Figure 14.12 Gantt chart

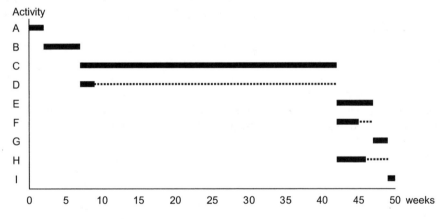

On this plan the installation of the new (E) and the old machinery (H) start at the same time. Since H has a 'float' of 3 weeks it might be preferable to delay its start, particularly if the same mechanics are involved in both operations. Also the existing staff could be given a few weeks break before arriving at the new premises where there would be little for them to do before week 49.

Many activities, such as 'Build new premises', have an uncertain duration. The time suggested here is 35 weeks. Is that realistic or is the estimate rather too optimistic? A standard method for dealing with this uncertainty is to use PERT (project evaluation and review technique) analysis. In PERT analysis the most optimistic, the most pessimistic and the most likely times are estimated instead of a definite duration. The expected duration defined as:

$$\frac{\text{most optimistic} + 4 \times \text{most likely} + \text{most pessimistic}}{6}$$

is used in the network analysis for timing the critical path.

Other uncertain activities are treated in the same way and a measure of the likely uncertainty in the duration of the whole project is estimated from the results. The probability of the whole project lasting longer than any specified time, such as 50 or 52 weeks, can be estimated.

A very simplistic approach has been taken in this example. It should be appreciated that network analysis is an essential part of the planning of vast projects and that it is usually carried out with the assistance of very sophisticated computer software, such as MS Project. However the principles are the same as those illustrated here.

14.9 Summary

Having studied this chapter you should have an idea of some of the techniques employed by operational researchers. It is not intended that you should be expert in any of them as we have only scratched the surface here. For this reason no exercise has been included in this chapter. It is, however, hoped that your interest in the subject might have been aroused.

Operational research realistically takes one or two semesters to study fully and is not usually included in first statistics courses which do, however, provide a good grounding for it. The wide variety of computer packages available enable the student to investigate realistic situations without having deep mathematical knowledge. The main requirement is an understanding of the processes taking place and the ability to interpret the computer output produced by them.

The application of operational research is essentially practical. All the techniques we have investigated here, at a very naïve level, are applicable to the workplace and, with the aid of a dedicated computer package, can analyse vast quantities of information. Any manager will appreciate the usefulness of quantitative information upon which to base his/her decisions when trying to optimise any situation within the company and that is where the operational researcher can come to his/her assistance. It must however be borne in mind that all models are a simplification of reality and should be validated by comparison with what is actually observed in the 'real world'.

15 Computer Analysis

This chapter includes SPSS and Minitab worksheets for all the topics included in the course. Some Excel worksheets are also included but their application is limited to the analysis available in Excel. Each worksheet should take about one hour to complete although this will depend on the individual student. Some topics are short and so more than one may be combined in one worksheet. There is also annotated output from all the worksheets in the lecturers' materials on the Internet. This is aimed at helping the student to interpret the results of the analysis.

This is obviously an 'either/or' situation in which you are only expected to use one of the computer packages depending on availability. Minitab is a popular teaching package and SPSS is more commonly met in the working environment. Both are widely used so should be employed in preference to Excel which is a spreadsheet rather than a statistical package.

15.1 Introduction to SPSS

SPSS, the Statistical Package for the Social Sciences, was originally developed in the USA to enable data from surveys and experiments to be analysed 'fully and flexibly'. It includes a wide range of procedures for both simple and highly complex methods of analysis. Its weaknesses are mainly in the output from the simpler forms of analysis which is not always immediately interpretable, although this is improving with each new version.

SPSS offers the facilities common to all Windows applications. It is supplied with an excellent Tutorial which you should work through.

On initially entering SPSS two windows are automatically set up. The 'SPSS Data Editor' is used for entering data. If you enter data from an existing file the heading includes the name of that file. The 'SPSS Viewer' window keeps a listing of all your commands and output including the charts. Each of these windows can be edited, saved, printed or pasted to another Windows application and printed.

Numerical data is entered into the grid Data View in the usual manner with each column containing the measurements on one particular variable and each row containing the measurements for a particular case. The characteristics of each variable are described in the Variable View grid.

The output which appears in the SPSS Viewer is in the form of 'Objects' which can be edited in SPSS, saved, deleted, printed and exported to other applications. The amount of output is rather copious so it is a good idea to delete regularly any which is not needed, especially before copying and pasting into a word processor for assignments, projects, and so on.

15.2 SPSS worksheets

Note: The commands used here are from SPSS Version 10, other versions may differ.

Throughout this tutorial *selections from menus, dialogue boxes or buttons* are shown in bold italics separated by the slash sign /; VARIABLES are given in capitals; and **characters you need to type** are in bold.

The assumption is that you have not used SPSS previously although you are probably familiar with Windows.

The numerical answers to all the questions in these worksheets are to be found in Section 15.3. (The full output from all the worksheets, including the graphics, is included in the lecturers' material on the Internet.)

15.2.1 Graphical presentation with SPSS

During this tutorial you will learn how to use SPSS to explore data graphically and also how to edit your graphs. We shall use the data from Tutorial Question 2.2.

2.1.1 Opening SPSS

The main menu on your local network may be set up in a variety of ways and the method of opening SPSS will differ from one to another.

> Open *SPSS for Windows*

You are now in the opening dialogue box. Select Type in Data **OK**. The SPSS data editor, Data View, opens. If you enter data from an existing file the heading includes the name of that file. The SPSS Output Viewer window will open automatically after your first use of the data to keep a listing of all your commands and output including Charts.

2.1.2 Putting your data into SPSS

The following figures represent the ages of a sample of 60 male employees of a firm Merlin plc:

35	44	54	33	46	20	32	19	50	39	33	37
42	40	20	25	34	52	27	22	18	40	23	17
41	45	21	34	49	27	60	46	32	58	23	52
24	64	41	47	54	37	40	41	40	36	46	29
34	39	39	40	37	50	41	34	47	34	45	36

In Variable View row 1 name the variable **Age**. Label it **Age of employee** and change the decimal places to 0. In Data View type all the ages in the table into column 1, working down the table columns from 35 to 34, 44 to 39 and so on. Check that the final row number is 60.

2.1.3 Checking your input

By printing the data into the Output Viewer you can check it at this stage and also have a record of it for printing out at the end of the session.

> *Analyse/Reports/Case Summaries*/Select **Age** and then click on the arrow to move it over to the active Variables box.

Any analysis is performed on the variables in this right hand box and not on the others remaining unselected in the original list. On pressing **OK** the data is printed into the Output Viewer window. Check the values with those above. If any is incorrect, just overtype the correct version into the data editor.

2.1.4   Saving your data as a file

Now that you are happy with the data save it to a disk.

    With the data window on top *File/Save as* **a:Merlin** and *Save*.

Your data has now been saved as an SPSS data file Merlin.sav on your floppy disk in the drive A.

2.1.5   Producing a histogram

We shall first produce the default histogram and then another more refined version.

    *Graphs/Histogram/*Select AGE as your variable and then **OK**.

The default histogram appears as a chart which can be printed out, saved as a separate file or exported into a Word file. It has no title and the mid-intervals are labelled. We shall improve on this.

    *Graphs/Histogram/*Select AGE, then *Titles* and type in **Histogram of ages**, and *Continue* then **OK**.

Your graph has a title. Do not worry about the mean and standard deviation; we shall consider them in Worksheet 15.2.2. We shall edit this histogram further as the next task.

2.1.6   Editing a graph

Double click anywhere within the graph to open up the SPSS Chart Editor tool bar. Pointing with the mouse at any of the icons tells you its specific purpose. Single clicking on any element within the chart window selects it for editing. Colour and pattern can be applied to the histogram bars using the 'pencil', 'colour', and the 'fill pattern'. Text and fonts can be altered, lines added to the graph, and so on. Try changing colour, pattern, and text. The range of each interval can be displayed (but not values at the interval ends only).

    SPSS does not offer the options of producing frequency or cumulative frequency polygons.

2.1.7   Producing a stem-and-leaf plot and a box plot

    *Analyse/Descriptive Statistics/Explore/*Move AGE into the Dependent List, Display *Plots* rather than *Both*.

Among other output you will find a stem-and-leaf plot with stem width of 10 and each case represented by one leaf and a box plot. You can see from both that the data distribution is symmetrical, that the lowest value is 17 and the highest 64 and, from the boxplot, that the middle half of the data ranges from about 31 to about 46. Make sure you can interpret both these graphs.

2.1.8   Printing out the session contents

When you have completed your tutorial you probably have many errors in your SPSS viewer window. These can be deleted by clicking on each of the unwanted sections in turn to select it and deleting it with the Delete key. When you are happy with the remaining material print it out, making sure that your cursor is in the Viewer window, then:

    *File/Print/***OK**

2.1.9 Saving data and session output (if required)

With the cursor in the data sheet:

File/Save as **a:Merlin.sav** to save the data as an SPSS file on your floppy disk.

(You will be told that you already have the file as you saved it earlier. Overwrite the existing file.)

With the cursor in the output window:

File/Save window as **a:Merlin.spo** to save your output window as a text file.

15.2.2 Summary statistics with SPSS

We shall again use the data which you typed into SPSS in Worksheet 15.2.1 as the file Merlin.sav and then saved on your floppy disk. (If, by any chance you do not have it, refer to Worksheet 15.2.1 and input the tabulated data again.)

This file contains information about the ages of 60 employees of the firm Merlin plc.

Inputting data from an SPSS datafile

2.2.1 Open SPSS and then from the Data Editor window select *File/Open* and from your floppy disk select **Merlin.** Your data appears in the Data View window.

2.2.2 Look at the data sheet. The ages of the 60 employees are displayed in the first column. If you have just typed them in, then check the numbers carefully with the tabulated data.

Data summary

2.2.3 Summarise the data by its mean and standard deviation.

Analyse/Descriptive Statistics/Descriptives and select AGE.

This is a quick way to obtain the main summary statistics.

- What is the mean age of the employees? . . . .
- What is the standard deviation of these ages? . . . .

2.2.4 *More information can be obtained by exploring the data:*

Analyse/Descriptive Statistics/Explore and select AGE.
Add *Percentiles* to *Statistics* and *Histogram* to *Plots.*

- What is the median of the ages? . . . .
- State the minimum, maximum and range of the ages . . . .
- State the quartiles and interquartile range of the ages . . . .
- Does the histogram appear to be reasonably symmetrical? . . . .

2.2.5 Double click anywhere within the histogram to open up the **SPSS Chart Editor.** From the top menu select *Chart/Options* and click *Display/Normal curve* to check for symmetry. *File/Close* returns you to the Viewer.

Comparing groups of data

2.2.6 Next split the employees into two separate groups, male and female, by coding the data. Click the **Goto Data** grid button. Click on column 2 in Data View and then type **1** in the first 40 cells of column 2 for the males and **2** in the remaining 20 cells for the females.

In Variable View name this new variable SEX, label it **Sex of employee**, and change the decimal places to 0. Code the variable label as 1 for Male and 2 for Female.

2.2.7   *Check that the number in each group is correct:*

*Analyse/Descriptive Statistics/Frequencies/*Select SEX as the variable.
Charts/Piecharts.

Double click anywhere within the piechart produced to open up the **SPSS Chart Editor**. From the top menu select *Chart/Options* and add *Values* and *Percents* to *Labels*.

• What percentage of the employees are male? . . . .
Save your revised datafile as **a:Merlin2.sav**

2.2.8   *The two groups can now be compared:*

*Analyse/Compare means/Means/*Move AGE into the Dependent List and SEX into the Independent List. From Options also select the median.

• State the median for each group . . . .
• State the mean and standard deviation for each group. . . . .
• Compare the median with the mean for each group. . . . .

2.2.9   *Looking for a more detailed comparison, **Explore** can be used on each group:*

*Analyse/Descriptive Statistics/Explore/*Move AGE into the Dependent list and SEX into the Factor list. Plots/select *Boxplots/Factor levels together*.

• For which sex are the ages higher, on average? Give two reasons . . . .
  . . . .
• For which sex are the ages more spread out, on average? Give two reasons . . . .
  . . . .
• Do the boxplots illustrate the same results?. . . . .

2.2.10   *Print out your output*

In the Viewer window *File/Print/all*

15.2.3 Estimation and hypothesis testing with SPSS

In this worksheet we shall use the data input in previous Worksheet 15.2.1, Merlin.sav, as our population. We shall calculate its summary statistics, and use it as a population to provide a random sample from which we shall estimate the population parameters and then test various hypotheses about that population (conveniently forgetting that we actually know their true values for the population parameters!).

2.3.1   Open SPSS and input your file, Merlin.sav, saved in Worksheet 15.2.1. If you have not saved the data turn back to that section and type it in.

File/Open/Merlin

2.3.2 Calculate the summary statistics for all the ages and look at their graphical descriptions:

> *Analyse/Descriptive Statistics/Descriptives*/Select AGE

- Make a note of the mean value.

2.3.3 Take a random sample of 10 cases:

> *Data/Select cases/Random sample of cases/Sample* Sample size exactly **10** from the first **60**. Leave unselected cases as *Filtered.*

Check in your data window and label filter variable as Sample1.

> With the column selected: *Data/Define variable/Variable name* **Sample1**

2.3.4 Check the sample for normality:

> *Analyse/Nonparametric tests/1 sample K-S/* Select AGE and make sure that Normal is ticked.

The Assymp. sig. is the probability that the data is normal.

- What is its value?. . . . .

You will probably find that it is over 0.05 and so the population is considered to be normally distributed.

2.3.5 Find a confidence interval for the mean of all the ages:

> *Analyse/Descriptive Statistics/Summarise* Select AGE

Under Descriptives you will find the upper and lower bounds of the 95% confidence interval for the mean.

- State the 95% confidence interval. . . . .
- Does this interval include the mean age found in task 2.3.2? . . . .

2.3.6 Forgetting that we actually know the true value of the population mean, test the hypothesis that the mean age of all the employees is 50.

> *Analyse/Compare means/One-Sample T Test*/Selecting AGE for the variable, set the test value at **50**, leaving the confidence interval at 95%.

The 'Sig. two tailed' gives the probability that the null hypothesis of 50 years is correct.

- State this value . . . .

You will probably find that this is lower than 0.05.

Repeat Task 2.3.6 for the null hypothesis that mean age is **40** years.

- State this value . . . .

You will probably now find that it is higher than 0.05 so 40 is acceptable as a claim for the mean age of the population at 5% significance.

- What do you conclude? . . . .

2.3.7 In a new column Type **1** in rows 1 to 30 and **2** in rows 31 to 60. Label the column **Sex**.

We shall assume that the first 30 employees are male and the last 30 female. Code this variable with values and value labels. Take a random sample of 20 to give a large enough sample from each sex (see Task 2.3.3).

Save this file as **Merlin3**.

2.3.8   Calculate separate confidence intervals to see if they overlap.

>   *Analyse/Descriptive Statistics/Explore*/Select AGE/*Factor list* SEX

- Do the intervals overlap? . . . .
- What does this mean? . . . .

2.3.9   Carry out a two sample t-test to see if the males and females in the whole population have different mean ages.

>   *Analyse/Compare means/Independent Samples T Test*/Select AGE for the Test variable, SEX for the Grouping variable. Define groups **1** and **2**, leave the confidence interval at 95%.

The Sig. (2-tailed) value on the last line gives the probability that there is no difference between the means.

- State this value . . . .
- What do you conclude? . . . .

15.2.4 Analysis of variance with SPSS

One-way ANOVA

One-way ANOVA can be thought of as an extension to the two-sample t-test.

2.4.1   *Open file*: Merlin3.sav saved while working through Worksheet 15.2.3.

2.4.2   Check by describing the variable, AGE, to be used in this analysis:

>   *Analyse/Descriptive Statistics/Descriptives/***AGE**

You should find a mean of 37.75 and a standard deviation of 11.04.

2.4.3   Carry out a 2-sample t-test on AGE grouped by SEX. (Reminder from last worksheet.)

>   *Analyse/Compare means/Independent Samples T Test* Select AGE for the Test Variable and SEX as the Grouping Variable, and Define groups: **1** and **2**.

- State the mean values for the males and the females . . . .
- The null hypothesis for this test is that the means are the same, i.e. that the difference is zero. What is the probability that this is true? . . . .
- Assuming equal variances, what do you conclude? . . . .

2.4.4   *Analyse/Compare means/One-Way ANOVA*/Select AGE as the dependent variable and SEX as the factor. Define its range as **1** to **2**.
From the *Options* activate *Descriptives* for the addition of the separate group means.

- State the null hypothesis . . . .
- What is the probability that it is true? . . . .
- What do you conclude? . . . .
- Look at the confidence interval for each of the means.
  Indicate why these lead to the same conclusion . . . .
- Compare with results of Task 2.4.3.

2.4.5 With the next empty row selected in the Variable View input the Job Category of each employee. Name the variable JOBCAT. Use Job category for the variable label with codes 1 = Clerical, 2 = Management, 3 = Production, 4 = Security. (See Worksheet 15.2.1 if unsure of method.)

Type in the following codes all down in one column without any spaces:

4 3 4 1 1   3 3 3 2 1   2 1 1 3 4   1 4 4 2 1   2 1 3 2 3   1 3 3 1 2
1 3 3 3 3   1 1 2 4 1   2 1 1 3 3   1 3 2 3 3   3 1 1 2 3   3 1 3 3 3

Save this updated datafile as **Merlin4**

2.4.6 *Analyse/Compare means/One-Way ANOVA*/Select AGE as the dependent variable and JOBCAT as the factor. From the Options activate *Descriptives* and from Post Hoc *Least significant difference. (LSD)*

- State the null hypothesis . . . .
- State the alternative hypothesis . . . .
- What is the probability that the null hypothesis is true? . . . .
- What do you conclude? . . . .
- Look at the confidence interval for each of the means.
  Indicate why these lead to the same conclusion. . . . .
- Which levels of JOBCAT differ in their mean ages? . . . .

Two-way ANOVA

Two-way ANOVA is the simplest extension of one-way ANOVA.

We shall now split AGE by *both* factors simultaneously.

2.4.7 *Analyse/General Linear Model/Univariate*/Select AGE as the Dependent Variable and JOBCAT and SEX as the Fixed Factors.

- State the three null hypotheses. . . . .
  . . . .
- State the three alternative hypotheses . . . .
  . . . .
- What are the probabilities that each null hypothesis is true? . . . .
- What do you conclude? . . . .

Since the interactions are not significant we can just consider the main effects

2.4.8 *Analyse/General Linear Model/Univariate*/Select AGE as the dependent variable and JOBCAT and SEX as the factors. From Model select *Custom* Build JOBCAT and SEX into the model and select *Main effects* (under Build terms)

- State the two null hypotheses. . . . .
  . . . .
- State the two alternative hypotheses . . . .
  . . . .
- What are the probabilities that each null hypothesis is true? . . . .
- What do you conclude? . . . .

2.4.9   Carry out a two-way analysis of variance using a main effects model as in Table 2.4.8 for the laboratories and brands of peanut butter as given in Tutorial Question 8.3.

You will need one column for all the fat contents, another column for the laboratory codes: 1 = A, 2 = B, etc., and a third for the brands.

Use the output to answer Tutorial Question 8.3.

2.4.10 Carry out a two-way analysis of variance using a main effects model as in Task 2.4.8 for the electronics firm data in Tutorial Question 8.4.

You will need one column for all numbers of monitors produced, another column for the employees: 1 = A, 2 = B, etc., and a third for the times of day.

Use the output to answer Tutorial Question 8.4.

15.2.5 Correlation and regression analysis with SPSS

During this tutorial you will learn how to use SPSS to investigate the association between two continuous variables and how to describe it graphically.

2.5.1   In this practical session you will analyse some bivariate data.

To enter the data:

File/Open worksheet/ **Merlin4** (saved in the ANOVA Worksheet 15.2.4)

In order to see what this file contains:

Analyse/Descriptive Statistics/Descriptives Select all the variables but not the filters.

We have three variables. Each is measured on 60 cases. There are no missing values. We shall give each of the employees a salary and then see if this is associated with their age.

In Variable View, in the first empty row name a new variable SALARY and label it Annual salary (£000). In Data View type the following in one column: (Work down these columns one after the other):

38.1	38.9	23.2	22.9	19.8	19.7	15.6	31.7	17.3	37.8
18.7	42.8	19.6	47.5	31.3	8.5	28.5	14.1	33.5	32.9
42.3	60.1	15.5	15.8	59.3	15.9	37.3	20.3	13.7	9.8
25.9	60.7	20.7	35.9	33.8	39.3	32.9	19.8	6.4	15.2
53.6	75.2	40.2	25.3	24.5	14.5	23.9	28.2	35.3	8.7
37.6	10.9	28.5	63.2	32.0	10.2	8.6	25.3	12.5	38.4

The variables of interest in this practical session are the continuous variables SALARY and AGE. We shall investigate the relationship between the salaries earned by the employees of Merlin and their ages.

2.5.2   Save the revised datafile as **Merlin5**

2.5.3   Produce a scatter plot

Graphs/Scatter/Define as Simple/Select SALARY for Y and AGE for X.

Give your graph a suitable title.

Examine the plot. You should find it does suggest a rather poor linear relationship.

• Does there appear to be a relationship?. . . . .
• Guess whether the relationship is likely to be significant or not. . . . .

2.5.4   Calculate the correlation coefficient.

 *Analyse/Correlate/Bivariate/*Select SALARY and AGE as the variables.

- What is the value of the correlation coefficient? . . . .
- What is the probability of it being zero? . . . .
- Is this significant at 5%? . . . .

If the p value is less than 0.05 the correlation coefficient is significant at the 5% level of significance.

2.5.5   Find the regression equation:

 *Analyse/Regression/Linear/*Select SALARY as Dependent, AGE as Independent. Use Method Enter.

The regression equation, as produced by SPSS, is not at all obvious. In the Coefficients table, under unstandardised coefficients and in the column under B you will find the constant, a, and the coefficient of Age, b.

- Write down the regression equation . . . .

2.5.6   Produce the regression line on your scatterplot.

 Graphs/Scatter/Define as simple/Select SALARY for Y and AGE for X and OK
 Double click on the graph to get into editing mode.

 Chart/Options/Fit line/Total

2.5.7   Carry out residual analysis:

 *Analyse/Regression/Linear/*Select SALARY as dependent and AGE as independent variables. Select *Plots/Standardised residual plots/histogram.* Select *Save/Residuals/Unstandardised*

You should see that your residuals appear reasonably normal on the histogram.
 To see if the mean is zero and the standard deviation low:

 *Analyse/Descriptive Statistics/Descriptives/*Select the SALARY and
 UNSTANDARDISED RESIDUALS

You should see that the mean of the residuals is nearly zero. (If you do not understand the value of the mean, ask your tutor for help.) The standard deviation should have been reduced (but not by much for these data).
 In the next three tasks we look at the males and females separately.

2.5.8   Produce the two regression lines on your scatterplot.

 Graphs/Scatter/Define as simple Select SALARY for Y and AGE for X and Set marker by SEX. OK
 Double click on the graph to get into editing mode.

 Chart/Options/Fit line/Subgroups

- Describe the general differences between the male and the female salaries . . . .
 . . . .

2.5.9 In the Data editor:

Data/Select cases/If condition is satisfied/If Sex=1. Continue.
Leave unselected cases as Filtered. OK

Repeat Task 2.5.4 and, if the correlation coefficient is significant, Task 2.5.5 for the males.

● Write down the correlation coefficient and the regression equation, if appropriate . . .

. . . .

2.5.10 In the Data editor:

Data/Select cases/All cases. Then **If condition is satisfied/If Sex=2.** Leave
unselected cases as Filtered.

Repeat tasks 2.5.4 and, if the correlation coefficient is significant, task 2.5.5 for the
females only.

● Write down the correlation coefficient and the regression equation, if appropriate.. . .

. . . .

15.2.6 Time series analysis and forecasting with SPSS

In this worksheet we will analyse seasonal data. Exponential smoothing and curve fitting
can be carried out quite easily in SPSS by following the instructions in the Help menu.

The quarterly sales of a departmental store have been monitored for the past five years
with the following information being produced (Tutorial Question 12.1):

		Total quarterly sales (£0000s)		
Year	Quarter 1	Quarter 2	Quarter 3	Quarter 4
1996	48	58	57	65
1997	50	61	59	68
1998	52	62	59	69
1999	52	64	60	73
2000	53	65	60	75

2.6.1 Type all the sales figures in chronological order in one column, heading it Sales.

Then **Data/Define dates** Select **Years, quarters/First case in Year 1996 quarter 1.**

Look at the new variables in both Data Editor grids. They describe the year, the quarter
and their combination for use in time series diagrams.

2.6.2 Plot a sequence graph of sales with date to see if an additive model is appropriate.

Graphs/Sequence/Variables: Sales/Time axis labels: Date

2.6.3 Assuming it is, carry out the seasonal decomposition using that model:

Analyse/Time Series/Seasonal Decomposition/Additive model/Endpoints
weighted by 0.5/Display casewise listing Variable SALES.

2.6.4 Some new variables have been produced. Produce a sequence plot, as in Task
2.6.2, adding the trend STC_1 to the graph.

2.6.5 Make use of the seasonal factors and the smoothed trend cycle for making forecasts.

For an additive model: Fitted values = Trend + Seasonal Factor so compute a new variable, named FITTED_1, describing the fitted values:

Transform/Compute/Target variable FITTED_1 = *STC_1* + *SAF_1*

2.6.6 Plot a sequence graph of the sales, the smoothed trend, STC_1, and the Fitted_1 values.

Graph/Sequence/Variables: Sales, STC_1, Fitted_1/Time axis labels: Date

2.6.7 Residual analysis:

Remember that the residuals should: (a) be small, (b) have a mean of 0, (c) have a standard deviation which is much smaller than that of Sales, (d) be normally distributed and (e) be random timewise. The residuals have been saved as ERR_1.

(a), (b), (c) Produce descriptive statistics of Sales and ERR_1.

(d) For ERR_1 produce a boxplot and a histogram with a normal plot.
Carry out the K-S hypothesis test for normality:

Analyse/Nonparametric tests/1 sample K-S/Normal distribution

(e) Produce a sequence plot of the errors
Edit the chart to put a reference line at ERR_1 = 0.

2.6.8, 2.6.9 Repeat Tasks 2.6.3 and 2.6.4 but use a multiplicative model

2.6.10 Make use of the seasonal factors and the smoothed trend cycle for making forecasts.

For a multiplicative model: Fitted values = Trend × Seasonal Factor so compute a new variable, named FITTED_2, describing the fitted values:

Transform/Compute/Target variable type FITTED_2 = *STC_2* * *SAF_2*

2.6.11 Plot a sequence graph of the sales, the smoothed trend, STC_2, and the Fitted_2 values.

Graph/Sequence/Variables: Sales, STC_2, Fitted_2/Time axis labels: Date

2.6.12 For the multiplicative model, subtract the fitted values from the sales figures to find a set of errors, ERR_3, which are comparable with those from the additive model.

2.6.13 Comparing residuals:

(a), (b), (c) Produce descriptive statistics of sales and ERR_1, ERR_3.

(d) Produce box plots and histograms with normal plots on ERR_1, ERR_3.
Carry out the K-S hypothesis tests for normality:

Analyse/Nonparametric tests/1 sample K-S/Normal distribution

(e) Produce sequence plots of both sets of errors on the same graph
Edit the chart to put a reference line at 0.

Which is the better model in your opinion. Why?

2.6.14 Assuming that the trend from the additive model is increasing by 0.3 per quarter, what would be your forecasts for the four quarters of 2001?

15.3 Numerical answers to SPSS worksheets

15.2.1 Graphical presentation

All graphical output. Full output is given in the lecturers' materials on the Internet.

15.2.2 Summary statistics

2.2.3 37.75, 11.04 years

2.2.4 39.00; 17, 64, 47; 32, 45.75, 13.75 years; Yes

2.2.7 66.7%

2.2.8 Male 39.5, Female 36.5 years;
Male 38.25, 11.08, Female 36.75, 11.17 years

2.2.9 Male averages higher; Female spreads higher

15.2.3 Estimation and hypothesis testing

2.3.2 37.75 years

2.3.4 0.530

2.3.5 27.38 to 44.02 years; Yes

2.3.6 0.004; 0.272

2.3.8 Yes, so mean ages could be the same.

2.3.9 0.163, mean ages could be the same.

15.2.4 Analysis of variance

2.4.3 38.9, 36.6 years; 0.411; they are the same.

2.4.4 0.411; they are the same; the confidence intervals overlap.

2.4.6 0.000; at least two are different; many do not overlap;
All different apart from production and security.

2.4.7 0.000, 0.804, 0.713; different for job category, same for sex and interaction.

2.4.8 0.000, 0.229; different for job category, same for sex.

2.4.9 Sig. (labs) = 0.383, sig.(brands) = 0.079; both same at 5% significance.

2.4.10 Sig. (shifts) = 0.028, sig.(employees) = 0.276 only shifts different.

15.2.5 Correlation and regression analysis

2.5.4 0.398; 0.002; Yes.

2.5.5 Salary = 7.73 + 0.554 × Age

2.5.9 Males: 0.483, Salary = 6.88 + 0.734 × Age; Females: not significant

15.2.6 Time series analysis and forecasting

Graphical output with most answers approximate.

15.4 Introduction to Minitab

Minitab is a powerful tool originally developed at Pennsylvania State University as a teaching aid for introductory statistics courses. It is now one of the most widely accepted statistical analysis packages for college instruction and is also an established research tool. It is becoming more sophisticated with each version and now includes many forms of multivariate analysis.

Minitab offers the facilities common to all Windows applications. Minitab does not offer a tutorial, as such, but it includes a comprehensive Help facility at any stage.

On initially entering Minitab a split window is automatically set up. The lower half is the Worksheet for entering data. If you enter data from an existing file the heading changes to the name of that file. The Session window keeps a listing of all your commands and output. Each of these windows can be edited, saved, pasted to another Windows application or printed out in the usual manner.

Numerical data only is typed into the grid with each column containing the measurements on one particular variable and each row containing the measurements for a particular case. The variables are named in the cells between the column numbers and row 1 of the data cells.

The output in the Session window can be edited before being saved, printed out or copied and pasted to another application, such as Word.

15.5 Minitab worksheets

Throughout this tutorial *selections from menus, dialogue boxes or buttons* are shown in bold italics separated by the slash sign /; VARIABLES are given in capitals; and **characters you need to type** are in bold. As your experience increases the degree of detail in the instructions decreases.

The assumption is that you have not used Minitab previously even though you are familiar with Windows.

Minitab is not fussy about capitals but it is very fussy about **having only numbers in its worksheet.** It remembers that letters have been typed into the grid even after they have been deleted so take care! In the Manip menu there is 'Change Data Type' which can be used to rectify this problem.

(The full output from all the sheets, including the graphics, is included in the lecturers' materials on the Internet.)

15.5.1 Graphical presentation with Minitab

5.1.1 Opening Minitab

Menus on your local network may be set up in a variety of ways and the method of opening Minitab will differ from one to another.

Open *Minitab for Windows*

You are now in Minitab with two windows open: the Worksheet window, into which you will put all your data, and the Session window, which holds the record of all your commands and the resulting output. Later you will use the Information window and the Chart window. Each of these windows can be saved and/or printed out during or at the end of the session.

5.1.2   Putting your data into Minitab

The following figures represent the ages of a sample of 60 male employees of a firm Merlin plc:

35	44	54	33	46	20	32	19	50	39	33	37
42	40	20	25	34	52	27	22	18	40	23	17
41	45	21	34	49	27	60	46	32	58	23	52
24	64	41	47	54	37	40	41	40	36	46	29
34	39	39	40	37	50	41	34	47	34	45	36

Place the cursor over the data window, the Worksheet, in the first cell of the row below C1, column 1, and click the mouse. You are now in the cell which will contain the column heading for the first variable. You can move around the worksheet using the arrow keys.

Type the word **Age** and then, with the down arrow, move the cursor down to row 1 of C1. Type all the values in the table into column 1, one number per cell, using the down arrow between each. Work down the first column from 35 to 34 then continue down with 44 to 39, etc., until you have all 60 ages in the first column. Be very careful not to type any words into the data cells. Check that your final number is in row 60.

5.1.3   Checking your input

By printing the data into the Session window you can check it at this stage and also have a record of it printed out at the end of the session.

> **Manip/Display Data**/Click on AGE to select your variable and then *Select*. This variable is entered into the Display box. On pressing **OK** the data is printed into the Session window. Check the values with those above. If any is incorrect, just overtype the correct version into the worksheet.

5.1.4   Saving your data as a file

Now that you are happy with the data save it to a disk.

> **File/Save Current Worksheet as a: Merlin**

This has now been saved as a Minitab data file Merlin.mtw on your floppy disk in the drive A.

5.1.5   Producing a histogram

We shall first produce the default histogram and then another more refined version.

> **Graph/Histogram** Click on AGE, then *Select*, then **OK**.

The default histogram appears as a chart which can be printed out, saved as a separate file or exported into a Word file. It has no title and the mid-intervals are labelled. We can improve on this. First we need to prepare a variable holding the cut-off positions.
Label C2 as **Cut_off1** and enter a column of figures

15	20	25	30	35	40	45	50	55	60	65

> **Graph/Histogram**/Click on AGE, then *Select*, then *Annotation, Title* and type in something like **Histogram of Ages, OK**. Select *Options* and change *Type of Intervals* to *CutPoint*. Click *Midpoint/CutPoint* positions, click the cursor in the empty box and select variable CUT_OFF1. Then **OK**, then **OK** again.

Do we have too many bars? Try a different grouping: Type a new set of cut-off values, **Cut_off2**, as **0 10 20 40 50 60 70 80**. Repeat the production of the histogram now using CUT_OFF2.

Which histogram do you prefer? We shall use the second one for the following tasks.

5.1.6 Editing a graph

From the top tool bar select *Editor* and then *Edit*, or double click anywhere within the graph to be in editing mode and produce the Editing toolbar at the side of your graph. Single clicking on any element within the chart window selects it for editing. Colour and pattern can be applied to the histogram bars using the paint roller. Text and fonts can be altered, lines added to the graph. Try making many changes!

5.1.7 Adding a frequency polygon to a histogram

Produce a fresh version of the last histogram as in Task 5.1.5. Double click for editing mode. In the top editing toolbar, click on the open polygon icon. In the graph click on the position (5,0), then, in turn, on the centre of the top of each bar and finally on position (75,0). Click again on the open polygon icon to deselect it.

5.1.8 Producing a cumulative frequency ogive

Produce a histogram as before but from *Options* select *Cumulative Frequency*. Use *Annotate/Title* to give your graph a suitable title. Edit as for the polygons selecting the open ended polygon icon. Click on the cumulative frequencies at the end of each interval starting with (10,0), then (20,3) through to (80,60). Click on the icon again to deselect.

Does the ogive look a bit untidy? It would be clearer if the histogram were removed. For each bar in turn, click on the right edge to select it; click on the broken line icon and select None. You will be left with just the cumulative frequency polygon but will have to redraw the baseline by using the line icon from the top toolbar.

5.1.9 Producing a stem-and-leaf plot

*Graph/Character Graphs/Stem-and-leaf/*Select AGE and **OK**.

You probably have stems of width 5. If you would prefer wider ones, repeat the command for the plot but, this time, type **10** in the increment box.

As with the histograms, either of these plots is quite acceptable. Make sure you can interpret this output.

Character graphs are part of your session window and are printed out with the rest of this output at the end.

5.1.10 Producing a dot plot

*Graph/Character Graphs/Dotplot/*Select AGE and **OK**.

For this plot each case is represented by a single dot, that is, the data is ungrouped.

5.1.11 Producing a box plot

*Graph/Character Graphs/Boxplot/*Select AGE and **OK** for a fairly crude boxplot.

*Graph/Boxplot/*Select AGE as the Y variable, **OK** for high resolution graphics. The Minitab boxplot is simpler than that drawn by SPSS. We can see that the middle half of the data ranges from about 31 to 46 and that the extreme values are at about 17 and 64.

5.1.12 Printing out the session contents and your graphs

When you have completed your tutorial you probably have many errors in your session window. These can be deleted by highlighting the unwanted sections and deleting them as you would in Word. When you are happy with the remaining material make sure that your cursor is in the session window, then print it out:

> *File/Print Window/***OK**

5.1.13 Saving data and session output (if required)

> *File/Save Current Worksheet as* **a:Merlin.mtw** to save as a datafile.

> *File/Save Session Window as* **a:Merlin.txt** to save your session window as a text file.

15.5.2 Summary statistics with Minitab

Inputting data from a Minitab datafile

We shall again use the data which you typed into Minitab in Worksheet 15.5.1 as the file Merlin.mtw and then saved on your floppy disk. (If, by any chance you do not have it, refer to Worksheet 15.5.1 and input the tabulated data again.)

This file contains information about the ages of 60 employees of the firm Merlin plc.

5.2.1 Inputting data from an Minitab datafile on your floppy disk: Open Minitab and then from the Data Editor window select *File/Open Worksheet* from your floppy disk select Merlin. Your data appears in the Worksheet window.

5.2.2 Look at the data sheet. The ages of the 60 employees are displayed in the first column. If you have just typed them in, then check the numbers carefully with the tabulated data.

Data summary

5.2.3 Summarise the data by its main summary statistics.

> *Stat/Basic Statistics/Display Descriptive Statistics* and select AGE as your Variable.

- What is the mean age of the employees?.....................................
- What is the standard deviation of these ages?..............................
- What is the median of the ages? ....
- State the minimum, maximum and range of the ages..........................
- State the quartiles and interquartile range of the ages....................

5.2.4 Repeat the descriptive statistics above but also produce some graphs.

> *Stat/Basic Statistics/Display Descriptive Statistics* and select AGE as your Variable.

> From *Graphs* select *Histogram of data* with *normal curve, Boxplot of data* and *Graphical summary.*

- Do the histogram and box plot show the data to be to be reasonably symmetrical? ....

For future reference note that the graphical summary is a good source of information.

Comparing two groups

5.2.5 Next split the employees into two separate groups, male (1) and female (2), by coding the data. Type the word **Sex** in the heading of the first empty column. Type **1** in the first 40 cells of the column and **2** in the remaining 20 cells.

5.2.6   Check that the number in each group is correct:

Stat/Tables/Tally. Display Counts. Select SEX as the variable.

5.2.7   *Graph/Pie Charts.* Select SEX for Chart data in

- What percentage of the employees are male? . . . .

5.2.8   The two groups can now be compared:

Stat/Basic Statistics/Display Descriptive Statistics and select AGE as your Variable, click in the *By variable* box and select SEX.

- State the median for each group . . . .
- State the mean and standard deviation for each group . . . .
- State the interquartile range for each group. . . . .
- For which sex are the ages higher, on average? Give two reasons?. . . . .
  . . . .
- For which sex are the ages more spread out, on average? Give two reasons? . . . .
  . . . .

5.2.9   Repeat the descriptive statistics above but also get the boxplots.

Stat/Basic Statistics/Display Descriptive Statistics and select AGE as your Variable. From *Graphs* select **Boxplot of data**.

- Do the box plots illustrate the same results? . . . .

5.2.10 Save this enlarged data file on your floppy disk:

File/Save Current Worksheet as . . . **Merlin2**

5.2.11 Print out your output:

In the Session window *File/Print window*

15.5.3 Estimation and hypothesis testing with Minitab

In this worksheet we shall use the data input in Worksheet 15.5.1, Merlin.mtw, as our population. We shall calculate its summary statistics, and use it as a population to provide a random sample from which we shall estimate the population parameters and then test various hypotheses about that population (conveniently forgetting that we actually know the true values for the population!).

5.3.1   Open Minitab and input your file, Merlin.mtw, saved in Worksheet 15.5.1. If you have not saved the data turn back to that section and type it in.

With your cursor in the worksheet *File/Open Worksheet* and select *Merlin*

5.3.2 Calculate the summary statistics for all the ages and look at their graphical descriptions:

> *Stat/Basic statistics/Display Descriptive statistics/* Select AGE
> *Stat/Basic statistics/Display Descriptive statistics/* Select AGE/ Select *Graphs* and *Graphical Summary*

Make a note of the mean value.

5.3.3 Take a random sample of 10 cases:

> *Calc/Random data/Sample from Columns* Type **10** in *Samples rows*, click in the box underneath and select AGE. *Store samples in* **C4**. Check in your data window and label column 4 as **Sample1**.

5.3.4 Test your sample for normality:

> *Stat/Basic Statistics/Normality Test/Kolmogorov-Smirnov/* Select Sample as variable

The Approximate P-value at the end gives the probability that the population is normal.

• What is your value?. . . . .

You will probably find that it is over 0.05 so the data can be considered to be normally distributed.

5.3.5 Find a confidence interval for the mean of all the ages:

> *Stat/Basic Statistics/Display Descriptive Statistics/* Select *Sample1/* Select *Graphs* and *Graphical Summary* Leave the confidence interval at **95%**

• Does this interval include the mean age found in Task 5.3.2?. . . . .

Repeat, changing the interval to 90%. Compare the two intervals.

5.3.6 Forgetting that we actually know the true value of the population mean, test the hypothesis that the mean age of all the employees is 50.

> *Stat/Basic Statistics/1-Sample t/* Select *Sample1* for the variable, test the mean of **50**, leaving the alternative hypothesis as *not equal.*

The P-value gives the probability that the null hypothesis of 50 years is correct.

• State this value. . . . .

You will probably find that this is lower than 0.05.

  Repeat for the null hypothesis that the mean age is 40 years.

• State this value. . . . .

You will probably now find that it is higher than 0.05 so 40 is acceptable as a claim for the mean age of the population at 5% significance.

  Unfortunately Minitab will not allow us to use different significance levels.

5.3.7 In a new column, C5, Type **1** in rows 1 to 30 and **2** in rows 31 to 60. Label the column **Sex**.

  We shall assume that the first 30 employees are male and the last 30 female.

  Take a new sample of 20 (see Task 5.3.3 if uncertain) selecting AGE and SEX as the columns and store the data in the next two unused columns to give a large enough sample from each sex. Label these two new columns **Age2** and **Sex2**

5.3.8 Calculate separate confidence intervals and see if they overlap.

> *Stat/Basic Statistics/Display Descriptive Statistics*/Select AGE2 for *Variables,* tick *By variable* and select SEX2.

Produce a graphical summary with a 95% confidence interval.

- Do the intervals overlap? . . . .
- What does this mean? . . . .

5.3.9 Carry out a two sample t-test to see if the males and females in the whole population have the same mean ages.

> *Stat/Basic Statistics/2-Sample t/Samples in one column/Samples* AGE2/*Subscripts* SEX2.

The P-value on the last line gives the probability that there is no difference between the means.

- State this value. . . . .
- What do you conclude? . . . .

5.3.10 Save this updated file as Merlin3.mtw on your floppy disk.

> *File/Save Current Worksheet as* **Merlin3.mtw**

15.5.4 Analysis of variance with Minitab

One-way ANOVA

One-way ANOVA can be thought of as an extension to the *two-sample t-test*.

5.4.1 *Open Worksheet* Merlin3 saved while working through the Worksheet 15.5.3.

5.4.2 Check by describing the variable, AGE, to be used in this analysis:

> *Stat/Basic Statistics/Display Descriptive Statistics* **AGE**

5.4.3 Carry out a 2-sample t-test on ages grouped by sex.

> *Stat/Basic Statistics/2-Sample t/Samples in one column/Samples* AGE *Subscripts* SEX/*Alternative not equal*

- State the mean values for the males and the females. . . . .
- The null hypothesis for this test is that the means are the same, that is, that the difference is zero. What is the probability that this is true?. . . . .
- What do you conclude? . . . .

5.4.4 *Stat/ANOVA/One-way/Responses* AGE/ *Factor* SEX

- State the null hypothesis . . . .
- What is the probability that it is true? . . . .
- What do you conclude? . . . .
- Look at the confidence interval for each of the means.
  Indicate why these lead to the same conclusion . . . .
- Compare with the results of Task 5.4.3.

5.4.5   In the first empty column type **Jobcat** for the heading and the following list of codes (without spaces which are there just to ease checking)

Type in the codes:

```
4 3 4 1 1   3 3 3 2 1   2 1 1 3 4   1 4 4 2 1   2 1 3 2 3   1 3 3 1 2
1 3 3 3 3   1 1 2 4 1   2 1 1 3 3   1 3 2 3 3   3 1 1 2 3   3 1 3 3 3
```

(1 = Clerical, 2 = Management, 3 = Production, 4 = Security)

Save your revised file as **Merlin4**

5.4.6   *Stat/ANOVA/One-way/Response Variable* AGE/*Factor* JOBCAT.
- State the null hypothesis . . . .
- State the alternative hypothesis . . . .
- What is the probability that the null hypothesis is true? . . . .
- What do you conclude? . . . .
- Look at the confidence interval for each of the means.
  Indicate why these lead to the same conclusion. . . . .
- Which levels of JOBCAT differ in their mean ages? . . . .

Two-way ANOVA

Two-way ANOVA is the simplest extension of *One-way ANOVA*.
  We shall now split the ages by both factors simultaneously.

5.4.7   *Stat/ANOVA/General Linear Model/Responses* AGE/ *Model* JOBCAT, SEX and JOBCAT * SEX
- State the three null hypotheses . . . .
  . . . .
- State the three alternative hypotheses . . . .
  . . . .
- What are the probabilities that each null hypothesis is true? . . . .
- What do you conclude? . . . .
Since the interactions are not significant we can just consider the main effects

5.4.8   *Stat/ANOVA/General Linear Model/Responses* AGE/*Model* JOBCAT and SEX
- State the two null hypotheses . . . .
  . . . .
- State the two alternative hypotheses . . . .
  . . . .
- What are the probabilities that each null hypothesis is true? . . . .
- What do you conclude? . . . .

5.4.9   Carry out a two-way analysis of variance, without interactions, for the laboratories and brand of peanut butter as given in Tutorial Question 8.3.
  You will need one column for all the fat contents, another column for the laboratory codes: 1 = A, 2 = B, etc., and a third for the brands.
  Use the output to answer Tutorial Question 8.3.

5.4.10 Carry out a two-way analysis of variance for the electronics firm data, without interactions, in Tutorial Question 8.4.

You will need one column for all numbers of monitors produced, another column for the employees: 1 = A, 2 = B, etc., and a third for the times of day.

Use the output to answer Tutorial Question 8.4.

15.5.5 Correlation and regression with Minitab

During this tutorial you will learn how to use Minitab to investigate the association between two continuous variables and how to describe it graphically

5.5.1 In this practical session you will analyse the some bivariate data.
To enter the data:

File/Open Worksheet/ **Merlin4** (saved in the ANOVA worksheet, 15.5.4)

In order to see what this file contains: Open the Information window; *Window/Info*. This window gives details of the data stored in the file merlin4.mtw which you are going to analyse.

We shall give each of the cases a salary, in £'000, and then see if it is associated with their age.

In the first empty column: name the variable Salary (£000) and type the following in one column (work down these columns one after the other):

38.1	38.9	23.2	22.9	19.8	19.7	15.6	31.7	17.3	37.8
18.7	42.8	19.6	47.5	31.3	8.5	28.5	14.1	33.5	32.9
42.3	60.1	15.5	15.8	59.3	15.9	37.3	20.3	13.7	9.8
25.9	60.7	20.7	35.9	33.8	39.3	32.9	19.8	6.4	15.2
53.6	75.2	40.2	25.3	24.5	14.5	23.9	28.2	35.3	8.7
37.6	10.9	28.5	63.2	32.0	10.2	8.6	25.3	12.5	38.4

The variables of interest in this practical session are the continuous variables SALARY and AGE. We shall investigate the relationship between the salaries earned by the employees of Merlin and their ages.

5.5.2 Save revised worksheet as **Merlin5.mtw**

5.5.3 Produce a Scatterplot to see if there appears to be a linear relationship?

*Graph/Plot/*Select SALARY for Y and AGE for X

● Examine the plot. Does it suggest a linear relationship? . . . .

The graph from the above command does not appear in the session printout. To produce one which does:

*Graph/Character Graphs/Scatter Plot/*Select SALARY as the Y-variable and AGE as the X-variable.

5.5.4 Calculate the correlation coefficient.

Stat/Basic Statistics/Correlation/Select SALARY and AGE as the variables.

● What is the value of the correlation coefficient? . . . .

● What is the probability of it being zero? . . . .

● Is this significant at 5%? . . . .

If the p value is less than 0.05 the correlation coefficient is significant at the 5% level of significance.

5.5.5   Find the regression equation:

   *Stat/Regression/Regression/*Select SALARY for Response, AGE for Predictors.

• Write down the regression equation . . . .

The last output was for the default setting. Minitab can calculate and store the fitted values and the standardised residuals for each observation.

   Edit/Edit Last Dialog The last dialogue box reopens.

   Under *Storage* select *Residuals, Standard resids and Fits.*

   Check that three new columns have been added to your worksheet.

5.5.6   Save this altered version of your file at this stage under a new name Merlin6

   File/Save Worksheet as . . **Merlin6**

5.5.7   Investigate the fitted values:

   Graph/Character Graphs/Scatter Plot

   Select FITS1 as the Y-variable and AGE as the X-variable.

This produces a straight line as all the fitted values lie on the regression line.
   To fit this line to a scatter plot requires a graphics plot:

   Graph/Plot SALARY against AGE as before.

   From *Frame* drop down menu select *Multiple Graphs, Overlay graphs on same page.*

   From *Annotation* drop-down menu select *Line,* click *Points* drop down menu,
   Use Variables, Click in *Use columns.* Then select AGE followed by FITS1.

   OK the three dialogue boxes that are open .

5.5.8   To print this graph which will not appear in your Session file:

   File/Print Window

5.5.9   To predict a Y-value for a given X-value, for example the salary of a 40 year old:

   Stat/Regression/Regression

   Select SALARY and AGE as before and then select *Options.*

   Type **40** in the prediction intervals for new observations.

The output gives the predicted value for y when x is 40 with a confidence interval and prediction interval for this predicted y-value.

• What is the predicted value of y when x is 40? . . . .

5.5.10 To produce the regression line with its confidence interval and prediction interval:

   Stat/Regression/Fitted Line Plot/Options: Display Confidence and Prediction bands.

   Select SALARY and AGE as before. Print this window as before.

5.5.11 To print your session, make sure that your Session window is in front of any others:

   File/Print Window

15.5.6 Time series analysis and forecasting with Minitab

Unfortunately Minitab does not combine a moving average trend with seasonal decomposition. We shall therefore look at its default method of combining a linear trend with seasonal decomposition and compare its output with a reproduction of the analysis previously worked by hand.

In this worksheet we will just analyse seasonal data. Exponential smoothing and curve fitting can be carried out quite easily in Minitab by following the instructions in the Help menu.

The quarterly sales of a departmental store have been monitored for the past five years with the following information being produced (Tutorial Question 12.1):

	Total quarterly sales (£0000s)			
Year	Quarter 1	Quarter 2	Quarter 3	Quarter 4
1996	48	58	57	65
1997	50	61	59	68
1998	52	62	59	69
1999	52	64	60	73
2000	53	65	60	75

5.6.1 Enter the data. Type all the sales figures in chronological order in one column heading it **Sales**.

5.6.2 Plot a sequence graph of sales to see if an additive model seems appropriate.

> *Stat/Time Series/Time Series Plot* SALES

5.6.3 Assuming the data to be seasonal, carry out the seasonal decomposition using an additive model:

> *Stat/Time Series/Decomposition/Seasonal length 4/Additive/Trend plus seasonal*
> Select SALES. and storing *Trend, Residuals* and *Fits*.

Also ask for four forecasts.

5.6.4 Plot a sequence graph of sales with trend to see if an additive model seems appropriate.

> *Stat/Time Series/Time Series Plot* SALES and TREND
> In *Frame* select *Multiple Graphs* and *Overlay graphs on the same page.*

5.6.5 *Residual analysis:*

Remember that the residuals should: (a) be small, (b) have a mean of 0, (c) have a standard deviation which is much smaller than that of sales, (d) be normally distributed and (e) be random timewise. The residuals have been saved as RESI1.

(a), (b), (c) Produce descriptive statistics of sales and RESI1.

(d) For RES1 produce a boxplot and a histogram with a normal plot.
Carry out the K-S hypothesis test for normality:

Stat/Basic Statistics/Normality Test/Kolmogorov-Smirnov

(e) Produce a time series plot of the errors.

Graph/Time Series Plot RESI1

Do these look to be a good set of residuals?

We are now going to build up a moving trend plus seasonal factor model.

5.6.6 Using Minitab to produce the moving average:

Stat/Time Series/Moving Average/MA length 4/Centre the moving averages.
Store Moving averages.

5.6.7 Head the next column **Seasonal** and type in the appropriate seasonal factors as produced by the deseasonal composition in Task 15.6.3. These were -8.83, $+1.92$, -1.14 and $+8.05$ for quarters 1 to 4 respectively.
Calculate the **FITTED** values as AVER1 + SEASONAL

Calc/Calculator/Store result in variable **Fitted**/*Expression* AVER1 + SEASONAL

5.6.8 Plot a sequence graph of sales, trend and fitted values to see if this model seems any better.

Stat/TimeSeries/Time Series Plot SALES, TREND and FITTED

In *Frame* select *Multiple Graphs* and *Overlay graphs on the same page.*

Does this model look a closer fit?

5.6.9 Calculate the residuals from this model as RESI2 = SALES − FITTED

5.6.10 Compare residuals:
(a), (b), (c) Produce descriptive statistics of Sales and RESI1, RESI2.
(d) For the errors produce box plots and histograms with a normal plots.
Carry out the K-S hypothesis test for normality:

Stat/Basic Statistics/NormalityTest/Kolmogorov-Smirnov

(e) Produce a time series plots of both sets of errors.

Graph/Time Series Plot RESI1 RESI2

Which set look preferable?

5.6.11 Assuming that the trend from the additive model is increasing by 0.3 per quarter, what would be your forecasts for the four quarters of 2001? Compare with those produced in Task 5.6.3.

15.6 Numerical answers to Minitab worksheets

15.5.1 *Graphical presentation*

All graphical output. Full output is given in the lecturers' materials on the Internet.

15.5.2 Summary statistics

5.2.3   37.75;   11.04;   39.00;   17, 64, 47;   32.0, 45.75, 13.75 years

5.2.4   Yes

5.2.7   66.7%

5.2.8   Male 39.5, Female 36.5 years;
Male 38.25, 11.08, Female 36.75, 11.17 years

5.2.9   Male 'averages' higher;   Female 'spreads' higher

15.5.3 Estimation and hypothesis testing

5.3.2   37.75 years

5.3.4   > 0.15

5.3.5   24.3 to 45.9 years;   Yes

5.3.6   0.012;   0.33

5.3.8   Yes, so mean ages could be the same.

5.3.9   0.88, mean ages could be the same.

15.5.4 Analysis of variance

5.4.3   38.9, 36.6 years;   0.41;   they are the same.

5.4.4   0.411;   they are the same;   the confidence intervals overlap.

5.4.6   0.000;   at least two are different;   many do not overlap;
all different apart from production and security.

5.4.7   0.804, 0.000, 0.713;   different for job category, same for sex and interaction.

5.4.8   0.229, 0.000;   different for job category, same for sex.

5.4.9   Sig. (labs) = 0.383, sig.(brands) = 0.079;   both same at 5% significance.

5.4.10 Sig. (shifts) = 0.028, sig.(employees) = 0.276 only shifts different.

15.5.5 Correlation and regression analysis

5.5.4   0.398;   0.002;   Yes.

5.5.5   Salary = 7.73 + 0.554 × Age

5.5.9   29.9, £29 900

15.5.6 Time series Analysis and Forecasting

Graphical output with most answers only approximate.

15.7 Introduction to Excel

Excel is a 'spreadsheet, graphics and database management tool' produced by Microsoft. It is widely used as a spreadsheet in business and finance but makes no claim to be a statistical package. Even with the 'Add-in' capabilities available, its scope is limited and there is occasionally conflict between the answers produced by the 'Add-in' and by the equivalent function in Excel itself. The Data Analysis Add-in was not produced by Microsoft and they are not willing to support it. However some types of statistical analysis, both graphical and numerical, can be carried out in Excel so it can be useful if neither SPSS nor Minitab are available. However, the results must be interpreted with caution.

Excel offers the facilities common to all Windows applications and is part of Microsoft Office. The version used in these worksheets is Excel 97 which is included in the Office 98 suite. No tutorial is included in the package but there is a fairly comprehensive Help facility. Many business textbooks include the use of Excel.

Numerical data and variable names are typed into the worksheet and the results may be produced on a different sheet or included in the current one. The output can be edited, saved or printed out. Probably the neatest method of display is to cut and paste it into Word, especially if it is to form part of a report or project.

15.8 Excel worksheets

The aim of these worksheets is to carry out statistical analysis in the most efficient manner available with Excel. No use will be made of formulae but rather of the functions provided by Excel itself or its Data analysis ToolPak from the Add-ins under Tools on the Toolbar.

Throughout this tutorial *selections from menus, dialogue boxes or buttons* are shown in *bold italics* separated by the slash sign / and the **characters you need to type** are in bold. The degree of detail in the instructions decreases as your experience increases.

The assumption is made throughout that you have not used Excel previously even though you are familiar with Windows.

All numerical answers to these worksheets are to be found in Section 15.9 but note that some are from the analysis of random samples so your answers will be different. (The full output from all the sheets, including the graphics, is included in the lecturers' materials on the Internet.)

15.8.1 Graphical presentation with Excel

Task

8.1.1 Opening Excel

Menus on your local network may be set up in a variety of ways and the method of opening Excel will differ from one to another.

Open *Microsoft Excel*

You are now in Excel with Sheet 1 of Book 1 open. This is where you will put all your data with appropriate variable names and present the graphs produced from it. Each cell, starting at A1, is identified by a letter for its column and a number for its row. The sheet has far more rows and columns than you will need for these worksheets.

8.1.2 Putting your data into Excel

The data we shall use in this worksheet represent the ages of a sample of 60 employees of a firm Merlin plc. Place the cursor in A1 and type **Ages of a sample of employees at Merlin plc.** In cell A3 type **Ages (years)**, this is the variable to be described. You can move around the worksheet using the arrow keys.

Now place the cursor in A4 and type in the first age, **35**, which will appear in the formulae bar and also in the appropriate cell. Carry on down column 1 filling in all the ages in that column, then work down column 2, and so on. Your final figure should be in cell A63.

The following figures represent the ages of a sample of 60 male employees of a firm Merlin plc:

35	44	54	33	46	20	32	19	50	39	33	37
42	40	20	25	34	52	27	22	18	40	23	17
41	45	21	34	49	27	60	46	32	58	23	52
24	64	41	47	54	37	40	41	40	36	46	29
34	39	39	40	37	50	41	34	47	34	45	36

8.1.3 Checking your input

You may find it easier to check figures on a hard copy so print out the data:

File/Print/Active sheet

Check the values with those above. If any is incorrect, just overtype the correct version into the worksheet.

8.1.4 Saving your data as a file

Now that you are happy with the data save it to a disk.

File/Save As **a:Merlin**

This has now been saved as an Excel data file Merlin.xls on your floppy disk in the drive A.

8.1.5 Producing a histogram

Excel produces an ordered bar chart rather than a histogram. We shall first produce the default histogram and then another more refined version.

Tools/Data analysis/Histogram/Input range Either type in **A4:A63** or select the same range with the cursor. Select *Output range* **C4** to determine the position of the output. (Any other suitable location may be used.)

By default the output has produced a frequency table split into 8 equal intervals which do not have very convenient limits. It also lacks a graph.

Type the numbers **20 30 40 50 60** and **70** in cells B4 to B9 and repeat the last commands adding the range **B4:B9** as the 'Bin range'. Also select *Chart output*.

8.1.6   Improving the graph

This improves the horizontal axis but the vertical may still leave much to be desired. Select the histogram by clicking on it. Increase its vertical scale by pulling down on one of the bottom black handles. This diagram is not a true histogram which should be continuous on the horizontal scale. It is really an ordered bar chart.

By selecting your histogram and selecting the appropriate dialogue box, colours, fonts, patterns, and so on can be edited. *Chart/Options* also allows editing. Have a play!

Charts can be positioned anywhere in the spreadsheet by selecting and dragging.

8.1.7   Producing a cumulative frequency diagram

Repeat the histogram command with the bin ranges as already selected and an output range somewhere free, probably C25. This time click on *Cumulative Percentage*.

There are no facilities for drawing stem-and-leaf, box and whisker or dot plots in Excel.

8.1.8   Printing out the Worksheet

When you have completed your session you probably have many errors in your worksheet. These can be deleted by highlighting the unwanted sections and deleting them as you would in Word. Charts may be dragged around to tidy the sheet up. When you are happy with the remaining material, print it out:

File/Print Active Worksheet for everything.

Alternatively all the output except the long column of data may be selected with the cursor and:

File/Print Selection can be used.

8.1.9   Saving data and graphical output (if required)

File/Save as **a:MerlinGr** to indicate that graphs have been added to Merlin.xls.

15.8.2 Summary statistics with Excel

Inputting data from an Excel datafile:

We shall again use the data which you typed into Excel in Worksheet 15.8.1 as the file Merlin.xls and then saved on your floppy disk. This file contains information about the ages of 60 employees of the firm Merlin plc. (If, by any chance you do not have it, refer to Worksheet 15.8.1 and input the tabulated data again.)

8.2.1   Inputting data from an Excel file on your floppy disk: Open Microsoft Excel and then:

File/Open and from your floppy disk select *Merlin*.

The data appears in the Worksheet.

8.2.2   Look at the data sheet. The ages of the 60 employees are displayed in the first column. If just typed them in, check the numbers carefully with the tabulated data in 8.1.2.

Data summary

8.2.3 Summarise the data by its main summary statistics. (Again the positioning of the output is only a suggestion.)

> *Tools/Data analysis/Descriptive Statistics/Input range* **A3:A63**/*Output range* **D4**
>
> Tick *Labels in first row* and *Summary statistics* Widen column D to read the terms.

- What is the mean age of the employees? . . . .
- What is the standard deviation of these ages? . . . .
- State the mode and the median of the ages . . . .
- State the minimum, maximum and range of the ages . . . .

Comparing two groups

8.2.4 Split the employees into two separate groups, male $=1$ and female $=2$, by coding the data. Type the word **Sex** into B3. Type **1** into B4. Pull the handle of the box surrounding B4 down to B43 to copy the '1' into the first 40 cells. Type 2 into B44 and copy down as far as B63. The first 40 cases are males, the last 20 females.

8.2.5 Save this enlarged data file on your floppy disk:

> *File/Save as* **a:Merlin2**

8.2.6 Check that the number in each group is correct:

> Type **0, 1, 2, 3** in cells C4 to C7 respectively.
>
> *Tools/Data analysis/Histogram/Input range* Either type in **B4:B63** or select the same range with the cursor. Then *Bin range* **C4:C7**/*Output range* **G4** to determine the position of the output. Check your frequencies.

8.2.7

> *Insert/Chart.* Select *Pie* for Chart/ *Next* Data range **H6:H7** (from frequency output)/ *Next/Data Labels/Show label and percent/Finish*

- What percentage of the employees are male? . . . .

Drag the graph to a reasonable position and resize it.

8.2.8 The two groups can now be compared:

> *Tools/Data analysis/Descriptive Statistics/Input range* **A3:A43**/*Output range* **D20**
>
> Tick *Labels in first row* and *Summary statistics*. (Add **Ages(male)** to title of this output.)
>
> *Tools/Data analysis/Descriptive Statistics/Input range* **A44:A63**/*Output range* **D36**
>
> Untick *Labels in first row* keep *Summary statistics*. (Add **Ages(female)** to the title.)

- State the median for each group . . . .
- State the mean and standard deviation for each group . . . .
- For which sex are the ages higher, on average? Give two reasons . . . .
  . . . .
- Looking at the standard deviation, for which sex are the ages more spread out? . . . . .

8.2.9   Print out your output:
Select the output you wish to print out:

 File/Print selection

8.2.10 Save your output:

 File/Save as **a:Merlin2Gr** to indicate that graphs have been added to Merlin2.xls.

15.8.3 Estimation and hypothesis testing with Excel

In this worksheet we shall use the data saved in Worksheet 15.8.1, Merlin.xls, as our population. We shall again calculate its summary statistics, and then use it as a population from which to provide a random sample. From this sample we shall estimate the population parameters and then test various hypotheses about that population (conveniently forgetting that we actually know the true values for the population!).

8.3.1   Open Excel and input your file, Merlin.xls, saved in Worksheet 15.8.1. If you have not saved the data turn back to that section and type it in.
 With your cursor in the worksheet *File/Open* and select *Merlin*

8.3.2   Calculate again the summary statistics for all the ages:

 Tools/Data analysis/Descriptive Statistics/Input range **A3:A63**/*Output range* **I4**

 Tick *Labels in first row* and *Summary statistics*. Widen column I to read the terms.

• Make a note of the mean value . . . .

8.3.3   Take a random sample of 10 cases:

 Tools/Data analysis/Sampling/Input range **A4:A63**/*Method Random*/
 No. of samples **10**/*Output range* **C4**

 Label column **Sample Age** in C3

8.3.4   Test your sample for normality. (Excel does not offer a normality test so a histogram will be used as an indication.)

 Type the numbers **20, 30, 40, 50** and **60** into D4:D8 to set as the bin range.

 Tools/Data analysis/Histogram/Input range Either type in **C4:C13** or select the same range with the cursor/*Bin range* **D4:D8**/*Output range* **I20** and ask for *Chart output*.

• Does your histogram look reasonably normal? . . . .

(Unless it seems a long way off normal, assume normality. If it does seem very skewed take a new sample.)

8.3.5   Find a confidence interval for the mean of all the ages: (Don't use the function wizard as this uses z instead of t in the calculation giving an incorrect result.)

 Tools/Data analysis/Descriptive statistics/Input range **C4:C13**/*Summary statistics* and *Confidence level.*

• Make a note of the sample mean . . . .

Despite Excel's description this result is not the confidence interval but the half interval on either side of the mean, $ts/\sqrt{n}$. If your result is c then your confidence interval is $\bar{x} \pm c$.
Calculate your interval.

• Does this interval include the mean age found in Task 8.3.2? . . . .

Repeat, changing the alpha value to 0.10.
Label these outputs **SampleAge** and compare the two intervals.

8.3.6   As Excel does not offer a one sample t-test the sample cannot be used to test for the value of the population mean. This is assumed to be within the 95% confidence interval found in the last task.

8.3.7   In a new column, E, Type **1** in rows 4 to 33 and **2** in rows 34 to 63 (see Task 8.2.4). Label the column **Sex**. We shall assume that the first 30 employees are male and the last 30 female.

Take two new samples of 10 (see Task 8.3.3 if uncertain), one for the males and one for the females and store the data in the next two unused columns, F and G. Label these columns **MaleAge** and **FemaleAge** respectively.

8.3.8   Calculate separate confidence intervals for the males and females and see if they overlap.

Produce summary statistics for both sexes, as in Task 8.3.5, putting the outputs in I45 and L45 respectively. Label the outputs **MaleAges** and **FemaleAges** respectively.
Calculate each 95% confidence interval as in Task 8.3.5.

• Do the intervals overlap? . . . .
• What does this mean? . . . .

8.3.9   Carry out a two sample t-test to see if the males and females in the whole population have the same mean ages. In order to decide which test to use the variances of the two samples must be compared for equality.

> *Tools/Data analysis/F-Test Two-sample Variances/Variable 1 range* **F4:F13**/ *Variable 2 range* **G4:G13**/*Hypothesised Mean Difference* 0/*Output range* **I62**.

• State value of p(F<=f) one-tail . . . .

If this value >=0.05 the two variances are not significantly different, i.e. they are equal; if < 0.05 they are unequal. Select the next test accordingly.

> *Tools/Data analysis/tTest for Two Samples assuming (Un)Equal variance/ Variable 1 range* **F4:F13**/*Variable 2 range* **G4:G13**/*Hypothesised difference* 0/*Alpha* **0.05**/*Output range* **L62**.

The $P(T \leq t)$ two tail is the probability of there being no difference between the population means.

• State this value. . . . .
• What do you conclude? . . . .

8.3.10   Save this updated file as **Merlin3Gr** on your floppy disk.

8.3.11   Delete any output produced and save the data as **Merlin3** on your floppy disk.

15.8.4 Analysis of variance with Excel

One-way ANOVA

One-way ANOVA can be thought of as an extension to the *two-sample t-test*.

8.4.1   *Open file* **Merlin3** saved while working through the Worksheet 15.8.3.

8.4.2   Check by describing the variable Age, to be used in this analysis:

Tools/Data analysis/Descriptive Statistics/Input range **A3:A63**/*Output range* **I4**
Tick *Labels in first row* and *Summary statistics*. Widen column C to read the terms.

• Make a note of the mean and standard deviation:. . . . .

8.4.3   Carry out an appropriate 2-sample t-test on Ages grouped by Sex. (Reminder from last worksheet.)

Tools/Data analysis/tTest for Two Samples assuming (Un)Equal variance/
Variable 1 range **F4:F13**/*Variable 2 range* **G4:G13**/*Hypothesised difference* **0**/
Alpha **0.05**/*Output range* **L4.**

The $P(T \leq t)$ two tail is the probability of there being no difference between the population means.

• State this value. . . . .
• What do you conclude? . . . .

8.4.4

Tools/Data analysis/Anova:Single factor/Input range **F4:G13**/*Alpha* **0.05**/*Output range* **I20**

• State the null hypothesis . . . .
• What is the probability that it is true? . . . .
• What do you conclude? . . . .

Compare with results of Task 8.4.3. You should reach the same conclusion even though this is an F-test and the previous one a t-test.

8.4.5   In column B type **Jobcat** (job category) for the heading and type in following list of codes (top row first):

```
4 3 4 1 1   3 3 3 2 1   2 1 1 3 4   1 4 4 2 1   2 1 3 2 3   1 3 3 1 2
1 3 3 3 3   1 1 2 4 1   2 1 1 3 3   1 3 2 3 3   3 1 1 2 3   3 1 3 3 3
```
(1 = Clerical, 2 = Management, 3 = Production, 4 = Security)

Save your revised file as **Merlin4** (to save typing in this data again).

8.4.6   Separating the ages for each of the Job categories

Data/Sort/Sort by JOBCAT in ascending order

Copy and paste the ages of each of the four Jobcat groups into separate columns labelling them accordingly.

8.4.7   Repeating Task 8.4.5 but for all the data as we now have four groups:

> *Tools/Data analysis/Anova: single factor/Input range* **A4:B63**/*Alpha* **0.05**/ *Output range* **I35**

- State the null hypothesis . . . .
- State the alternative hypothesis . . . .
- The p-value of 6.62×10^{-10} is so small that you can take it as zero. What do you conclude? . . . .

If you look closely at the output you will find that, even though four groups have been analysed, only one degree of freedom has been used in the analysis. Obviously this result is not valid.

8.4.8   Save this updated file as **Merlin4Gr** on your floppy disk.

8.4.9   Delete any output produced and save the data as **Merlin4** on your floppy disk.

15.8.5 Correlation and regression with Excel

During this tutorial you will learn how to use Excel to investigate the association between two continuous variables and how to describe it graphically

8.5.1   In this practical session you will analyse some bivariate data. To enter the data:

> *File/Open* **Merlin** (saved in the first worksheet, 15.8.1)

We shall give each of the cases a salary, in £000, and then see if this is associated with their age.
    In column B name the variable Salary, and type the following figures into one column (work down these columns one after the other):

38.1	38.9	23.2	22.9	19.8	19.7	15.6	31.7	17.3	37.8
18.7	42.8	19.6	47.5	31.3	8.5	28.5	14.1	33.5	32.9
42.3	60.1	15.5	15.8	59.3	15.9	37.3	20.3	13.7	9.8
25.9	60.7	20.7	35.9	33.8	39.3	32.9	19.8	6.4	15.2
53.6	75.2	40.2	25.3	24.5	14.5	23.9	28.2	35.3	8.7
37.6	10.9	28.5	63.2	32.0	10.2	8.6	25.3	12.5	38.4

The variables of interest in this practical session are the continuous variables, Salary and Age. We shall investigate the relationship between the salaries earned by the employees of Merlin and their ages.

8.5.2   Save revised worksheet as **Merlin5**

8.5.3   Produce a Scatterplot

> Select the *Chart wizard* on the top tool bar. Select the *XY (Scatter)* and then the version without any lines. *Next/Data range* **A4:B63**/*Series in columns/Next/Chart title* **Salary v Age**/*Value (X) Axis* **Age**/*Next/Value (Y) Axis* **Salary (£000)**/*Place as object in Sheet 1/Finish*

(You may need to reposition and increase the height of the chart.)

- Examine the plot. Does it suggest a linear relationship? . . . .

8.5.4   Calculate the correlation coefficient.

   Tools/Data analysis/Correlation
   Input range **A3:B63**/*Labels in first row/Output range* **D22**.

- What is the value of the correlation coefficient? . . . .
- Given the critical value is 0.250 for a sample of 64 (Table D6),
  is it significant at 5%?. . . . .

8.5.5   Find the regression equation:

   Tools/Data analysis/Regression/Input Y range **B4:B63**/*Input X range* **A4:A63**

The equation is not immediately apparent. You will find the values of *a* and *b* under 'coefficients'.

- What is the regression equation. . . . .

The last output was for the default setting. Excel can also calculate and store the fitted values and the residuals for each observation.

   Tools/Data analysis/Regression/Input Y range **B4:B63**/*Input X range* **A4:A63**
   Add *Residuals, Residual plots, Line fit plots* and *Normality plots*.

This command has put the regression line through the data, the residuals and predicted values have been saved and also some residual plots produced. (You may need to separate out your plots and possibly change their vertical scales for easier interpretation.)

8.5.6   Save this altered version of your file at this stage under a new name MerlinGr6

   File/Save as. **Merlin6Gr**

8.5.7   Investigate the graphs in the output:
- Consider the fitted line plot: does the data seem a close fit to the line? . . . .
- Consider the X Variable 1 residual plot: do the residuals seem to be random
  when plotted against X?. . . . .
- Consider the normal probability plot: are the residuals plotted on a
  straight line, indicating normality? . . . .

All are reasonable but none ideal.

8.5.8   The residuals have rather large values so we shall analyse them.

   Tools/Data analysis/Descriptive statistics/Input range (the range of cells holding
   your residuals, possibly F70 to F129)

The mean is nearly zero but the standard deviation should be much smaller. This reflects the wide spread of the original data about the regression line.

8.5.9   Save this updated file as **Merlin6Gr** on your floppy disk.

8.5.10   Delete any output produced and save the data as **Merlin6** on your floppy disk.

15.8.6 Time series analysis and forecasting with Excel

Unfortunately Excel does not combine the calculation of a moving average trend with seasonal decomposition. We shall therefore look at its default method of calculating a centred moving average of four values but cannot use this package for forecasting as the only method available for this is linear regression which is unsuitable for seasonal data.

The quarterly sales (£0000s) of a departmental store have been monitored for the past five years with the following information being produced (Tutorial Question 12.1):

		Total quarterly sales (£0000s)		
Year	Quarter 1	Quarter 2	Quarter 3	Quarter 4
1996	48	58	57	65
1997	50	61	59	68
1998	52	62	59	69
1999	52	64	60	73
2000	53	65	60	75

8.6.1   Enter the data all in column A headed **Quarterly Sales (£0 000)**: Type all the sales figures in chronological order in this one column.

8.6.2   Plot a sequence graph of sales to see if an additive model seems appropriate.

> *Chart wizard/Line/Next/Input data A2:A21/Series in columns/Next/*
> *Chart title Quarterly Sales/Category (X) axis Quarters/Value (Y) axis Sales/*
> *Next/As object in sheet 1/Finish*

Increase the height of the graph and double click within it to alter the Scale Minimum to 40. The pattern looks promising, doesn't it?

8.6.3   Assuming quarterly data, carry out a moving average analysis of time period 4:

> *Tools/Data analysis/Moving average/Input range A1:A21/Labels in first row/*
> *Interval 4/Output range C20/Chart output*

Edit this graph as in Task 8.6.2. Note that the forecast in the legend is the moving average trend for the seasonal data and not the appropriate forecast for seasonal data.

8.6.4   Print out the graphs and save the file if you wish.

15.9 Numerical answers to Excel worksheets

Full output is given in the lecturers' materials on the Internet.

15.8.1 Graphical presentation

All graphical output.

15.8.2 Summary statistics

8.2.3 37.75; 11.04; 34, 39; 17, 64, 47 years

8.2.4 Yes

8.2.7 67%

8.2.8 Male 39.5, Female 36.5 years;
Male 38.3, 11.08, Female 36.8, 11.17 years

8.2.9 Female 'spreads' are wider.

15.8.3 Estimation and hypothesis testing

Note: Most of these answers are produced from random samples, so you may have produced values which are different from these.

8.3.2 37.75 years

8.3.5 31.7 to 42.9 years; 32.8 to 41.9 years; Second interval narrower.

8.3.8 33.6 to 41.4 years; 22.8 to 40.6 years; Yes, overlap so could be same.

8.3.9 Mean ages of male and female populations could be the same.

15.8.4 Analysis of variance

8.4.2 37.75, 11.04 years

8.4.3 38.9, 36.6 years; 0.10; No significant difference.

8.4.4 0.193; No significant difference.

8.4.7 6.62×10^{-10}; At least two means are different.

15.8.5 Correlation and regression analysis

8.5.4 0.398; Yes

8.5.5 Salary $= 7.73 + 0.554 \times$ Age

15.8.6 Time series analysis and forecasting

All graphical output without any numerical answers.

16 Revision

16.1 Introduction

You have now completed the course and so no doubt will be faced with some type of assessment. This chapter is intended to help you prepare for this assessment, whether in the form of a multi-choice test or an examination.

For each topic, some of which are grouped as they might appear logically in examination questions, you are offered a very brief summary of the theory covered in the relevant chapter followed by a series of revision questions. These brief summaries are no substitute for re-reading the detail in the relevant chapters. The questions are presented with their **numerical** answers so that you know immediately if you are on the right track and if not can rectify your working before going on to the following question. Make sure that you are confident about the theory which is also examinable.

After the separate topics you are presented with includes two typical exam papers such as those you might meet for an end-of-course examination. The emphasis in these is on the earlier chapters from the course, which might be assessed part way through the course, though some of the later ones are not excluded. The final section an assortment of multi-choice questions which you might find useful before meeting that type of assessment. These deal with the later topics in more depth but may also include some earlier material.

Time spent on sensible revision can increase you exam marks considerably and can, as a last resort, make the difference between success and failure. Do take advantage of the material included here.

16.2 Descriptive and summary statistics

Data can be described **pictorially** by some form of graphical display such as a pie chart or histogram. A picture is generally a very good means of communication. Not only can it provide an immediate overall impression but can include additional information when looked at more closely.

In Chapter 2 you studied bar charts and pie charts for categorical data and histograms, cumulative frequency diagrams and box plots for measurable data.

Nominal and ordinal data are generally described graphically by pie or bar charts (see Figure 16.1).

Interval data can be described by a wider range of diagrams of which histograms are the most common. Those in Figure 16.2 describe the salaries earned by a group of bank employees in US dollars.

Make sure that you are able to construct these diagrams by hand and can also interpret fully any printed diagram of the types usually met in the media.

Figure 16.1 Employment categories in a bank

(a)

(b)

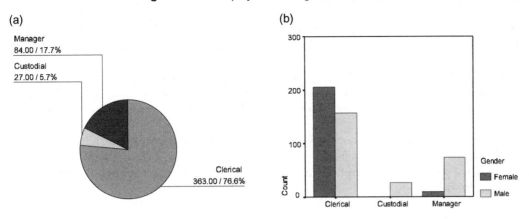

Figure 16.2

(a) Histogram

(b) Box plot

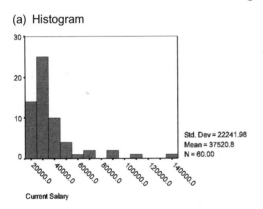

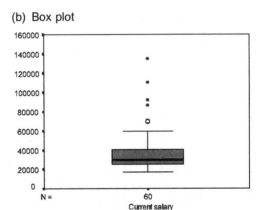

(c) Stem-and-leaf plot

(d) Cumulative frequency diagram

```
Current Salary

Frequency    Stem  &  Leaf
    4.00       1   .  7799
   10.00       2   .  0223344444
   16.00       2   .  5556666666777789
    9.00       3   .  000011344
    4.00       3   .  5678
    6.00       4   .  000133
    1.00       4   .  7
    3.00       5   .  124
    1.00       5   .  9
    6.00   Extremes  (>=69250)
Stem width:   10000

Each leaf:    1 case(s)
```

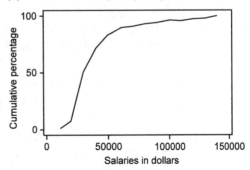

From the histogram you should be able to estimate the mode by using crossed diagonals; from the boxplot estimate approximately the median and interquartile range; from the stem-and-leaf plot identify the median and interquartile range; and from the cumulative frequency diagram estimate the median, quartiles, value below which a given percentage earn and value earned by the top (or bottom) x % by drawing horizontal and vertical lines.

If in doubt refer to Chapter 2 for the methods in detail.

Numerical description (Chapter 3)

Nominal data can only be summarised by frequencies and percentages. For example, how many employees are there in the bank? How many are there of each gender?

Ordinal data can be summarised by medians – the middle members when the data sets are ordered – and range, interquartile range. Frequencies and percentages are also used.
    For example, if job categories are considered to be ordinal, which is the middle one?

Interval data are generally summarised by their mean – the arithmetical average – and their standard deviation which is a measure of their spread. These measures are best found from your calculator but can also be calculated using the formulae in the prelims and Appendix C.
    For example, what is the mean current salary of all the employees and what is their standard deviation?

Revision questions

Note: Answers indicated by $\approx$ are approximations from graphs.

16.1   The following information was collected about the times spent by 200 patients in a doctor's waiting room:

Seat occupation times	Frequency
0 minutes and less than 4 minutes	6
4 minutes and less than 6 minutes	12
6 minutes and less than 8 minutes	19
8 minutes and less than 10 minutes	25
10 minutes and less than 12 minutes	32
12 minutes and less than 16 minutes	36
16 minutes and less than 20 minutes	27
20 minutes and less than 30 minutes	25
30 minutes and less than 40 minutes	18

(a) Calculate the frequency densities, per minute, of this data. Draw a histogram and estimate the modal waiting time. Add a frequency polygon.
                                                                (≈ 10.7 min)

(b) Draw an ogive of the data and estimate the median waiting time and the interquartile range of the times. Estimate how many patients waited for less than 5 minutes and how many more for more than 25 minutes.
                                        (≈ 12.5, ≈ 10 min, ≈ 12, ≈ 31)

(c) Use your calculator to estimate the mean and standard deviation of all waiting times.   (15.14 min and 8.63 min)

(d) What waiting time was exceeded by the 10% of patients who waited longest?
                                                                (≈ 29 min)

16.2 The following table shows the distributions of weekly turnover for 200 newsagents shops owned by ABC Ltd and 300 similar shops owned by XYZ Ltd:

	Number of shops owned by:	
Weekly turnover (£100)	ABC Ltd	XYZ Ltd
5 and under 10	18	3
10 and under 15	42	16
15 and under 20	62	23
20 and under 25	30	42
25 and under 30	20	76
30 and under 35	14	83
35 and under 40	8	42
40 and under 50	6	15
Total	200	300

(a) Express the frequencies per £100 interval for each firm. Use them to draw histograms for both sets of data on one graph and estimate the modal weekly turnover of each firm. ($\approx$ £1690 and $\approx$ £3070)

(b) Write out the cumulative frequency distribution for each firm.
Express these figures as percentage cumulative frequencies and plot the ogives for each firm on the same graph.
Estimate the median weekly turnover and the interquartile range for each firm. ($\approx$ £1820, $\approx$ £1090 and $\approx$ £2930, $\approx$ £1010)

(c) Calculate the mean and standard deviation of each distribution for all the shops. (£1998, £876 and £2869, £789)

(d) With reference to parts (a), (b) and (c) compare the turnovers of the two firms.

16.3 The figures below represent the lifetimes in hours of 30 electronic components from a faulty batch.

2.1	4.9	2.2	6.0	10.1	7.8
5.5	2.6	6.5	3.9	2.3	2.0
8.9	1.5	2.6	3.4	4.3	4.9
3.0	2.0	1.7	1.6	1.4	4.8
2.8	0.8	1.9	2.1	1.3	4.3

(a) Construct a histogram, stem and leaf plot and cumulative frequency diagram of the data and from them estimate the median and interquartile range. ($\approx$ 2.7, $\approx$ 2.9 hours)

(b) From the figures directly find the mean and standard deviation. (3.64, 2.355 hours)

16.4 A survey of insurance claims was conducted for 31 companies based on 31 635 claims. The following table gives the amount (£) of the claim settlements.

Amount of claim (£)	Number of claims	Amount of claim (£)	Number of claims
0 and < 100	4365	1500 and < 2000	1265
100 and < 200	5000	2000 and < 2500	950
200 and < 300	3450	2500 and < 5000	1865
300 and < 400	2500	5000 and < 10 000	1265
400 and < 500	1580	10 000 and < 50 000	1580
500 and < 1000	5315	>50 000	315
1000 and < 1500	2185		

(a) Calculate the frequency density per £100 and construct a histogram to represent the data.

(b) From your histogram estimate the modal claim size.   ($\approx$ £129)

(c) Add a frequency polygon to your graph.

(d) Calculate the cumulative frequencies. Construct a cumulative frequency diagram.

(e) Use your cumulative frequency diagram to estimate:
  (i)   the median and quartiles   ($\approx$ £430, $\approx$ £170 and £1350)
  (ii)   the interquartile range   ($\approx$ £1180)
  (iii) the number of claims over £20 000   ($\approx$ 1500)
  (iv)   the value exceeded by the highest 10% of the claims   ($\approx$ £5000)
  (v)   the highest claim from the lowest 20%.   ($\approx$ £140)

(f) From the data estimate the mean and standard deviation of the claims.
          ($\approx$ £3220, $\approx$ £9700 depending on the closure of the top interval)

(g) For this particular set of data do you think that the mean and standard deviation are better summary statistics than the median and interquartile range? Explain your answer.
          (Median and interquartile range because the data are so skewed)

16.3 Probability, contingency tables and chi-squared tests

Probability describes the likelihood of an event happening. Its value can be calculated from symmetry, as in gambling, or from the relative frequency of past events. Calculation from relative frequency is the more common method and the one we have concentrated on in this course.

Probability is calculated from symmetry by taking the ratio of the number of possibilities giving the desired effect to the number of all possibilities. We do this instinctively as in the probability of drawing an ace from a pack of 52 cards, which is 4/52 or 1/13.

Probability from relative frequency is obtainable by calculating the ratio of all favourable events in the past to all possible events. If, on average, it has rained on 12 days out of the 30 in June in the past the probability that it will rain on any one day in June in the future is 12 out of 30 or 2/5.

If we are considering two variables, the results are cross-tabulated in contingency tables with the cells containing the frequencies of the past events counted on both variables. These frequencies are related to the totals or subtotals to give the relative frequencies and hence the probabilities. Conditional probabilities can also be calculated from contingency tales by considering only the relevant subtotals and ignoring the rest.

In order to see if there is any significant association between the two variables under consideration a chi-squared test is carried out. This compares the observed frequencies with those that would be expected if the null hypothesis of no association between them were true. If there is very little difference between the observed and expected cell counts then the difference probably happened by chance. If the difference is large then it must have been produced by a strong association between the two variables. The chi-squared test is used to see whether this association is significant or not.

The formula for calculating the test statistic is in the prelims and Appendix C and the chi-squared table is in Appendix D.

You studied probability and contingency tables in Chapter 4 and chi-squared testing in Chapter 10. These two topics are however often combined in examination papers so are combined here for revision purposes.

Revision questions

16.5   The following table gives the numbers of male and female drivers calling for petrol between 5 p.m. and 6 p.m. on a given day at four garages in a city selling the same type of petrol.

Is there any evidence that the proportion of male to female varies from one garage to another? (Use 5% level)

| | Garages | | | |
Sex of driver	A	B	C	D
Male	25	50	20	25
Female	10	50	5	15

(CV $= 7.82$, TS: $\chi^2 = 10.34$, there is a difference, females prefer Garage B)

16.6   At the end of a semester, the grades for Statistics students were tabulated in the following 3×2 contingency table to see if there is any association between class attendance and grades received.

Number of days absent	Grade received: Pass	Fail
0–3	135	110
4–6	36	4
7–45	9	6

(a) Calculate the probability that a student selected at random:
   (i)   was absent for less than four days
   (ii)   was absent for less than seven days
   (iii) passed
   (iv) passed given that he/she was absent for less than four days
   (v)   passed or was absent for less than four days
   (vi) passed and was absent for less than four days

((i) 0.817; (ii) 0.950; (iii) 0.600; (iv) 0.550 (v) 0.967; (vi) 0.450)

    (b) Calculate the expected value for the number of days absence.   (3.19 days)

    (c) At 5% significance, do the data indicate that the proportions of students who pass differ between the three absence categories?

$$(\chi^2 = 17.45; \chi^2_{0.05}(2) = 5.99; \text{Reject } H_0; \text{proportions differ})$$

    (d) Calculate the 95% confidence intervals for the percentage of students who passed and the percentage of them who failed. Interpret your findings.

(54.5% to 65.5%; 34.5% to 45.5%; No overlap so percentages different)

    (e) Briefly summarise your results so that they can be understood by a non-statistician.

16.7   In an effort to determine whether family status and type of course taken are related the following data were collected from a random selection of students in a technical college.

Technical College Programme	Lower	Social Status Middle	Upper
Academic	25	32	58
Commercial	40	60	70
General	35	68	42
Vocational	10	15	20

    (a) What is the probability of any student opting for an academic course?

(0.242)

    (b) What is the probability of a student with upper social status opting for an academic course?

(0.305)

    (c) What is the probability of a student with upper social status opting for either an academic or commercial course?

(0.674)

    (d) Test at 1% significance if social status and programme undertaken are associated. $(\chi^2 = 14.81; \chi^2_{0.01}(6) = 16.81; \text{Reject } H_0; \text{they are not associated})$

16.8   An electronic supply centre wants to determine whether there are any differences in the proportion of service calls for four major brands of television sold by them in a certain city. The following data were collected during a two-year period.

	Brand A	Brand B	Brand C	Brand D
Service	20	30	55	45
No service	280	289	350	89

    (a) What is the probability of any set requiring a service?   (0.130)

    (b) What is the probability of a Brand A set requiring a service?   (0.0667)

    (c) What is the probability that a set which required servicing is Brand A?

(0.133)

    (d) What is the probability that a set which required servicing is Brand A or Brand B?   (0.333)

    (e) Can the supply centre conclude, at 1% significance, that the proportions of defective televisions differ among the brands?

$$(\chi^2 = 64.6; \chi^2_{0.01}(3) = 11.35; \text{Reject } H_0; \text{conclude that they do differ})$$

16.9 (a) Use the data in the following table to test the claim that the number of cigarettes smoked per day and the smoker's blood pressure level are related, at 5% significance.

| Blood pressure | Number of cigarettes smoked | | | | | |
	Under 5	6–10	11–15	16–20	21–25	Over 25
High	12	6	3	15	15	14
Slightly high	13	4	7	8	6	7
Normal to low	15	11	10	10	2	0

($\chi^2 = 30.1$; $\chi^2_{0.05}(10) = 18.3$; Reject H_0; conclude that they are related)

(b) What is the probability of any smoker having high blood pressure?   (0.411)

(c) What is the probability of a someone who smokes under 5 a day having high blood pressure?
(0.300)

(d) What is the probability of a someone who smokes over 25 a day having high blood pressure?
(0.667)

(e) What is the probability of a someone who smokes over 15 a day having high blood pressure?
(0.571)

16.4 Normal distribution

Many naturally occurring data sets are found to be normally distributed. Any data which are grouped symmetrically about a modal value with the frequency tailing off the further the value is from the mode is likely to be normal.

In industry where production aims at a given target value, such as a prescribed length, the output will be grouped about this length with the frequency of lengths tailing off either side of it. The discrepancies from the target, the errors, will therefore be normally distributed. This is one reason why the normal distribution is so important in statistics as the study of errors, or residuals, is a major aspect of statistical modelling.

Because the normal distribution has been so widely studied tables have been produced which describe the area under the standard normal probability curve between any given points. Any data we are studying therefore needs to be first standardised (normalised) using the formula in the prelims and Appendix C. From the standardised value, making use of normal tables (Appendix D), we can find the area under the curve above (or below) this value. This area describes the probability of any case falling above (or below) the value or alternatively the proportion of the data which we would expect to find above (or below) the given value. The method is described in detail in Chapter 5.

The table can be used inversely to find a value above (or below) which a certain proportion of the data fall.

Revision questions

16.10 The weights of sugar in what are nominally 2 kilo bags are actually normally distributed with mean 2.1 kg and standard deviation 0.1 kg.

(a) What percentage of bags will weigh less than 2.0 kg?   (15.9%)

(b) What percentage will weigh between 2.0 kg and 2.25 kg?   (77.5%)

(c) If only 4% of the bags were to contain less than the stated minimum weight, what should this value be? (1.93 kg)

(d) If a random sample of 25 bags from another machine has a mean weight of 2.0 kg and a standard deviation of 0.5 kg would its mean production be any different? (95% C.I. 1.79 kg to 2.21 kg so no different)

16.11 A business man has two small stores. Their daily takings are approximately normally distributed.

(a) The mean daily takings of store A are £83.00 with standard deviation £4.00. On what percentage of the days will takings exceed £87.50? (13.0%)

(b) The mean daily takings at store B are £84.00 with standard deviation of £5.00. What value of takings will be exceeded on only 14% of the days? (£89.4)

(c) He appointed a manager to look after his stores. Under this new management, a random sample of takings for 30 days showed that store A had a mean of £80 and store B a mean of £85 with the standard deviation remaining unchanged at £4.00 and £5.00 respectively.
   Calculate a 99% confidence interval for each store and use them to decide whether or not the mean takings had changed under the new management.
   (A £78.10 to £81.90; B £82.60 to £87.40; A had changed, B had not changed)

16.12 If the trunk length of thirty-year-old fir trees is normally distributed with mean 15 m and standard deviation 3 m:

(a) What percentage of trees are useful for telegraph poles if these need trunks longer than 13 m? (74.8%)

(b) What percentage will be sold as Christmas trees if these have trunks less than 8 m? (0.98%)

(c) A sample of 25 similar trees from another wood had a mean length of 13m and a standard deviation of 2.5m. Using a 95% confidence interval find out if these trees are different. (11.9m to 14.0m so mean height is different)

16.13 A mill finds that the quantity of fibre used per week is approximately normally distributed with a mean of 1000 tonnes and a standard deviation of 150 tonnes. If delivery of fibre is possible only at weekly intervals, to what level should stocks be raised to give only a 2.5% chance of running out during the ensuing week?
(1294 tonnes)

16.14 A machine which puts soup into tins is found to be putting in an average weight of 160 g with a standard deviation of 2.0 g. Assuming the weights to be normally distributed, calculate:

(a) The percentage of tins containing over 164 g (2.28%)

(b) the percentage of tins containing between 157 g and 163 g (86.6%)

(c) the probability that a tin selected at random will contain less than 156 g (0.0228)

(d) the minimum weight to be stated if only 5% are to be underweight (156.7 g)

16.15 An automatically machined component has a diameter which varies with a known standard deviation of 2.0 thou. If the machine is set to give a mean diameter of 1200 thou:

(a) What percentage of the components will have a diameter of between 1198.6 and 1202.6 thou?
(66.12%)

(b) What percentage will have a diameter greater than 1203.6 thou? (3.59%)

(c) What diameter will be exceeded by 2.5% of the components? (1203.92 thou)

16.5 Confidence intervals

When a sample is taken from a population and analysed, the exact mean for the sample can be calculated, but can we claim that the same figure is the mean for the whole population? Obviously not as different samples will produce different mean values.

It seems safer to quote an interval centred on the sample mean as the range for the most likely population mean. It seems reasonable that the width of this interval, the confidence interval, should depend upon how variable the sample is found to be and also its size. Because of the uncertainty inherent in analysing samples an interval is always quoted with the degree of confidence we have that it does actually include the true population parameter; the wider the interval the higher our level of confidence. This level of confidence determines the t or z value taken from the standard tables to be incorporated in the calculating formula.

Confidence intervals can be calculated for any population parameters which are estimated from samples but, in this course, we have concentrated on means and proportions in the form of percentages.

You studied the theory of confidence intervals in Chapter 6. The formulae for calculating them are listed in the prelims and repeated in Appendix C and the tables from which the t or z values can be found are in Appendix D. The use of t-tables or normal, z, tables is determined by two points: if the sample taken is large (≥ 30) or if we actually know the population standard deviation the normal table can be used. If neither of these conditions is satisfied we have to use the t-table which gives a wider, and therefore safer, confidence interval.

Revision questions

16.16 Explain what is meant by the term 'confidence interval'.

Measurements of a random sample of 200 ball-bearings made by a machine during one week gave a mean of 0.944 cm. and a standard deviation of 0.048 cm.

Find (a) 95% and (b) 99% confidence intervals for the mean diameter of all the ball-bearings made during that week. (0.937 to 0.951 cm and 0.935 to 0.953 cm)

16.17 The records of a large shoe shop show that over a given period 520 out of 1000 people who entered the shop bought at least one pair of shoes.

(a) Treating this as a random sample of all potential customers find a 95% confidence interval for the actual percentage of the people entering the shop who will buy at least one pair of shoes. (48.9% to 55.1%)

(b) Does this support the firm's claim that they actually sell shoes to half of their potential customers? Why? (Yes, interval includes 50%)

16.18 A supermarket in Hull undertook a survey of customer buying habits. They randomly selected 100 customers who visited the store and noted the total sale for each. 72 of the customers were female and their purchases averaged £14.80, with a standard deviation of £1.40.

The sales to the males were found to average £17.30 with a standard deviation of £1.50.

(a) Find the 95% confidence interval for average amount spent by all female customers
(£14.47 to £15.13)

(b) Find a 99% confidence interval for the proportion of all customers who are male
(0.16 to 0.40)

(c) Is there any evidence to show that the mean spending of all male customers is different from the mean spending of all female customers?
(Yes, 95% CI for males £16.72 to £17.88)

16.19 The same supermarket then decided to investigate the spending habits of husbands and wives. They were thinking of starting late 'family shopping' evenings and as an experiment asked both partners to shop separately. The amounts spent by 14 husbands and their wives were selected randomly from all the pairs with the following results (rounded to the nearest £1)

Family	A	B	C	D	E	F	G	H	I	J	K	L	M	N
Husband (£)	9	20	19	9	26	16	20	13	15	10	18	13	16	23
Wife (£)	23	30	13	23	12	17	29	35	18	26	32	23	26	14

(a) Calculate the 95% confidence interval for the mean amount spent by the wives.
(£18.72 to £27.14)

(b) Calculate the 99% confidence interval for the mean amount spent by the husbands.
(£12.05 to £20.37)

(c) The store manager thinks that, on average, women spend £20 per head. Does the confidence interval in (a) from the sample support this claim? Explain your answer.
(Yes, £20 in interval)

(d) Is there any evidence that the mean amounts spent by wives and their husbands are different? (Calculate the 95% confidence interval for the *differences* in each family)
(Yes, £0.72 to £12.70)

16.6 Hypothesis testing

Hypothesis testing is another method of investigating population parameters by means of the analysis of a sample. In this case the interest lies in finding whether the population parameter is likely to take a particular value or not rather than finding an interval for its most likely value.

As with confidence intervals, hypothesis tests can be carried out on any parameter whose value is hypothesised for a population and which can be calculated for a sample taken from that same population. In Chapter 7 we tested hypotheses about means and proportions of populations; in Chapter 8 we carried out F-tests in the analysis of variance; in Chapter 9 we tested correlation coefficients for significance; and in Chapter 10 we used chi-squared tests of association, so hypothesis testing has figured widely in this course.

Hypothesis testing is a very important and well established technique. It follows a set logical procedure through a series of steps from the null hypothesis to the conclusion reached about it.

Again, because we are working with samples, there is inevitably uncertainty about the results and we have to admit the probability of reaching the wrong conclusion a small proportion of the time. This previously decided proportion determines the value of t or z taken from the standard tables, in Appendix D, when calculating test statistics from the appropriate formulae found in the prelims and included in Appendix C.

As with confidence intervals the use of t-tables or normal, z, tables is determined by two points: if the sample taken is large (≥ 30) or if we actually know the population standard deviation the normal table can be used. If neither of these conditions is satisfied we have to use the t-table which has a slightly higher value which compensates for the added uncertainty caused by having to also estimate the standard deviation.

Revision questions

16.20 Explain what is meant by the term 'level of significance' and explain its importance in hypothesis testing.

A small office recorded information about overdue invoices. A random sample of 16 of these were selected and the amount overdue was correlated with the amount of time by which their payment was overdue. The correlation coefficient was found to be 0.876.

Carry out a hypothesis test to see whether this degree of correlation is significant or not at the 5% level
(CV = 0.497, TS r = 0.876, correlation is significant)

16.21 The mean height of 20 male students in a class was found to be 71" with a standard deviation of 1". Does this evidence support, at the 5% level, the belief that the mean height of all men is 70"?
(CV = 2.10, TS: t = 4.47, No, the null hypothesis is rejected)

16.22 A doctor claims that 12% of all his appointments are cancelled. Over a six week period, 21 of the doctor's 200 appointments were cancelled.

Test at the 5% level to determine if the true proportion of all appointments that are cancelled is different from 12%.
(CV = 1.96, TS: z = 0.65, No evidence on which to reject doctor's claim)

16.23 A machine is supposed to produce steel pins of length 2 cm. A sample of 10 pins was taken and their lengths measured in cm. with the following results:

1.98   1.96   1.99   2.00   2.01   1.95   1.97   1.96   1.97   1.99

Assuming the lengths to be normally distributed, calculate the mean and standard deviation of this sample and test at the 1% level of significance whether the machine is in good working order.
(CV = 3.25, TS: t = 3.60, It is not in good working order)

16.24 A random sample of 300 shoppers in a shopping mall is selected and 182 are found to favour longer shopping hours.

Is this sufficient evidence to conclude that less than 65% of all the shoppers favour longer shopping hours?
(CV = 1.96, TS: z = 1.57, could be hypothesised proportion of 65%)

16.25 A new teaching method, N, is to be compared to a standard teaching method, S, which was believed to have a mean score of 65. Children were paired, one of each pair was taught by each method, and both were given the same reading test with the following results

Pair number	1	2	3	4	5	6	7	8	9	10
S method score	56	59	61	48	39	56	75	45	81	60
N method score	63	57	67	52	61	71	70	46	93	75

(a) Is 65 a reasonable estimate for the mean score of all children taught by method S?

(CV $= 2.26$, TS: $t = 1.73$, 65 could be the mean mark for all the children)

(b) Calculate the difference in scores for each pair of children and test to see if, at the 5% level, new method N gives a better mean score than standard method S.

(CV $= 1.83$, TS: $t = 2.80$, Method N does give a higher mean score.)

16.7 Analysis of variance

Analysis of variance can be used as means testing which can be extended to look at the difference between more than two group means and also consider more than one grouping variable at a time.

The variation between the group means is compared to the overall variation within the sample. If this ratio is large the difference between the group means is significant; if it is small it may have occurred by chance and the means may all be the same. The null hypothesis is that all the group means are equal; the alternative hypothesis is that at least one is different.

The method, described in Chapter 8, may seem complicated but it has the advantage of comparing all the groups together at the stated significance level rather than doing multiple pair-wise tests which would increase the probability of error considerably.

For the method in detail refer back to Chapter 8. The production of the analysis of variance table always follows the same route so should be followed pedantically. The subsequent testing of the null hypothesis of no difference between group means is carried out by working through the standard hypothesis testing steps.

Revision questions

16.26 The times given alongside are a random sample of those needed to complete a task on a production line using three different methods.

Test at the 1% level whether or not there is a significant difference between these production lines.

Method 1	Method 2	Method 3
5.3	7.5	5.0
4.0	4.8	3.6
6.9	4.4	4.0
3.7	4.8	3.5
4.9	4.8	4.3
5.0	6.5	3.7
4.5	4.0	2.4
6.1	2.1	3.6

($F_{times} = 2.71$ $F_{0.01}(2, 21) = 5.78$. No significant difference between method times at 1%)

16.27 In order to test the yield of three different varieties of peas, a field is split up into six blocks. Each block is then subdivided into three equal areas and assigned one of the pea varieties at random. The yields in kilograms were as follows:

Block	Variety		
	A	B	C
1	13.9	16.3	14.3
2	12.3	14.9	14.8
3	11.9	16.7	11.9
4	12.8	13.9	12.7
5	7.8	10.4	8.2
6	14.3	17.3	15.0

(a) Carry out a one-way ANOVA at 5% significance to see if there is any difference between the yields of the three different varieties of peas.

$(F_{(varieties)} = 2.04, F_{0.05}(2, 17) = 3.68$, varieties not significant)

(b) Carry out a two-way ANOVA at 5% significance to see if there is any difference between the yields taking the blocks into consideration.

$(F_{(varieties)} = 15.5, F_{0.05}(2, 10) = 4.10$, varieties significant when blocks included)

16.28 Four salesmen in your company are competing for the title 'Salesman of the year'. Each has the task of selling 'cold' in three different types of location. Their resulting sales, in £000, were as follows:

Area	Salesmen			
	A	B	C	D
1	52.8	49.4	58.6	42.9
2	60.1	48.1	61.0	50.3
3	62.0	56.4	63.3	61.2

(a) Is there any significant difference, at a 5% level, between the sales of the men if the location is not taken into account?

$(F_{salesmen} = 2.14, F_{0.05}(3, 8) = 4.07$, no significant difference)

(b) Is there any significant difference, at a 5% level, between the sales of the men if the location is taken into account? $(F_{salesmen} = 5.88, F_{0.05}(3, 6) = 4.76,$ significant difference when locations taken into consideration)

(c) Which salesman won? Did he do significantly better than his nearest rival?
(Salesman C, not significantly better than Salesman A, LSD = 5.53.)

16.29 Your school wishes to compare students' reactions to the three different levels of printing facilities provided in different computer laboratories, which are identical in all other aspects of their provision. Room A has two central printers at the front but no local printers; Room B has local printers at pairs of workstations; Room C sends all printing to a fast central printing room where it can be collected from the pigeon holes.

In order to provide the necessary data for making the comparisons all the three rooms were used by the same eight students who then filled in the same questionnaires. Later analysis of these questionnaires provided the preference scores overleaf:

| Treatments | Students – Blocks | | | | | | | |
---	1	2	3	4	5	6	7	8
Room A	21	19	15	18	21	18	23	20
Room B	25	24	21	22	23	23	20	21
Room C	17	14	15	17	16	13	17	16

(a) Why is it preferable to use two-way rather than one-way analysis of variance when analysing the data produced in the experiment described above?

(b) Calculate the sums of squares between both the treatments, SSTr, and the blocks, SSB, and also the total sum of squares, SST.

$$\text{SSTr} = 183.0, \text{SSB} = 32.6. \text{SST} = 260.6$$

(c) Construct an ANOVA table in order to carry out the appropriate analysis.

(d) Test to see if there is any difference between the preferences for the different types of printing facilities provided.

$$(F_{\text{rooms}} = 28.5, F_{0.05}(2,14) = 3.74, \text{difference significant})$$

(e) If appropriate, carry out a test in order to identify the source of this difference.
$(t(14 \text{ df}) = 1.76 \text{ so LSD} = 1.57, \text{all rooms significantly different from each other})$

16.30 Carry out a one-way ANOVA on the following rates (pages per hour) of production of text from a word processor by four administrative assistants and see if there is any significant difference between them at 5% significance.

| Administrative assistant | | | |
A	B	C	D
3.52	3.48	3.06	4.01
3.02	2.82	1.35	3.11
3.25	2.56	3.36	2.92
3.86	1.72	2.73	2.99
3.31	2.53	3.07	2.71
3.56	1.83	3.33	3.47
	2.75	3.31	
		3.11	

$(F_{\text{assistants}} = 3.30, F_{0.05}(3,23) = 3.03;$ there is a significant difference between speeds)

16.8 Correlation and regression

Correlation assesses the degree of linear association between two continuous variables and regression describes the form the relationship between them takes. We have assumed, in this course, that the relationship is linear but it may take other non-linear forms which are best analysed by a computer package (see Chapter 9).

The first step in this type of analysis is the plotting of the bivariate data to see what form it takes as it needs to be reasonably linear for this analysis to be appropriate. Both the correlation coefficient and the regression equation are easiest produced from a statistical calculator in linear regression mode as described in its specific calculator handbook. Alternatively the formulae in Appendix C can be used for their calculation.

In Chapter 9 we first produced a correlation coefficient, r, and then tested it for significance to check if the degree of association was higher than the value which could have occurred by chance (correlation tables in Appendix D). If strong enough the nature of the linear relationship was identified from the regression coefficients, produced by the calculator, in the form of an equation. This equation was then used for predictive purposes.

Revision questions

16.31 The following data refers to the sales and advertising expenditure of a small local bakery.

Year	Advertising (£000)	Sales (£000)
1990	3	40
1991	3	60
1992	5	100
1993	4	80
1994	6	90
1995	7	110
1996	7	120
1997	8	130
1998	6	100
1999	7	120
2000	10	150

(a) Plot a scatter diagram of sales against advertising.

(b) Calculate the correlation coefficient.   (0.958)

(c) Test it for significance at the 5% level.   (CV = 0.602, significant)

(d) If significant, find the equation of the regression line.
                                                (Sales = 15.2 + 14.1 × advertising)

(e) What practical use could be made of this equation?

(f) What percentage of the variation in sales is explained by your model?
                                                                                (92%)

16.32 Merlin plc has observed from a random sample of its outlets the quantity of one of its products sold at various price levels. The results are shown in the following table:

Price per gallon (x) (pence)	Quantity (y) (100s gallons)
120	26
122	24
125	20
118	32
115	38
120	28

The company is confident that business conditions will remain the same in the near future and they wish to prepare a forecast of sales based on this data.

(a) Plot the scatter diagram for this data.

(b) Calculate the correlation coefficient. (−0.984)

(c) Calculate the regression line and add it to the graph. ($y = 247.3 - 1.83x$)

(d) Forecast the quantity of this product which Merlin can expect to sell if the price were 116 pence per gallon. (3531 gallons)

(e) Is this data suitable for forecasting the sales at 150 pence? Explain your answer. (No)

16.33 Calculate the correlation coefficient and test it for significance at the 5% level. If it is found to be significant, calculate a regression equation from the following data, relating the ages of husbands and wives at time of marriage, which is suitable for estimating the expected age of the bride of a thirty year old man.

Husband	27	28	28	29	29	30	30	30	31	31	32	32	33	33
Wife	26	26	20	24	21	25	29	26	32	26	24	28	31	29

($r = 0.574$; CV $= 0.532$; $y = -5.3 + 1.04x$; 26 years old)

16.34 Find the correlation coefficient between x and y. Test it for significance and, if significant, find the regression equation which best fits the following pairs of data.

x	77	81	94	50	72	63	88	95
y	82	77	85	66	65	72	89	95

($r = 0.858$; $y = 32.7 + 0.59x$)

16.35 The table below lists the 400-metre freestyle swimming times (sec) for men since 1924

Year	Time	Year	Time
1924	304.2	1960	258.3
1928	301.6	1964	252.2
1932	288.4	1968	250.0
1936	284.5	1972	240.27
		1976	231.93
		1980	231.31
1948	281.0	1984	231.23
1952	270.7	1988	226.95
1956	267.3	1992	218.41

Find the regression equation and use it to predict the men's time for 2000.

($y = 308.8 - 5.017x$, 208.5 or $y = 2717 - 1.254x$, 208.5)

16.36 The following heart rates have been recorded for the maximum heart rate of patients of various ages on an intensive exercise programme. Find the correlation coefficient between the variables and test it for significance.

Age	10	20	20	25	30	30	30	40	45	50
Rate	210	200	195	195	190	180	185	180	170	165

Find the regression line and use it to predict the heart rate of a 28 year old.

($r = -0.971$; $y = 219.8 - 1.093x$; 189 beats per minute)

16.37 Compute the Pearson's correlation coefficient, r, for the following sample of paired data representing the number of hours (x) studying for an exam and the marks received (y) on the exam by a sample of six students.

Student	A	B	C	D	E	F
Hours study (x)	1	2	4	4	7	12
Mark (y)	41	50	65	80	80	86

Calculate the regression equation and use it to predict the marks for a student who studied for 14 hours. $(r = 0.8295; y = 48.06 + 3.79x;$
101%! but 14 hours is outside the range of the model)

16.9 Index numbers

Index numbers are used for monitoring changes over time. They may measure absolutely anything and, since they are ratios, they have no units. The ratio of the value in any period to that of the corresponding value in its base period, when it was 100, is converted to a percentage and is referred to in terms of 'percentage points'.

When an index series reaches a relatively high value and the percentage point change becomes about four times the true percentage change, it is rebased by being brought back to 100. You need to be able to bridge this discontinuity by producing a smooth series of either the old numbers or the new.

Index series with the same base year can be constructed for any time series and used to compare the progress of, say, two competing firms or that of one firm with the industry as a whole. Prices are often compared to the Retail Price Index upon which many pensions and other payment rates are based.

Revision questions

16.38

Year	Index
1	100
2	110
3	120
4	135
5	150

(a) Construct an index with Year 3 = 100
(83.3 91.7 100.0 112.5 125.0)

(b) Construct an index with Year 5 = 100
(66.7 73.3 80.0 90.0 100.0)

(c) If the index concerns the price of a loaf of bread, which was 65p in year 3, then calculate the price of a similar loaf in each of the other years.
(54p 60p 65p 73p 81p (to the nearest 1p))

16.39

Year	'Old'	Indexes 'New'
1	100	
2	120	
3	160	
4	190	100
5		130
6		140
7		150
8		165

(a) Scale to 'New' the 'Old' indexes for years 1, 2, and 3.   (52.6 63.2 84.2)

(b) Scale to 'Old' the 'New' indexes for years 5, 6, 7
(247.0 266.0 285.0 313.5)

(c) If a company's profits were £3.5 million in Year 3, what would they be for the other years?
(2.19 2.63 (3.50) 4.16 5.40 5.82 6.23 6.86 £million)

16.40 The production of refrigerators can be summarised by the following table:

Year	Year 1	Year 2	Year 3	Year 4	Year 5
Production (000s)	4500	4713	5151	5566	6000

(a) Calculate index numbers for the above data taking Year 3 as the base year.
(87.4 91.5 100.0 108.1 116.5)

(b) If the production of cookers followed the same index and 550 thousand were made in year 1, how many thousand were made in each of the other years?
((550) 576 630 680 733)

16.41 The table below refers to the Annual Average Retail Price Index.

Year	1	2	3	4	5	6	7
RPI_1	351.8	373.2	385.9	394.5			
RPI_2				100.0	106.9	115.2	126.1

(a) Calculate the percentage change between consecutive years.
(6.1% 3.4% 2.2% 6.9% 7.8% 9.5%)

(b) Calculate the percentage point change between consecutive years after Year 4.
(6.9 8.3 10.9)

16.42 The following table shows the prices of three commodities in three consecutive years:

	Prices		
	Year 1	Year 2	Year 3
Tea	8	12	16
Coffee	15	17	18
Chocolate	22	23	24

(a) Calculate the simple aggregate index for Year 2 and Year 3 using Year 1 as the base year.
(115.6 128.9)

(b) Calculate the mean price relative index for Year 2 and Year 3 using Year 1 as the base year.
(122.7 143.0)

16.10 Time series analysis and forecasting

Forecasting is a very useful technique in business for estimating such items as demands in order to optimise production levels and minimise losses.

All methods are based on analysing past data, time series analysis, and, with the assumption that no significant changes will take place, projecting the same pattern or trend into the near future, forecasting. Several methods were described in Chapters 12 and 13 but the stress in this course is on seasonal decomposition using an additive model. This method produces a model which is the sum of an overall trend plus an additional amount, the seasonal factor, which may be positive or negative and is due to it being a particular season. This same model is used to produce the forecasts.

When the model is projected backwards in time it is found that the observed data did not fit it exactly. These past discrepancies are used to measure how good we expect the forecasts from the model to be in the future. If they were small we would expect a good forecast; if large it is unlikely to be accurate.

Revision questions

Note: SPSS and Minitab outputs differ in all numerical answers after Question 16.45. Use the output for whichever package has been included in your course.

16.43 The following quarterly data represents the output of a small manufacturing company, in £0000, for four consecutive years:

Year	Q_1	Q_2	Q_3	Q_4
1997	58	195	573	102
1998	81	171	507	94
1999	60	183	479	96
2000	69	127	397	113

Summaries of the analysis performed by SPSS and Minitab on this data follow.

(a) Using the values in the computer output, plot the given data on graph paper as a time series, leaving room for your forecasts for 2001.

(b) Plot the smoothed trend-cycle for SPSS, trend for Minitab on your graph.

(c) State the four seasonal factors and use with your graph to forecast demand for outward passenger movement for each of the four quarters of Year 5, stating your forecasts clearly and showing how they were calculated.

(d) Estimate the likely error in your forecasts.

(e) Demonstrate how the seasonally adjusted series for SPSS, deseasonal for Minitab, for each of the quarters of Year 4 have been found. Explain how these figures might be used.

(f) With reference to your graph and the summary statistics given in the SPSS or Minitab output, discuss the suitability of the additive model.

SPSS output for use with Question 16.43

Additive Model. Centered MA method. Period=4.

DATE	OUTPUT	Moving averages	Ratios	Seasonal factors	Seasonally adjusted series	Smoothed trend-cycle	Irregular component
Q1 1997	58.000	.	.	-137.875	195.875	213.722	-17.847
Q2 1997	195.000	.	.	-40.667	235.667	235.097	.569
Q3 1997	573.000	234.875	338.125	299.250	273.750	239.194	34.556
Q4 1997	102.000	234.750	-132.750	-120.708	222.708	233.412	-10.704
Q1 1998	81.000	223.500	-142.500	-137.875	218.875	222.986	-4.111
Q2 1998	171.000	214.250	-43.250	-40.667	211.667	213.963	-2.296
Q3 1998	507.000	210.625	296.375	299.250	207.750	210.306	-2.556
Q4 1998	94.000	209.500	-115.500	-120.708	214.708	210.079	4.630
Q1 1999	60.000	207.500	-147.500	-137.875	197.875	206.431	-8.556
Q2 1999	183.000	204.250	-21.250	-40.667	223.667	206.407	17.259
Q3 1999	479.000	205.625	273.375	299.250	179.750	202.750	-23.000
Q4 1999	96.000	199.750	-103.750	-120.708	216.708	201.634	15.074
Q1 2000	69.000	182.500	-113.500	-137.875	206.875	185.208	21.667
Q2 2000	127.000	174.375	-47.375	-40.667	167.667	173.630	-5.963
Q3 2000	397.000	.	.	299.250	97.750	166.375	-68.625
Q4 2000	113.000	.	.	-120.708	233.708	162.102	71.606

Descriptive Statistics

	N	Minimum	Maximum	Mean	Standard deviation
Output (£0000)	16	58	573	206.56	176.28
Errors	16	-68.62500	71.60648	1.3564815	28.57182

Output (£000)

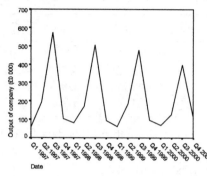

Output and trend

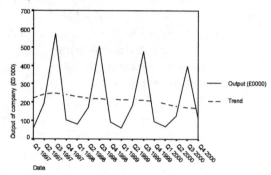

Output, trend and fitted values

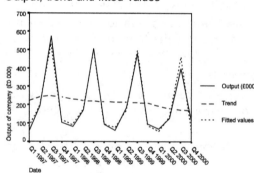

Errors

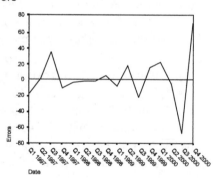

Minitab output for use with Question 16.43

Row	Output	Trend	Seasonal	Deseasonal	Residuals	Fitted values
1	58	218.838	-141.281	199.281	-19.5570	77.557
2	195	217.201	-42.031	237.031	19.8298	175.170
3	573	215.565	297.594	275.406	59.8415	513.158
4	102	213.928	-114.281	216.281	2.3533	99.647
5	81	212.291	-141.281	222.281	9.9901	71.010
6	171	210.654	-42.031	213.031	2.3768	168.623
7	507	209.018	297.594	209.406	0.3886	506.611
8	94	207.381	-114.281	208.281	0.9004	93.100
9	60	205.744	-141.281	201.281	-4.4629	64.463
10	183	204.107	-42.031	225.031	20.9239	162.076
11	479	202.471	297.594	181.406	-21.0643	500.064
12	96	200.834	-114.281	210.281	9.4474	86.553
13	69	199.197	-141.281	210.281	11.0842	57.916
14	127	197.560	-42.031	169.031	-28.5290	155.529
15	397	195.924	297.594	99.406	-96.5173	493.517
16	113	194.287	-114.281	227.281	32.9945	80.006

Time series analysis of company's output

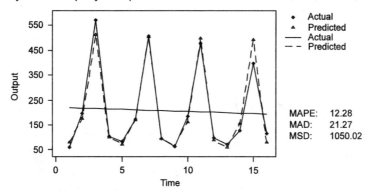

Variable	N	Mean	Median	TrMean	StDev	SE Mean
Output	16	206.6	120.0	191.0	176.3	44.1
Residuals	16	-0.00	2.37	2.62	33.47	8.37

Variable	Minimum	Maximum	Q1	Q3
Output	58.0	573.0	84.2	346.5
Residuals	-96.52	59.84	-15.78	17.64

16.44   The following quarterly data represents the number of marriages, in thousands, for four consecutive years (Source: Office of Population Censuses):

Year	Q_1	Q_2	Q_3	Q_4
1	71.6	111.0	135.7	79.6
2	62.2	108.8	138.0	78.0
3	61.9	108.9	140.5	78.0
4	61.3	115.0	146.2	73.3

A summary of the analysis performed on this data, using both SPSS and Minitab, is shown overleaf.

(a) Plot the given data on graph paper as a time series, leaving room for your forecasts for Year 5.

(b) Calculate the missing values indicated by the three question marks (?) on the table in the printout.

(c) Plot the smoothed trend-cycle, trend for Minitab, on your graph.

(d) State the four seasonal factors and use with your graph to forecast the expected number of marriages for each of the four quarters of Year 5, stating your forecasts clearly and showing how they were calculated.

(e) Estimate the likely error in your forecasts.

(f) Demonstrate how the Seasonally adjusted series for SPSS, or Fitted values for Minitab, of the number of marriages for each of the quarters of Year 4 have been found.

(g) With reference to your graph and the summary statistics given in the SPSS or Minitab outputs, discuss the suitability of the additive model.

SPSS output for use with Question 16.44

```
->* Seasonal Decomposition.
->/VARIABLES=marriage
->/MODEL=ADDITIVE
->/MA=CENTERED.
```

		Moving		Seasonal	Seasonally adjusted	Smoothed trend-	Second
DATE	MARRIAGE	averages	Ratios	factors	series	cycle	residuals
Q1 1	71.600	.	.	-35.718	107.318	101.004	6.314
Q2 1	111.000	.	.	13.207	97.793	99.973	-2.181
Q3 1	135.700	98.300	37.400	40.891	94.809	97.912	-3.103
Q4 1	79.600	96.850	-17.250	-18.380	97.980	96.976	1.005
Q1 2	62.200	96.863	-34.662	-35.718	97.918	96.980	.938
Q2 2	108.800	96.950	11.850	13.207	95.593	96.799	-1.206
Q3 2	138.000	96.713	41.287	40.891	97.109	96.757	.353
Q4 2	78.000	96.688	-18.688	-18.380	96.380	96.653	-.273
Q1 3	61.900	97.012	-35.112	-35.718	97.618	97.080	.538
Q2 3	108.900	97.325	11.575	13.207	95.693	97.144	-1.451
Q3 3	140.500	97.250	43.250	40.891	99.609	97.512	2.097
Q4 3	78.000	97.938	-19.938	-18.380	96.380	97.764	-1.384
Q1 4	61.300	?	?	-35.718	97.018	99.146	?
Q2 4	115.000	99.538	15.463	13.207	101.793	99.788	2.005
Q3 4	146.200	.	.	40.891	105.309	99.594	5.715
Q4 4	73.300	.	.	-18.380	91.680	99.497	-7.817

Summary Statistics

Variable	Mean	Std Dev	Minimum	Maximum	N	Label
MARRIAGE	98.12	30.79	61.3	146.2	16	Number of marriages (0,000)
FIRST	-.04	30.83	-38.0	47.0	16	First residuals
SECOND	-.04	3.35	-7.81690	6.31389	16	Second residuals

Time series of marriages (0,000)

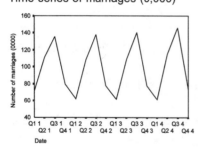

Marriages with trend line added

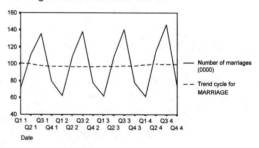

Marriages with trend and fitted model

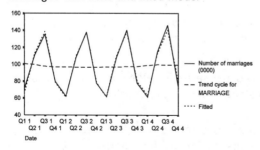

Scatter plot of errors

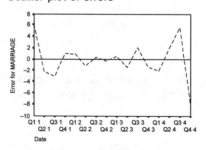

Histogram of residuals

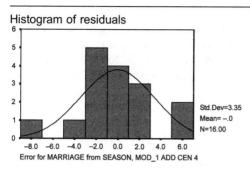

Std.Dev=3.35
Mean= –.0
N=16.00

Error for MARRIAGE from SEASON, MOD_1 ADD CEN 4

Box plot of residuals

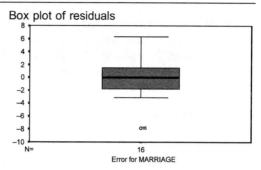

N=   16
Error for MARRIAGE

Minitab output (from an older version) for use with Question 16.44

ROW	QUARTER	THE DATA	TREND	1ST.RESD	SEASONAL	FITTED	2ND.RESD
1	1	71.6	*	*	*	*	*
2	2	111.0	*	*	*	*	*
3	3	135.7	98.3000	37.4000	40.6458	138.946	-3.24583
4	4	79.6	96.8500	-17.2500	-18.6250	78.225	1.37500
5	5	62.2	96.8625	-34.6625	-35.9625	60.900	1.30000
6	6	108.8	96.9500	11.8500	12.9625	109.912	-1.11250
7	7	138.0	96.7125	41.2875	40.6458	137.358	0.64166
8	8	78.0	96.6875	-18.6875	-18.6250	78.063	-0.06250
9	9	61.9	97.0125	-35.1125	-35.9625	61.050	0.85000
10	10	108.9	97.3250	11.5750	12.9625	110.287	-1.38750
11	11	140.5	97.2500	43.2500	40.6458	137.896	2.60417
12	12	78.0	97.9375	-19.9375	-18.6250	79.313	-1.31250
13	13	61.3	?	?	-35.9625	63.450	?
14	14	115.0	99.5375	15.4625	12.9625	112.500	2.50000
15	15	146.2	*	*	*	*	*
16	16	73.3	*	*	*	*	

Plot of the data and the trend line

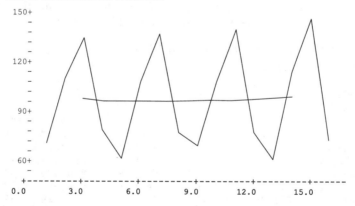

Summary Statistics

FOR THE DATA
  MEAN = 98.125
  ST.DEV. = 30.791

FOR THE FIRST RESIDUALS
  MEAN = -0.24479
  ST.DEV. = 30.775

FOR THE SECOND RESIDUALS
  MEAN = 3.178914E-07
  ST.DEV. = 1.8536

16.45 Whiterose Brewers are a small brewery supplying a number of public houses in the Huddersfax area. Ten years ago they introduced a new 'Strong Bitter'. Having allowed six years for the sales to settle down, they require you to analyse the sales for the past four years, given in gallons, and estimate demands for the next year.

Year	Q_1	Q_2	Q_3	Q_4
1	1485	1560	1605	1842
2	1576	1620	1700	1804
3	1602	1817	1975	1998
4	1813	1831	2006	2110

A summary of the analysis performed on this data, using SPSS and Minitab, is shown below and overleaf.

(a) Plot the given data on graph paper as a time series, leaving room for your forecasts for Year 5.

(b) Calculate the missing values indicated by the three question marks (?) on the table in the printout.

(c) Plot the smoothed trend-cycle for SPSS, trend for Minitab, on your graph.

(d) State the four seasonal factors and use them with your graph to forecast the expected demand for 'Strong Bitter' for each of the four quarters of Year 5, stating your forecasts clearly and showing how they were calculated.

(e) Estimate the likely error in your forecasts.

(f) Demonstrate how the seasonally adjusted series for SPSS and fitted values for Minitab, of demand for 'Strong Bitter' for each of the four quarters of Year 4 have been found. Explain how these figures might be used.

(g) With reference to your graph and the summary statistics given in the SPSS output, discuss the suitability of the additive model.

SPSS output for use with Question 16.45

```
->* Seasonal Decomposition.
->/VARIABLES=sales
->/MODEL=ADDITIVE
->/MA=CENTERED.
```

| | | | | | | Seasonally | Smoothed | |
| | | | Moving | | Seasonal | adjusted | trend- | Second |
	DATE	SALES	averages	Ratios	factors	series	cycle	residuals
Q1	1 1485.000		.	.	-114.854	1599.854	1576.764	23.090
Q2	1 1560.000		.	.	-50.396	1610.396	1593.604	16.792
Q3	1 1605.000		1634.375	-29.375	34.438	1570.563	1627.285	-56.722
Q4	1 1842.000		1653.250	188.750	130.813	1711.188	1659.688	51.500
Q1	2 1576.000		1672.625	-96.625	-114.854	1690.854	1674.650	16.204
Q2	2 1620.000		1679.750	-59.750	-50.396	1670.396	1678.711	-8.315
Q3	2 1700.000		1678.250	21.750	34.438	1665.563	1676.840	-11.278
Q4	2 1804.000		1706.125	97.875	130.813	1673.188	1702.465	-29.278
Q1	3 1602.000		1765.125	-163.125	-114.854	1716.854	1759.762	-42.907
Q2	3 1817.000		1823.750	-6.750	-50.396	1867.396	1828.600	38.796
Q3	3 1975.000		1874.375	100.625	34.438	1940.563	1881.729	58.833
Q4	3 1998.000		1902.500	95.500	130.813	1867.188	1898.576	-31.389
Q1	4 1813.000		?	?	-114.854	1927.854	1910.317	?
Q2	4 1831.000		1926.000	-95.000	-50.396	1881.396	1921.044	-39.648
Q3	4 2006.000		.	.	34.438	1971.563	1944.049	27.514
Q4	4 2110.000		.	.	130.813	1979.188	1955.551	23.637

Summary Statistics

Variable	Mean	Std Dev	Minimum	Maximum	N	Label
SALES	1771.50	187.12	1485	2110	16	Sales of Strong Bitter
FIRST	3.40	101.98	-158	182	16	First residuals
SECOND	3.40	35.41	-56.72222	58.83333	16	Second residuals

Sales of strong bitter

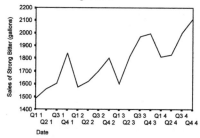

Sales with trend added

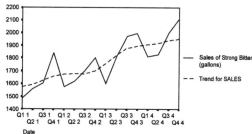

Sales with trend and fitted model

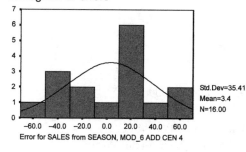

Scatter plot of errors

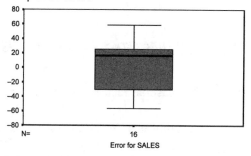

Histogram of errors

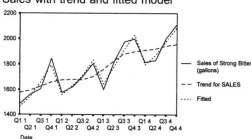

Std.Dev=35.41
Mean=3.4
N=16.00

Box plot of errors

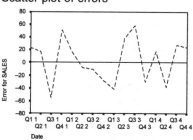

Minitab output (from an older version) for use with Question 16.45

ROW	QUARTER	THE DATA	TREND	1ST.RESD	SEASONAL	FITTED	2ND.RESD
1	1	1485	*	*	*	*	*
2	2	1560	*	*	*	*	*
3	3	1605	1634.37	-29.375	31.000	1665.37	-60.3750
4	4	1842	1653.25	188.750	127.375	1780.62	61.3750
5	5	1576	1672.62	-96.625	-118.292	1554.33	21.6666
6	6	1620	1679.75	-59.750	-53.833	1625.92	-5.9166
7	7	1700	1678.25	21.750	31.000	1709.25	-9.2500
8	8	1804	1706.13	97.875	127.375	1833.50	-29.5000
9	9	1602	1765.13	-163.125	-118.292	1646.83	-44.8334
10	10	1817	1823.75	-6.750	-53.833	1769.92	47.0834
11	11	1975	1874.38	100.625	31.000	1905.37	69.6250
12	12	1998	1902.50	95.500	127.375	2029.87	-31.8750
13	13	1813	?	?	-118.292	1789.83	?
14	14	1831	1926.00	-95.000	-53.833	1872.17	-41.1666
15	15	2006	*	*	*	*	*
16	16	2110	*	*	*	*	*

Plot of the data and the trend line

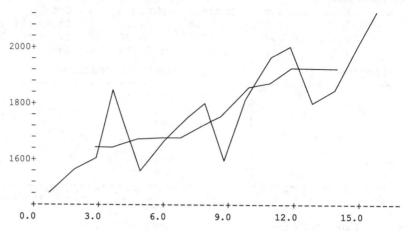

Summary Statistics

FOR THE DATA
  MEAN = 1771.5
  ST.DEV. = 187.12

FOR THE FIRST RESIDUALS
  MEAN = -3.4375
  ST.DEV. = 105.87

FOR THE SECOND RESIDUALS
  MEAN = 0.000000000
  ST.DEV. = 43.895

Answers to time series and forecasting questions

$r = 0.8578; \quad y = 32.71 + 0.5957x$

16.43 (c) Seasonal factors $-137.9, -40.7, 299.3, -120.7$ (£0000) (SPSS)
                                 $-141.3, -42.0, 297.6, -114.3$ (£0000) (Minitab)

Forecasts (in the region of) 20, 110, 450, 20 (£0000) (SPSS)
                              50, 150, 460, 70 (£0000) (Minitab)

(d) Maximum likely error = 59 (SPSS) or 67 (Minitab) (£0000)

(f) Yes. Regular seasonal quarterly pattern; Data and fitted values close on graph; Second residuals have very small mean and standard deviation much reduced.

16.44 (b) Moving average = 99.41, Ratio = -38.11, Second residual = -2.3 or -2.2

(d) Seasonal factors $-35.718, 13.207, 40.891, -18.380$ thousand
Forecasts (in the region of) 65, 114.0, 142, 84 thousand

(e) Maximum likely error = 6.7 thousand

(f) Deseasonalised values for year 4:   97.0, 101.8, 105.3, 91.7 thousand (SPSS)
                                         97.3, 102.1, 105.6, 91.9 thousand (Minitab)

(g) Yes. Regular seasonal quarterly pattern; Data and fitted values close on graph; Second residuals have mean of nearly zero and standard deviation much reduced.

16.45 (b) Moving average = 1908.1, Ratio = −95.1, Second residual = 17.54

(d) Seasonal factors −114.9, −50.4, 34.4, 130.8 thousand (SPSS)
−118.3, −53.8, 31.0, 127.4 thousand (Minitab)

Forecasts (in the region of) 1830, 1920, 2030, 2140 thousand

(e) Maximum likely error = 71 or 87 thousand

(f) Deseasonalised values for year 4: 1928, 1881, 1972, 1971 thousand (SPSS)
1830, 1885, 1975, 1983 thousand (Minitab)

(g) Not a very good model. Seasonal quarterly pattern not so regular; data and fitted values not very close on graph; second residuals have low mean but the standard deviation is still fairly high and the residuals do not appear to be random on the plot.

16.11 Examination type revision questions

Note: All numerical answers are in Appendix A2.

16.46 A research exercise was carried out in the university in order to find out whether a new word processing package was proving disproportionately popular with any particular group of users. From a random sample of all its users the results were as follows:

	Academics	Administrators	Students
Like package	20	50	80
Dislike package	50	40	20
No opinion	0	20	20

(a) What is the probability that any user selected at random liked the package? (3 marks)

(b) What is the probability that a student liked the package? (4 marks)

(c) Carry out a chi-squared test, at 5% level, on all the data in order to see if opinions differ significantly between the academic staff, the administrative staff and the students. (15 marks)

(d) Comment briefly on your findings identifying, if applicable, the main differences in opinion. (3 marks)

Total 25 marks

16.47 A book publisher has produced seven comparable textbooks with the following costs:

Quantity produced (000):	1	2	4	5	7	9	13
Manufacturing costs (£000):	5	5.9	6.5	7.5	8	9.5	10.8

(a) Calculate the correlation coefficient for the association between quantity produced and manufacturing costs. Test it for significance at 5%. (5 marks)

(b) Plot the data on a scatter diagram. (6 marks)

(c) Calculate the regression line for predicting manufacturing costs from quantity produced, interpret its coefficients and add it to the scatter diagram. (8 marks)

(d) Estimate how much of the variation in costs is accounted for by the model.

(3 marks)

(e) Predict the manufacturing costs of an eighth textbook which has an expected production run of 12 000 copies.

(3 marks)

Total marks 25

16.48 It is thought that the variability of 'user friendliness' in three different computer packages, which have the same function, is causing different amounts of stress in their usage. In order to test this hypothesis the three packages were installed in the same laboratory and six students were selected at random and assigned the task of carrying out a simple analysis with each of the packages.

Following the exercise the students were each asked to fill in the same questionnaire. The analysis of the questionnaires produced the following measures of stress caused to each student while carrying out each test.

| Packages | Students | | | | | |
	1	2	3	4	5	6
Package A	15	14	10	13	16	13
Package B	14	13	10	11	12	12
Package C	18	14	15	17	16	13

(a) In order to analyse this data using a one-way analysis of variance, check that the values for the total sum of squares, SST, and the sum of squares of the treatments (packages), SSTr, are 86 and 37 respectively. (7 marks)

(b) Construct an ANOVA table in order to carry out the appropriate analysis.

(5 marks)

(c) Test to see if there is any significant difference, at the 5% level, between the stress levels caused by the three different packages. (5 marks)

(d) If appropriate, carry out a test in order to identify the source of this difference.

(6 marks)

(e) If it were considered likely that the students differed in their resilience to stress, how would you account for this in your analysis?
(One or two sentences only needed.) (2 marks)

Total marks 25

16.49 Most new students are interested in improving their keyboard skills and the staff in Computer Services are interested in running helpful courses. A keyboard course was designed and, so that its effectiveness could be judged, the random selection of students who were to be the first trainees agreed to undertake speed tests both before and after they had been on the course.

The results were as follows (words per minute):

Student	1	2	3	4	5	6	7	8
Speed before	22	41	35	27	44	18	28	36
Speed after	29	51	42	35	53	29	30	39

(a) Assuming the data to be normally distributed, construct a 99% confidence interval and use it to find out whether an estimate of 25 words per minute for the mean typing speed of students before taking the course was reasonable or not. (5 marks)

(b) Test at 5% significance the claim by the staff running the course that there has been an average improvement in typing speed of at least 10 words per minute. (10 marks)

(c) It was later suggested that the second set of marks might have become confused and out of order. Treating the speeds before and after as no longer being produced by the same student, would you change the conclusion reached in part (b) about the claim of 10 words per minute improvement? (10 marks)

Total marks 25

16.50 Merlin Packaging Ltd have purchased a new machine for their jars of instant coffee. To test the initial setting of the machine they weighed the contents of 100 jars taken at random from the first day's production. The weights they found were as follows:

Weights	Number of jars
Less than 97 g	0
97 g and less than 98 g	6
98 g and less than 99 g	20
99 g and less than 100 g	38
100 g and less than 101 g	28
101 g and less than 102 g	7
102 g and less than 103 g	1
More than 103 g	0

(a) Estimate the mean and standard deviation of the first day's production. (3 marks)

(b) Assuming the data to be normally distributed and using your results from (a), calculate a 95% confidence interval for the mean contents of all the packages from the machine.

State, with justification, whether you consider the machine setting to be satisfactory for the filling of jars labelled 100 g? (6 marks)

(c) Assuming the weights of the whole production to be normally distributed with a mean of 101.2 g and a standard deviation of 0.8 g find:

(i) The percentage of the filled jars likely to contain less than 100 g.

(ii) The percentage of the jars likely to contain between 100 and 102 g.

(iii) What is the value exceeded by 5% of jars which have the highest contents? (Give your answer correct to one decimal place.) (16 marks)

Total marks 25

16.51 The advertising department of a company selling three similar products X, Y and Z wish to know if the choice of product is dependent upon the type of employment of the customer.

They conducted a survey of three general classes of customer producing the following results:

	Customer group by employment		
Product	Professional	Clerical	Manual
X	170	146	154
Y	20	14	24
Z	10	40	22

(a) What is the probability that a customer selected at random:

    (i)   chose product X?

    (ii)   from the clerical group chose product Y?

    (iii) was in professional employment, if it is known that he/she did not choose product X?   (10 marks)

(b) Do the survey results suggest any difference in product preference between the employment groups? Carry out a chi-square test at 1% significance.

                                         (15 marks)

                                         Total marks 25

16.52 A manager who needs to predict sales of a product wishes to understand the relationship between sales of the product and the price of the product. The sales are not seasonal in nature. The table alongside gives details of the quantity sold (£000s) and the price (£) for a random sample of 10 similar outlets.

Price (£) X	Quantity sold (£000s) Y
4.10	180
4.80	60
4.40	115
4.62	80
4.20	166
4.60	100
4.35	136
4.90	50
4.80	90
4.24	160

(a) Plot a scatter diagram of the data and comment on it.   (4 marks)

(b) Calculate the value of the correlation coefficient and test its value at the 5% level of significance.   (5 marks)

(c) Find the regression equation of the line which could be used to predict the quantity sold in terms of the price of the product.

    Plot this line on your diagram.

    Interpret the value of the gradient of the line.   (7 marks)

(d) Calculate the value of the goodness of fit, R^2 %, and interpret its value.

                                         (4 marks)

(e) Predict the quantity sold if the price is:

    (i) £4.50   (ii) £5.20

    Comment on the likely accuracy of these two forecasts.   (5 marks)

                                         Total marks 25

16.53 The quarterly sales of a product for 1996 to 2000 are given below:

Year	Quarter 1	Quarter 2	Quarter 3	Quarter 4
		Sales (£00 000s)		
1996	87.8	97.4	95.2	90.4
1997	91.1	102.1	99.2	98.1
1998	94.6	104.2	102.1	98.1
1999	98.8	108.6	104.7	100.6
2000	99.3	110.7	103.5	102.0

The SPSS analysis of these data is given after the question.

(a) Plot the given data as a time series, leaving room for your forecasts for 2001.
                                                                  (5 marks)

(b) Calculate the missing values indicated by the 3 question marks in the
     following table.   (3 marks)

(c) Plot the smoothed trend-cycle on your graph.   (2 marks)

(d) Use your graph to forecast sales for each of the four quarters of 2001.
     State your forecasts clearly and show how they were calculated.
     Estimate the likely error in your forecasts.   (7 marks)

(e) Find the deseasonalised sales figures for the last two quarters of 2000.
     Explain how these figures might be used.   (3 marks)

(f) With reference to your graph and the summary statistics given in the SPSS
     output, discuss the suitability of the fitted model.   (5 marks)

                                                          Total marks 25

SPSS ouput for use with Question 16.53

->* Seasonal Decomposition.

DATE	SALES	Moving averages	First residual	Seasonal factors	Smoothed trend-cycle	Second residual
Q1 1996	87.800	.	.	.	.	.
Q2 1996	97.400	.	.	.	.	.
Q3 1996	95.200	93.113	2.087	1.512	93.176	.512
Q4 1996	90.400	94.113	−3.713	−2.763	94.007	−.844
Q1 1997	91.100	95.200	−4.100	−4.288	95.221	.167
Q2 1997	102.100	96.663	5.438	5.540	96.651	−.091
Q3 1997	99.200	98.063	1.138	1.512	98.021	−.333
Q4 1997	98.100	98.763	−.663	−2.763	98.996	1.867
Q1 1998	94.600	99.388	−4.788	−4.288	99.332	−.444
Q2 1998	104.200	99.750	4.450	5.540	99.629	−.969
Q3 1998	102.100	100.275	1.825	1.512	100.310	.278
Q4 1998	98.100	101.350	−3.250	−2.763	101.296	−.433
Q1 1999	98.800	102.225	−3.425	−4.288	102.321	.767
Q2 1999	108.600	102.863	5.737	5.540	102.884	.176
Q3 1999	104.700	103.237	1.463	1.512	103.232	−.044
Q4 1999	100.600	?	?	−2.763	103.540	?
Q1 2000	99.300	103.675	−4.375	−4.288	103.665	−.077
Q2 2000	110.700	103.700	7.000	5.540	103.862	1.298
Q3 2000	103.500	.	.	.	.	.
Q4 2000	102.000	.	.	.	.	.

Quarterly sales (£00 000)

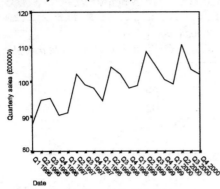

Sales and trend

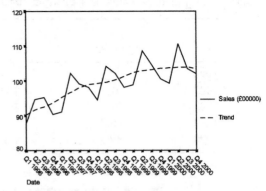

Sales, trend and fitted model

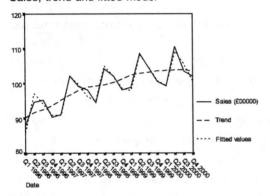

Second residuals against time

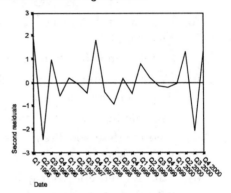

Summary statistics

Variable	Mean	Std Dev	Minimum	Maximum	Valid N	Label
SALES	99.43	5.79	87.80	110.70	20	Sales (£00 000s)
1st RESIDS	0.12	4.05	-4.79	7.00	16	First residual
2nd RESIDS	-0.02	0.84	-1.98	1.87	20	Second residuals

16.54 The financial director of White-houses, a group of estate agents, believes that experience is the best predictor of the annual sales of the various salespeople at its Yorkshire branches.

The data alongside were collected for a random sample of fifteen salespeople:

Experience (years)	Annual sales (£0 000)
1.3	50
5.1	161
6.2	195
5.4	172
3.9	132
4.1	133
6.1	181
1.9	69
2.2	78
3.4	124
7.1	131
2.1	64
4.5	80
3.8	110
4.4	127

(a) Plot the annual sales (y) against the number of years of experience (x).

(5 marks)

(b) Calculate the correlation coefficient (r) and test, at the 5% level of significance, to see if there is a linear relationship between the annual sales and the number years of experience.

(6 marks)

(c) Calculate the regression equation which can be used to forecast the annual sales given the number of years experience and draw this line on your scatter diagram. Interpret the coefficients in your equation.

(6 marks)

(d) What is the percentage of the variation in annual sales which is explained by this regression model?

(2 marks)

The salespeople's sales for the previous year were also used to predict current annual sales and the Minitab printout in Figure 16.3 gives the results of that analysis.

(e) State the regression equation for this second model and interpret its coefficients.

(2 marks)

(f) Which of the two models is likely to give the most accurate prediction for current annual sales and why?

(2 marks)

(g) Have you any reservations about your answer to part (f)?

(2 marks)

Figure 16.3

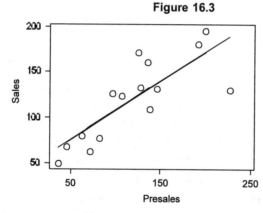

Presales

Note:
'sales' is current annual sales
'presales' is previous year's
sales

```
Correlation of presales and sales=0.808

The regression equation is
sales = 44.8 + 0.638 presales

Predictor       Coef       Stdev       t-ratio          p
Constant       44.75       16.87          2.65      0.020
presales       0.6377      0.1289         4.95      0.000

s=27.50   R-sq=65.3%   R-sq(adj) = 62.6%

Analysis of Variance
SOURCE            DF          SS         MS          F          p
Regression         1       18498      18498      24.46      0.000
Error             13        9830        756
Total             14       28328

Unusual Observations
Obs.     presales      sales       Fit    Stdev.Fit    Residual    St.Resid
11            227     131.00    189.51        15.66      -58.51      -2.59R
```

Total marks 25

16.55 The values of the houses on a house agent's lists are approximately normally distributed with a mean value of £68 000 and a standard deviation of £13 000.

(a) What percentage of the houses have values below £45 000? (6 marks)

(b) A customer is interested in buying a house between £70 000 and £80 000. What percentage of houses are in this price range? (7 marks)

(c) The house agent is doing a newspaper promotion on the higher priced properties. They have decided to concentrate on the top 15% of the price range. What is the minimum value to be considered for this promotion? (6 marks)

(d) A sample of 40 houses in the Wakefield area was selected at random and found to have a mean of £61 250 with a standard deviation of £12 500. Calculate a 95% confidence interval for the mean price of all the houses in the Wakefield area. Are houses cheaper in Wakefield? Why? (6 marks)

Total marks 25

16.56 Two hundred properties which had been sold from the Halifax branch were selected at random and their addresses were classified into three main areas. The length of time which it took to complete each sale was noted.

	Length of time to complete sale (months)			
Area	0 and <6	6 and <12	12 and <24	24 and over
A	21	48	19	7
B	10	26	3	4
C	5	24	10	23

(a) Test at the 1% level of significance to see if there is an association between area and the length of time to complete a sale. (14 marks)

(b) Calculate the probability that the length of time to complete the sale of a property in Halifax selected at random:

(i) is between 6 and less than 12 months

(ii) is 24 or more months, given that it is in area A

(iii) is less than 6 months and from area B (5 marks)

(c) Assuming a maximum value of 36 months, calculate the expected value for the length of time to complete a sale. (6 marks)

Total marks 25

16.57 The index of house prices in the Yorkshire region was revised in 1997. The values of the old and the new indices are given below.

	Index of house prices in Yorkshire region						
Year	1994	1995	1996	1997	1998	1999	2000
Index 1	175	172	169	161			
Index 2				100	99	103	110

(a) (i) Explain what is meant by the term 'base year' for an index number.

(ii) What is the base year for Index 2?

(iii) If the index had not been revised, what would the values of Index 1 have been in years 1998, 1999 and 2000?

(iv) What values would Index 2 have in years 1994, 1995 and 1996?

(8 marks)

(b) The table below gives the values of Index 1 for house prices in the South East.

	Index of house prices in the South East						
Year	*1994*	*1995*	*1996*	*1997*	*1998*	*1999*	*2000*
Index 1	210	206	191	175	179	198	219
Index 2							

(i) Calculate the 'revised' figures for this region (Index 2), using the same base year as for the Yorkshire region.

(ii) On one set of axes, draw graphs to show how house prices have changed in the two regions over the period 1994 to 2000.

(iii) Comment upon the main features of the graphs. (9 marks)

(c) Categorise the following information about houses as nominal, ordinal, interval or ratio data:

(i) Postcode

(ii) Price (£)

(iii) Number of bedrooms

(iv) Area of garden classified as small, medium or large (4 marks)

(d) What type of random sampling method should be used in each of the following cases and why?

(i) A sample survey of sellers' opinions, where the house agent will visit the client and wishes to minimise travelling.

(ii) A sample survey of buyers' opinions which will be done by postal questionnaire and it is expected that house prices and area of property are likely to be relevant. (4 marks)

Total marks 25

16.58 The Minitab printout overleaf gives the time series analysis of the number of houses sold at the Brighouse branch over the period from quarter 1 of 1996 to quarter 1 of 2000.

(a) Draw a graph of the data. (5 marks)

(b) Calculate the missing trend and first residual values (marked ? in the table) and draw the trend on your graph. (5 marks)

(c) Describe briefly the pattern in house sales over this period. (3 marks)

(d) Forecast the house sales for the remaining three quarters of 2000, explaining clearly the method you used. (4 marks)

(e) From the mean and the standard deviation of the second residual values, give a measure of the likely accuracy of your forecasts in part (d). (4 marks)

(f) Does this model fit the data well? Give three reasons to support your decision. (4 marks)

Total marks 25

Minitab output for question 16.58

Row	QUARTER	THE DATA	TREND	1ST.RESD	SEASONAL	FITTED	2ND.RESD
1	1	200	*	*	*	*	*
2	2	212	*	*	*	*	*
3	3	229	211.375	17.625	13.0625	224.438	4.56250
4	4	207	209.750	-2.750	-4.6250	205.125	1.87500
5	5	195	207.125	-12.125	-8.2500	198.875	-3.87500
6	6	204	204.875	-0.875	0.0833	204.958	-0.95833
7	7	216	205.000	11.000	13.0625	218.062	-2.06250
8	8	202	206.375	-4.375	-4.6250	201.750	0.25000
9	9	201	207.625	-6.625	-8.2500	199.375	1.62500
10	10	209	208.625	0.375	0.0833	208.708	0.29167
11	11	221	209.875	11.125	13.0625	222.937	-1.93750
12	12	205	?	?	-4.6250	207.125	-2.12500
13	13	208	214.000	-6.000	-8.2500	205.750	2.25000
14	14	217	216.250	0.750	0.0833	216.333	0.66667
15	15	231	218.500	12.500	13.0625	231.563	-0.56250
16	16	213	*	*	*	*	*
17	17	218	*	*	*	*	*

SUMMARY STATISTICS

FOR THE DATA
Mean of THE DATA = 211.06
Standard deviation of THE DATA = 10.034

FOR THE FIRST RESIDUALS
Mean of 1ST.RESD = 1.0673
Standard deviation of 1ST.RESD = 9.1172

FOR THE SECOND RESIDUALS
Mean of 2ND.RESD = 0.0000011738
Standard deviation of 2ND.RESD = 2.2620

Houses sold

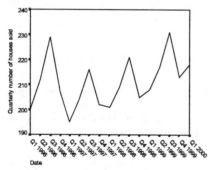

Houses sold with trend

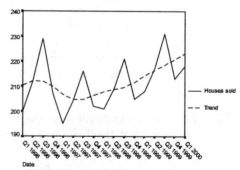

Houses sold, trend and fitted values

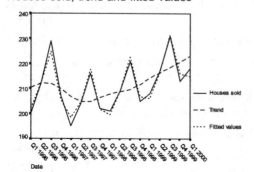

Second residuals against time

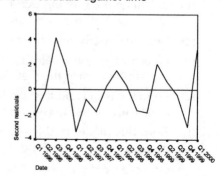

16.59 An investment manager studying haulage companies calculates, for a random sample of six such firms, the percentage capital investment in vehicles (% vehicles) and the profit before tax (% profit) as a percentage of turnover. The results were as follows:

% vehicles	37	47	10	22	41	25
% profit	14	21	−5	16	19	8

(a) Draw a scatter diagram of the data, plotting % profit against % vehicles.
(4 marks)

(b) Calculate the value of the correlation coefficient (r) and test to see if it is significantly different to zero, at the 5% level of significance. (6 marks)

(c) Calculate the regression equation for estimating % profit in terms of % vehicles and draw the regression line on your graph. (5 marks)

(d) Comment upon the value of r, with reference to your graph. (3 marks)

(e) Use your equation in part (c) to estimate % profit when % vehicles is:

(i) 30

(ii) 90

Briefly comment upon the validity of your answers. (4 marks)

(f) If the investment manager wanted to estimate the minimum value of the % vehicles in order to break even (that is, when % profit $= 0$), *explain* how he should do this, but *do not* perform the calculations. (3 marks)

Total marks 25

16.60 After an intensive three-week training course, new sales representatives at Merlin plc sit a comprehensive examination. The minimum pass mark is 75.

You can assume the marks to be normally distributed with a mean mark of 84 and standard deviation of 5.1?

(a) What percentage of the new employees are expected to pass the examination? (5 marks)

(b) What percentage are expected to have marks between 75 and 85? (6 marks)

(c) At what mark should the distinction grade be set, if Merlin wish to award distinctions to the top 5%? (6 marks)

(d) Merlin believes that the mean mark of the new sales representatives might be altering. A random sample of 20 of them was selected. Their marks in the test had a mean of 76. Assuming that the standard deviation remains unchanged, calculate an appropriate 95% confidence interval and say whether these results support Merlin's belief or not. (8 marks)

Total marks 25

16.61 The table below gives the number of saloon cars and hatchbacks sold by a random sample of dealers over the first six months of the year.

Car type	Jan	Feb	Mar	Apr	May	Jun
Saloon	6	6	8	22	32	24
Hatchback	48	30	21	24	38	36

(a) Test at the 5% level of significance the hypothesis that the type of car sold is independent of the month of sale. (14 marks)

(b) Using the above data, calculate a 95% confidence interval for the percentage of cars sold by all such dealers in the first six months of the year which are hatchbacks. (6 marks)

(c) Briefly summarise your results to (a) and (b) so that they can be understood by a non-statistician. (5 marks)

Total marks 25

16.62 (a) The following table gives the index of sales figures for INP Magazines over the past five years. Which is the base year?

1996	1997	1998	1999	2000
86	92	100	108	113

(1 mark)

(b) Calculate the index of sales figures for INP for this same period using 1996 as the base year (5 marks)

(c) The following table gives the index of sales figures for the overall sector, for the same period.

1996	1997	1998	1999	2000
100	105	114	128	137

Draw a graph to illustrate how the sales performance of INP compares to that of the overall sector over the period 1996 to 2000 and comment upon it. (5 marks)

(d) For the overall sector, calculate:

(i) the percentage point increase from 1999 to 2000.

(ii) the percentage increase from 1999 to 2000. (4 marks)

(e) If INP's sales in 2000 were £1 680 000, calculate their sales in 1997. (3 marks)

(f) INP publishes a range of magazines of general (non-specialist) interest, which are sold at newsagents and other retail outlets. In order to improve their circulation figures they decide to survey their readers and readers of similar publications, by means of an interview questionnaire.

(i) Why would it be difficult to select a simple random sample? (1 mark)

(ii) What would be the disadvantage of selecting a quota sample? (1 mark)

(iii) What would be an advantage of selecting a cluster sample? (1 mark)

(iv) Give, in your own words, four guidelines which should be followed when compiling the questionnaire. (4 marks)

Total marks 25

16.63 An entrance examination of average difficulty was expected to produce a mean mark of 50%. A large group of students thought a particular entrance exam had been too difficult and felt certain that the mean mark must be lower than this. The lecturer asked a random sample of them for their marks which he recorded opposite:

Student	A	B	C	D	E	F	G	H	I	J
Mark	32	41	62	31	57	37	48	40	50	22

(a) Perform a hypothesis test at 5% significance to see if the students were right.

(5 marks)

After a semester studying a maths and statistics module the lecturer gave his students a similar test to the entrance exam to see if they were still of the same standard. The marks of the same ten students are tabulated below:

Student	A	B	C	D	E	F	G	H	I	J
Mark	37	44	59	36	60	33	55	40	57	32

(b) Calculate a 95% confidence interval for the mean mark of all the students for this second paper and use it to investigate whether the mean of all the marks could still be 50%. (5 marks)

(c) Investigate whether the module has been effective or not by using:

   (i) separate 95% confidence intervals for each set of marks

   (ii) a single confidence interval for the change in the marks   (11 marks)

(d) Comment on your answers to part (c).   (4 marks)

Total marks 25

(Answers to these examination-type questions are given in Appendix A2)

16.12 Multiple choice questions

Select the answer nearest to your own. (All answers are given in Appendix A3.)

The annual salaries, £000, of the employees of a wholesale cash-and-carry firm are illustrated in the histogram below. The frequencies are per £2000 interval. Use the diagram to answer Questions 1 to 5.

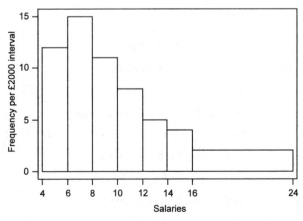

Answer

1   This distribution is:

   (a) Positively skewed   (b) Negatively skewed

   (c) Symmetrical   (d) None of these   _ _ _ _ _

2   The value of the modal income (£000) could be:

    (a) 15   (b) 7

    (c) between 6 and 8   (d) 24   _____

3   The number of employees earning between £16 000 and £24 000 is:

    (a) 2   (b) 8   (c) 16   (d) 24   _____

4   The total number of employees is:

    (a) 15   (b) 24   (c) 57   (d) 63   _____

5   The range of the incomes, in £000, is exactly:

    (a) 24   (b) 20

    (c) 15   (d) Impossible to tell   _____

6   The mean of the incomes, in £000, is:

    (a) 7.0   (b) 8.9   (c) 9.07   (d) 10.1   _____

250 students have taken a Statistics exam. The cumulative distribution of marks is shown below. Use the diagram to answer Questions 7 to 11.

7   What is the median mark in the Statistics exam?

    (a) 42   (b) 50   (c) 60   (d) 72   _____

8   What is the 30th percentile mark in the Statistics exam?

    (a) 0   (b) 30   (c) 33   (d) 49   _____

9   What percentage of students have Statistics marks over 50?

    (a) 33%   (b) 45%   (c) 55%   (d) 65%   _____

10   What percentage of students have Statistics marks between 40 and 50?

    (a) 2%   (b) 10%   (c) 22%   (d) 65%   _____

11   If the pass mark was 40% how many students passed?

    (a) 40   (b) 60   (c) 100   (d) 145   _____

The following Minitab output represents the distribution of the exam marks for a group of trainees. Use the diagrams to answer Questions 12 to 18.

```
Stem-and-leaf of Exam
Leaf Unit=1.0
    1    2  8
    5    3  0059
   14    4  244578899
   (9)   5  000024789
   18    6  034455679
    9    7  3578
    5    8  699
    2    9  01
```

```
Boxplot
                               ----------------
               ----------------I     +       I--------------------
                               ----------------
        +---------+---------+---------+---------+---------+------ Exam
        24        36        48        60        72        84
```

12 The range of the marks is:
    (a) 63   (b) 62   (c) 8   (d) 7   _____

13 The modal mark is:
    (a) 9   (b) 50   (c) 54   (d) 91   _____

14 The number of students who took the exam is:
    (a) 8   (b) 41   (c) 49   (d) 59   _____

15 The median mark is:
    (a) 57   (b) 52   (c) 50   (d) 9   _____

16 If 45% was needed to pass, the number of failures was:
    (a) 8   (b) 9   (c) 32   (d) 33   _____

17 The interquartile range is:
    (a) 20   (b) 27   (c) 57   (d) 63   _____

18 Which of the following groups of statements is correct?
    (a) range = 63, median = 59, interquartile range = 20
    (b) median = 57, interquartile range = 20, range = 63
    (c) interquartile range = 27, range = 62, median = 50
    (d) median = 57, range = 62, interquartile range = 27   _____

The sets of data below are samples from large populations for use with Questions 19–28:

Sample A:	23	42	17	33	25	23		
Sample B:	2.4	5.7	4.6	4.6	1.9			
Sample C:	1.8	−4.1	0	3.6	−2.4	1.8	0	0

19 The range of A is:

(a) 23 to 23 (b) 0 (c) 25 (d) 17 to 42 _ _ _ _ _

20 The range of B is:

(a) 3.8 (b) 0.5 (c) 1.9 to 5.7 (d) 1.9 to 2.4 _ _ _ _ _

21 The mode of A is:

(a) 23 (b) 25 (c) 17 (d) 33 _ _ _ _ _

22 The mode of C is:

(a) 1.8 (b) −4.1 (c) 0.09 (d) 0 _ _ _ _ _

23 The median of A is:

(a) 23 (b) 24 (c) 25 (d) none of these _ _ _ _ _

24 The median of C is:

(a) 0 (b) 0.6 (c) 1.8 (d) 3.6 _ _ _ _ _

25 The mean of A is:

(a) 25.6 (b) 24.0 (c) 23.0 (d) 27.2 _ _ _ _ _

26 The mean of B is:

(a) 3.84 (b) 4.60 (c) 3.92 (d) 4.10 _ _ _ _ _

27 The estimated standard deviation of the population from which B was taken is:

(a) 1.73 (b) 1.62 (c) 1.45 (d) 1.40 _ _ _ _ _

28 The estimated standard deviation of the population from which C was taken is:

(a) 1.63 (b) 2.45 (c) 2.29 (d) 3.24 _ _ _ _ _

The following set of numbers represents a sample of student heights. Use it to answer Questions 29 and 30.

Heights	Frequency
60" and less than 64"	3
64" and less than 66"	5
66" and less than 68"	7
68" and less than 69"	10
69" and less than 70"	18
70" and less than 72"	13
72" and less than 74"	4
74" and less than 76"	2

29 The mean value of all student heights is estimated to be:

   (a) 69.10"   (b) 68.90"   (c) 69.40"   (d) 69.05"   _____

30 The standard deviation of all student heights is estimated to be:

   (a) 4.20"   (b) 2.70"   (c) 2.69"   (d) 2.72"   _____

31 If 20 invoices from the South average £60 and 10 invoices from the North average £30 the overall mean is:

   (a) 50   (b) 45   (c) 30   (d) 60   _____

32 If the mean of five numbers is 4.2 and four of them are 3, 4, 4, and 5 the fifth must be:

   (a) 3   (b) 4   (c) 5   (d) 6   _____

33 The variable 'weight', for example, 56 kg, is:

   (a) nominal   (b) ordinal   (c) interval   (d) ratio   _____

34 The variable 'satisfaction', for example, low, medium, high is:

   (a) nominal   (b) ordinal   (c) interval   (d) ratio   _____

35 The variable 'colour', for example, red, is:

   (a) nominal   (b) ordinal   (c) interval   (d) ratio   _____

36 The variable 'cost', for example, £24, is:

   (a) nominal   (b) ordinal   (c) interval   (d) ratio   _____

37 If three coins are tossed the probability of getting exactly two heads is:

   (a) 2/3   (b) 3/8   (c) 2/8   (d) 1/3   _____

38 If a pair of dice are rolled the probability of getting at least one six is:

   (a) 11/36   (b) 10/36   (c) 6/36   (d) 1/36   _____

39 Adam, Barry, Charles and David are the semi-finalists in a snooker contest. Barry and David each have a probability of 0.20 of winning the trophy. If the probability of Charles winning is 0.25 then that for Adam is:

   (a) 0.55   (b) 0.45

   (c) 0.35   (d) insufficient information   _____

Questions 40 to 42 refer to a large batch of invoices from a particular company. You are asked to assume that the values of the invoices (£) have a normal distribution with mean of £200 and standard deviation of £30

40 What percentage of the invoices have values of less than £170?

   (a) 16%   (b) 26%   (c) 36%   (d) 85%   _____

41 What percentageof invoices have values over £150?

   (a) 21%   (b) 45%   (c) 75%   (d) 95%   _____

42 What percentage of the invoices have values between £170 and £210?

   (a) 29%   (b) 47%   (c) 76%   (d) 95%   _____

43 What percentage of the invoices have values between £170 and £190?

    (a) 21%   (b) 47%   (c) 53%   (d) 79%   _____

44 What is the value which is exceeded by 40% of the invoices?

    (a) £58   (b) £108   (c) £158   (d) £208   _____

45 What is the value below which 25% of the invoices fall?

    (a) 58   (b) £158   (c) £180   (d) £220   _____

Questions 46 to 48 refer to the annual commission, in £000, earned by the whole of the salesforce of your company. You are asked to assume that they follow a normal distribution with a mean of 12 and a standard deviation of 3.5

46 What percentage of the sales force earned less than £6 000 commission?

    (a) 95.7%   (b) 45.7%   (c) 4.3%   (d) 1.7%   _____

47 What percentage of the salesmen earned between £10 000 and £15 000 commission?

    (a) 1.4%   (b) 8.8%   (c) 48.0%   (d) 52.0%   _____

48 What is the commission which needs to be earned, in £000, in order for a salesman to be in the top 20% of commission earners?

    (a) 9   (b) 15   (c) 19   (d) 20   _____

The times taken by a random selection of 10 workers to complete a task were:

   3.5 2.7 2.9 3.4 2.7 3.0 3.3 2.9 3.1 and 3.6 minutes

Use this information for Questions 49 to 52

49 The mean and standard deviations needed in order to calculate a 95% confidence interval for the mean time are:

    (a) $\bar{x} = 3.11; s = 0.308$ (b) $\bar{x} = 3.11; s = 0.325$

    (c) $\bar{x} = 3.46; s = 0.308$ (d) $\bar{x} = 3.46; s = 0.325$ _____

50 The table value to make use of in the calculation of the 95% confidence interval is:

    (a) 1.83   (b) 1.96   (c) 2.23   (d) 2.26   _____

51 The confidence interval produced is:

    (a) from 2.36 to 3.86 min   (b) from 2.88 to 3.34 min

    (c) from 2.90 to 3.32 min   (d) from 2.91 to 3.31 min   _____

52 Which of the following statements is true about the confidence interval produced?

    (a) It contains 95% of the times taken by the sample of workers.

    (b) There is a 95% chance that it contains all the times taken by the workers.

    (c) There is a 95% chance that it contains the mean time taken by all the workers.

    (d) There is a 95% chance that it contains the mean time taken by the sample of workers.   _____

(All answers are given in Appendix A3.)

Appendix A Answers

A1 Answers to tutorials and supplementary exercises

Tutorial 2   Graphical presentation

(Numerical answers are accurate but diagrams are only sketches.)

2.1   (a)   Frequency

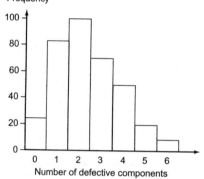

Number of defective components

(b)

Defectives	Frequency	Cumulative frequency
0	25	25
1	85	110
2	99	209
3	70	279
4	51	330
5	14	344
6	6	350

Cumulative frequency

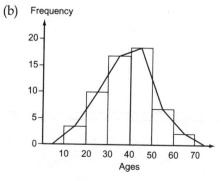

Number of defective components

2.2 (a)

Age	Frequency
less than 10	0
10 and < 20	3
20 and < 30	11
30 and < 40	18
40 and < 50	19
50 and < 60	7
60 and < 70	2

(b)   Frequency

Ages

(c)

Frequency	Stem & Leaf
3	1 | 789
11	2 | 00123345779
18	3 | 223344444566777999
19	4 | 00000111112455666779
7	5 | 0022448
2	6 | 04

Stem width: 10
Each leaf: 1 case(s)

(d)

Age	Cumulative frequency	% Cumulative frequency
< 10	0	0.0
< 20	3	5.0
< 30	14	23.3
< 40	32	53.3
< 50	51	85.0
< 60	58	96.7
< 70	60	100.0

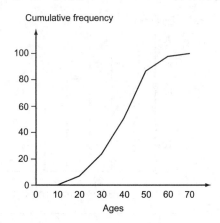

2.3 (a)

Height	Frequency	Range	Frequency/ inch	(c) Cumulative frequency	% Cumulative frequency
60" and < 64"	2	4"	0.5	2	4
64" and < 66"	6	2"	3.0	8	16
66" and < 68"	11	2"	5.5	19	38
68" and < 69"	9	1"	9.0	28	56
69" and < 70"	10	1"	10.0	38	76
70" and < 72"	8	2"	4.0	46	92
72" and < 74"	2	2"	1.0	48	96
74" and < 80"	2	6"	0.3	50	100

(b)

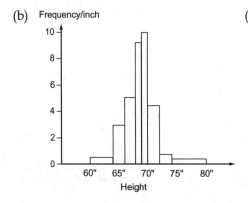

(c)

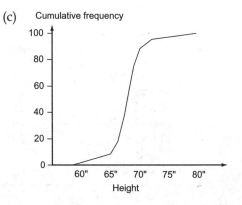

Supplementary Exercise 2

Note: Numerical answers are accurate but diagrams are only sketches.

2.4 (a) Employees

(b)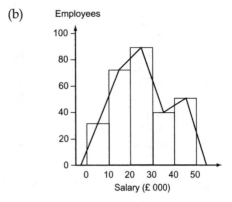

(c)

Salary (£000)	Cumulative frequency
< 10	35
< 20	110
< 30	206
< 40	248
< 50	300

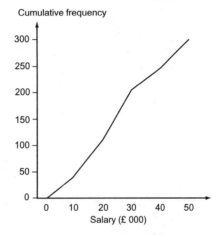

2.5 (a)

Times (sec)	Frequency
less than 50	1
50 and < 100	2
100 and < 150	4
150 and < 200	6
200 and < 250	10
250 and < 300	13
300 and < 350	8
350 and < 400	3
400 and < 450	2
450 and < 500	1

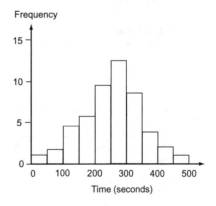

2.5 (b)

Times (sec)	Cumulative frequency
< 50	1
< 100	3
< 150	7
< 200	13
< 250	23
< 300	36
< 350	44
< 400	47
< 450	49
< 500	50

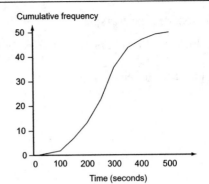

2.6 (a)

Profits (£000)	Frequency	Frequency/ £10k
less than 20	3	1.50
20 and < 30	5	5.00
30 and < 40	10	10.00
40 and < 50	21	21.00
50 and < 60	12	12.00
60 and < 100	9	2.25

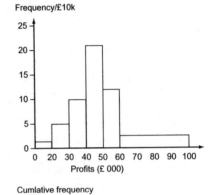

(b)

Profits	Cumulative frequency
< £20 000	3
< £30 000	8
< £40 000	18
< £50 000	39
< £60 000	51
< £100 000	60

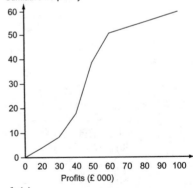

2.7 (a)

Pay (£)	Frequency
350 and > 375	2
375 and > 400	6
400 and > 425	7
425 and > 450	9
450 and > 475	6
475 and > 500	6
500 and > 525	2
525 and > 550	1
550 and > 575	1

(b) and (c)

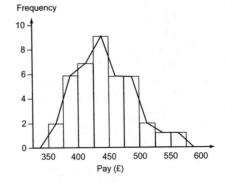

(b)

Pay (£)	Cumulative frequency	% Cumulative frequency
< 375	2	5.0
< 400	8	20.0
< 425	15	37.5
< 450	24	60.0
< 475	30	75.0
< 500	36	90.0
< 525	38	95.0
< 550	39	97.5
< 575	40	100.0

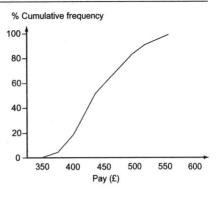

2.8 (a)

Exam scores	Frequency Yr1	Frequency/ 10marks 1	Frequency Yr2	Frequency/ 10marks 2
less than 30	5	1.67	2	0.67
30 & < 40	14	14.00	8	8.00
40 & < 50	29	29.00	20	20.00
50 & < 60	20	20.00	35	35.00
60 & < 70	8	8.00	15	15.00
70 and over	4	1.33	10	3.33

(b) Frequency density

(c)

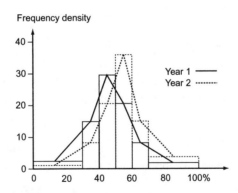

(e)

Exam scores	Cumulative frequency Yr 1	% Cumulative frequency Yr 1	Frequency Yr 2	% Cumulative frequency Yr 2
< 30	5	6.25	2	2.22
< 40	19	23.75	10	11.11
< 50	48	60.00	30	33.33
< 60	68	85.00	65	72.22
< 70	76	95.00	80	88.89
< 100	80	100.00	90	100.00

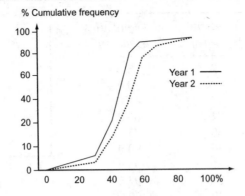

% Cumulative frequency

Tutorial 3   Summary statistics

Note: Answers from calculators are accurate but those from graphs are estimates only.

3.1   (a) 18   (b) 199   (c) 200   (d) 4.944

3.2   (a) A $\bar{x} = 4.50$ $s = 0.301$ 0.86 g/denier
            B $\bar{x} = 4.40$ $s = 0.154$ 0.47 g/denier

3.3 $n = 1000$ $\bar{x} = 2.00$ $s = 0.999$ defective components

3.4 $n = 50$ $\bar{x} = 64.0$ $s = 6.36$ hours

3.5 $n = 100$ $\bar{x} = 97.0$ $s = 9.27$ marks

3.6   Mode = 2 defectives; median = (175th/176th box) containing 2 defectives

3.7   Estimated mode = 41 years, estimated median = 39 years, estimated upper quartile = 47 years and estimated lower quartile = 31 years giving an interquartile range of 16 years.

6% under 21 and 15% over 50 years old.

3.8   Estimated mode = 69.2 inches, estimated median = 68.7, estimated upper quartile = 70.0 inches and estimated lower quartile = 66.8 inches giving an interquartile range of 3.2 inches. 8% of students are over six feet tall.

Supplementary exercise 3

Note: Answers from calculators are accurate but those from graphs are estimates only.

3.9   (a) £22 800   (b) £24 200   (c) £19 200
      (d) $\bar{x} = £25000$, $s = £12 500$

3.10 (a) $\bar{x} = 252$ s, s.d. $= 93.2$ s   (b) 270 s
      (c) 260 s   (d) 115 s   (e) 5/6 bills

3.11 (a) £46 000   (b) £46 000   (c) £18 000
      (d) $\bar{x} = £47 200$, $s = £17 800$ (e) 10%

3.12 Answers will vary slightly with the class intervals used. These are for £25 intervals.

      (a) $\bar{x} = £442.50$, $s = £46.75$ (b) £437
      (c) £440   (d) £67   (e) 20%, 10%

3.13 Year 1 values given first.

    (a) 46%, 54%   (b) 47%, 54%   (c) 15%, 16%

    (d) $\bar{x} = 47.9\%, 55.1\%$; $s = 14.6\%, 14.6\%$ (e) 40%, 67%

    (f) The marks of the two year groups are evenly spread but those for Year 2 are, on average, about 7% higher than those of Year 1.

Tutorial 4 *Probability*

4.1   0.8

4.2   (a) 1/6   (b) 1/2   (c) 1/3   (d) 0

4.3   (a) 1/13   (b) 1/4   (c) 1/52   (d) 4/13

    (e) 3/13   (f) 1/2   (g) 1/26   (h) 3/26

4.4   (a) 8   (b) 1/8   (c) 3/8   (d) 3/8

    (e) 1/8   (f) 1

4.5   (a) 3/36   (b) 5/12   (c) 1/6   (d) 1/2

    (e) 1/4   (f) 5/12

4.6   (a) 1/3   (b) 1/2   (c) 5/6   (d) 1/6

4.7   (a) 0.042   (b) 0.543   (c) 0.415

4.8   (a) 0.850   (b) 0.818   (c) 0.889   (d) 0.471

    (e) 0.529

4.9   (a) 0.700   (b) 0.500   (c) 0.500   (d) 0.600

    (e) 0.800   (f) 0.571   (g) 0.429

4.10 (a) 0.640   (b) 0.128   (c) 0.240   (d) 0.144

    (e) 0.872   (f) 0.776   (g) 0.550   (h) 0.075

    (i) 0.710   (j) 0.290

Supplementary Exercise 4

4.11 (a) 0.050   (b) 0.362   (c) 0.588

4.12 (a) 0.159   (b) 0.032   (c) 0.000

4.13 (a) 0.198   (b) 0.036   (c) 0.005

4.14 0.110

4.15 (a) 0.829   (b) 0.171

4.16 0.2

4.17 (a) 0.625   (b) 0.665   (c) 0.110   (d) 0.894

Tutorial 5 *Normal distribution*

5.1   (a) 0.0161   (b) 0.746   (c) 0.21%   (d) 8.41 metres

5.2   (a) 0.0284   (b) 5 days   (c) 39 days   (d) 171 cups

    (e) 26 sandwiches

5.3   928

5.4   (a)(i)   382   (ii) 6888   (iii) 730   (b) 1.04 kg

5.5   (a) 64%   (b) 87%

5.6   (a) 4.78%   (b) 0.9044   (c) 4 cups   (d) 0.04%

5.7   (a) 5.48%   (b) 33.6%
       (c) 21 working days   (d) 0.38%

5.8   3 years 7 months

5.9   (a) 99.7%   (b) 68.5%   (c) 0.62%

5.10   (a) 0.202   (b) 0.0487   (c) 27.8 kg

Supplementary Exercise 5

5.11   (a) 0.71%   (b) 0.0%   (c) 0.96%   (d) 79.4%
       (e) £74.35   (f) £76.63   (g) £89.92

5.12   (a) 53 students   (b) 5 students   (c) 299 students   (d) 143 students
       (e) 71.1 kg

5.13   (a) 6 workers   (b) 0 workers   (c) 66.8 s   (d) 76.2 s

5.14   153.4 cm

5.15   (a) 0.0668   (b) 0.401   (c) 0.175

5.16   454 to 541 g

5.17   21.2% small, 67.3% medium, 11.5% large

5.18   (a) 0.171   (b) 0.329   (c) 0.248   (d) 0.253
       (e) 0.962   (f) 0.279   (g) 0.580

5.19   37.9 m.p.g.

5.20   £33.37, 0.0%

Tutorial 6   Confidence intervals (mainly to 3 sf)

6.1   (a) $27.6 < \mu < 29.0$ (b) $27.4 < \mu < 29.2$
       (c) $27.1 < \mu < 29.5$

6.2 $£26.10 < \mu < £30.10$

6.3 $0.979 < \mu < 1.043$

6.4 $63.1\% < \pi < 70.2\%$

6.5   Firm A: $£338.90 < \mu < £347.10$, Firm B: $£335.40 < \mu < £342.50$
       Overlap, so could be same, Firm B correct.

6.6 $-0.104 < \mu < 0.722$ Zero included, no difference between
                                                   methods

6.7 $12.7 < \mu < 15.3$ and $15.7 < \mu < 20.3$ No overlap, two different population means

6.8 $-2.1 < \mu_d < +12.1$ Training may not be effective

6.9 $62.2\% < \pi < 73.8\%$.   75% outside range so claim not upheld

6.10 $92.9\% < \mu < 99.1\%$ Claim not upheld, mark lower than 100

Supplementary exercise 6

6.11 $1382 < \mu < 1528$ hours   1500 included so no change

6.12 $1.02 < \mu < 1.06$ kg   Mean of whole batch over 1 kg

6.13   (a) $11.0\% < \pi < 19.0\%$ (b) $9.7\% < \pi < 20.3\%$

6.14 $-0.096 < \mu < 1.536$ Zero included so claim rejected

6.15 $4.20 < \mu < 5.58$ tonnes   Yield has improved from 4.1 tonnes

6.16 $0.03 < \mu < 1.72$ Zero excluded so training effective

6.17 $55.7 < \mu_a < 83.1$; $65.9 < \mu_b < 96.4$ Overlap so B not better than A

6.18 $26.6 < \mu < 28.4$ and $26.1 < \mu < 27.6$ Both groups performed similarly

6.19 $176.6 < \mu < 179.4$ and $172.1 < \mu < 175.9$ cm   No overlap so different.

6.20 $-4.62 < \mu < 10.02$ Zero included so method not effective

Tutorial 7   Hypothesis testing

7.1   CV $= 1.64$ TS $= 1.94$ H_0 rejected, mean less than £95

7.2   CV $= 1.64$ TS $= 4.63$ H_0 rejected, she does spend longer

7.3   CV $= 1.81$ TS $= 4.38$ H_0 rejected, mean weight more than 1 kg

7.4   CV $= 2.58$ TS $= 1.58$ H_0 not rejected, mean life could be 1500 hrs

7.5   CV $= 1.83$ TS $= 2.87$ H_0 rejected, drug gives more hours sleep

7.6   CV $= 2.58$ TS $= 1.98$ H_0 not rejected, coin could be fair

7.7   CV $= 1.89$ TS $= 1.70$ H_0 not rejected, training may be ineffective

7.8   CV $= 1.64$ TS $= 1.86$ H_0 rejected, could be less than 84 scoops

7.9   CV $= 2.82$ TS $= 2.27$ H_0 not rejected, yields could be same

7.10   CV $= 1.83$ TS $= 1.20$ H_0 not rejected, study has not been effective

Supplementary exercise 7

7.11   CV $= 1.64$ TS $= 1.41$ H_0 not rejected, incidents not increasing

7.12   CV $= 2.45$ TS $= 2.05$ H_0 not rejected, interviewers not different

7.13   CV $= 1.64$ TS $= 1.73$ H_0 rejected, percentage lower than 60

7.14 CV $=2.62$ TS $=2.15$ H_0 not rejected, mean load could be 10 tonnes

7.15 CV $=2.45$ TS $=2.01$ H_0 not rejected, yields could be same

7.16 CV $=2.33$ TS $=1.17$ H_0 not rejected, claim of 70% upheld

7.17 CV $=1.75$ TS $=2.28$ H_0 rejected, increase in temperature

7.18 CV $=1.64$ TS $=2.07$ H_0 rejected, less than 70% will vote Labour

7.19 CV $=2.26$ TS $=0.67$ H_0 not rejected, mean score could be 60%

7.20 CV $=1.73$ TS $=1.86$ H_0 rejected, method B better

7.21 CV $=1.96$ TS $=2.76$ H_0 rejected, the two groups not the same

7.22 CV $=1.64$ TS $=3.0$ H_0 rejected, A could last longer than B

7.23 CV $=2.33$ TS $=2.68$ H_0 rejected, women get better mean marks

7.24 CV $=2.33$ TS $=1.66$ H_0 not rejected, Brown quicker by 4 minutes.

Tutorial 8 Analysis of variance

8.1 TS $=0.20$ $F_{0.05}(3,16) = 3.24$
We have no evidence that the mean typing speeds of the four trainees are different.

8.2 TS $=4.41$ $F_{0.05}(2,37) = 3.26$
Results of all three instructors are not the same.

8.3 (a) Brands: 3.72 $F_{0.05}(2,9) = 4.26$ No difference between brands
(b) Brands: TS $=3.97$ $F_{0.05}(2,6) = 5.14$;
(c) Laboratories: TS $=1.25$ $F_{0.05}(3,6) = 4.76$;
There is no difference between the mean results of the brands or laboratories.

8.4 Employees: TS $=1.55$, $F_{0.05}(4,8) = 3.84$ Shifts: TS $=5.76$, $F_{0.05}(2,8) = 4.46$
There is a significant difference in mean production between shifts but not between workers.

8.5 (a) Employees $F_{Emp} = 0.02$, $F_{0.05}(2,18) = 3.55$ No significant difference

(b) Employees $F_{Emp} = 0.05$, $F_{0.05}(2,12) = 3.89$ Still no significant difference

(c) Weeks $F_{Week} = 4.59$, $F_{0.05}(6,12) = 3.00$ At least one week's sales different. CD $= 1.45$

Week 1 different from weeks 2, 4, 5, 6 and 7; week 3 different from weeks 5 and 7; week 5 different from week 6. All other differences non-significant.

Supplementary exercise 8

8.6 $F_{Packers} = 2.34$, $F_{0.05}(3,12) = 3.49$ No significant difference between packers

8.7 $F_{Shifts} = 0.14$, $F_{Packers} = 8.23$; Shifts: $F_{0.05}(2,6) = 5.14$, Packers: $F_{0.05}(3,6) = 4.76$
No difference between shifts, but at least two of the packers different

8.8 $F_{\text{Route}} = 4.53$, $F_{\text{Day}} = 8.20$; Routes: $F_{0.05}(3, 12) = 3.49$, Days: $F_{0.05}(4, 12) = 3.26$
Both significant
Routes: 1 and 2 different from 3 and 4 (CD $= 1.74$); Days: Monday different from the rest (CD $= 1.94$); Tuesday and Wednesday different from Thursday and Friday

8.9 (a) $F_{\text{Fert}} = 2.14$, $F_{0.05}(3, 8) = 4.07$ No significant difference

(b) $F_{\text{Fert}} = 5.88$; $F_{0.05}(3, 6) = 4.76$,   There is a significant difference

(c) Fertilisers: A and C different from B and D (CD $= 5.53$)

8.10 (a) Rope structures: $F = 16.93$, $F_{0.05}(2, 12) = 3.89$ Significant difference between the strength of the different rope structures
Interaction: $F = 5.29$, $F_{0.05}(6, 12) = 3.00$, interaction significant

(b) $F = 11.36$, $F_{0.05}(3, 12) = 3.49$ Humidity did affect the strength of the threads

8.11 Districts: $F = 33.73$; Heights: $F = 0.32$; Tests: $F = 2.15$; $F_{0.05}(4, 12) = 3.26$
So difference between at least two districts but not between heights. The different tests produce consistent results

Tutorial 9   Correlation and regression

9.1 $r = 0.560$ CV $= 0.576$ No correlation between expenses and profits.

9.2 $r = 0.968$ CV $= 0.707$ $y = 0.068 + 0.705x$ 5.4% increase in sales

9.3 $r = 0.247$ CV $= 0.707$ not significant so regression equation not appropriate
6.1%

9.4   (b) $r = 0.976$ (c) $y = 21.7 + 3.47x$ (e) 95.3%
(f) 74%   (g) 143%!   (h) outside range of given data

9.5 $r = -0.668$ $y = 14.9 - 0.564x$ For every additional £1000 salary an extra half day is likely to be missed   6 days

9.6 $r = 0.987$ CV $= 0.765$ correlation significant

$y = 0.113 + 0.103x$ For every extra £1000 turnover an extra profit of £103 is expected

Supplementary exercise 9

9.7   Spearman's correlation coefficient $= 0.842$;   CV $= 0.632$;   correlation significant

9.8   (a) $r = 0.656$ CV $= 0.729$ Sales not rising significantly over time
(b) not appropriate

9.9   (b) $r = 0.965$ CV $= 0.497$ so significant
(c) $y = 39.7 + 1.58x$ (d) 93%   (e) 1620

9.10 (b) $r = 0.997$, significant, $y = 501 + 10.0x$;   (c) £2507   99.4%

9.11 Spearman's correlation coefficient $= 0.006$, CV $= 0.632$ not significant.

9.12 (a) $r = 0.864$ CV $= 0.514$ so significant   (b) $y = -0.075 + 0.073x$
(c) £659 000

9.13 Spearman's correlation coefficient $= 0.817$ CV $= 0.666$ significant correlation

Tutorial 10   Chi-squared tests

10.1   CV 5.99   TS$=3.96$ Lager preference is not gender dependent

10.2   CV$=13.28$ TS$=5.63$ Demand for new brand is not regionalised

10.3   CV$=5.99$ TS$=14.46$ Magazine read is associated with income

10.4   CV$=12.59$ TS$=4.57$ No differences of opinion between departments

10.5   CV$=16.81$ TS$=38.86$ Opinions differ among the different professions

Supplementary exercise 10

10.6   CV$=7.82$ TS$=1.72$ Brand share is independent of region

10.7   CV$=16.81$ TS$=20.91$ Perceived value does depend on industry

10.8   CV$=9.49$ TS$=22.00$ Opinion is not independent of income

10.9   CV$=9.49$ TS$=21.50$ View of prospects depends on profession

10.10 CV$=13.28$ TS$=28.52$ Expenditure and mode of travel are associated

10.11 CV$=5.99$ TS$=5.94$ Driving capability is not gender dependent

10.12 CV$=16.81$ TS$=13.16$ Proportions of defective tubes produced similar

10.13 CV$=16.92$ TS$=21.34$ Number of subscriptions does depend on income

10.14 CV$=5.99$ TS$=19.62$ Type of ownership and size of house are associated

10.15 CV$=3.84$ TS$=0.11$ Machine productions are of similar quality

Tutorial 11   Index numbers

Note: Some values will vary slightly due to rounding errors depending upon the method taken for calculating them. One decimal place shown but final answer may be an integer.

11.1   (a) 100, 105.2, 110.0, 113.1   (b) 5.2, 4.8, 3.1
       (c) 5.2%, 4.6%, 2.8%

11.2   (a) 100, 103.3, 109.6, 95.7   (b) 104.5, 108.0, 114.5, 100
       (c) 3.5, 6.5, −14.5   (d) 3.3% 6.0% −12.7%

11.3   (a) 182.0, 208.8, 233.8, 275.6, 59.9, 74.9, 91.6
       (b) 23 850, 29 3 810, 36 490, 39 830, 43 410, 49 790, 55 760, 65 720 (4 sf)
       (c) 25%, 22.4%, 9.2%, 9.0%, 14.7%, 12.0%, 17.9%

11.4   114.2

11.5   (a) 102.3   (b) 102.0   (c) 102.1

11.6   (a) 133.7   (b) 33.7%   (c) 25.2%

Supplementary exercise 11

11.7 (a) 79.4, 84.9, 91.3, 100.0, 110.3, 115.1, 119.0, 120.6

(b) 65.8, 70.4, 75.7, 82.9, 91.4, 95.4, 98.7, 100.0

(c) 7, 8, 11, 13, 6, 5, 2

(d) 7.0%, 7.5%, 9.6%, 10.3%, 4.3%, 3.4%, 1.3%

11.8 (a) 419.7, 473.6, 523.6, 566.0, 64.9, 72.2, 88.3

(b) £9450, £11 560, £13 090, £14 270, £16 100, £17 800, £19 240
(c)(i) 28, 62, 45, 34.7, 53.9, 50.0, 42.4 (ii) 7.3, 16.1, 11.7, 9.0, 14.0, 13.0, 11.0
(d) 11.2%, 22.3%, 13.2%, 9.0%, 12.8%, 10.6%, 8.1%

11.9 100, 99.2, 100.8, 102.5, 101.2, 102.1, 100.6, 99.9

11.10 (a) Year 2: 104.5; Year 3: 110.3 (b) Year 2: 111.6, Year 3: 109.4
(c) Year 2: 105.5, Year 3: 111.8 (d) Year 2: 106.0, Year 3: 112.5
(e) Year 2: 105.7, Year 3: 112.1

11.11 (a) May: 98.4, June: 101.0, July: 100.5
(b) May: 90.7, June: 84.4, July: 67.9
(c) May: 94.5, June: 92.3, July: 82.6

Tutorial 12 Time series

12.1 (a) graph of time series (b) 62.25, 61.75, 2.250
(c) addition of trend to graph (d) −8.906, +1.938, −1.219, +8.406
(e) £619 100

12.2 (a) 388.750, 391.750, 55.250 (b) graph of time series and trend

12.3 (a) graph of time series and trend

Supplementary exercise 12

12.4 (a) Graph of data
(b) (5455 + 9645 + 13297 + 6633) = 35030; 35030/4 = 8757.50
(9645 + 13297 + 6633 + 5548) = 35123; 35123/4 = 8780.75
(8757.50 + 8780.75)/2 = 8769.13
(c) Addition of trend line to graph
(d) First residuals

	Q_1	Q_2	Q_3	Q_4
1997			4528	−2161
1998	−3326	757	4780	−2175
1999	−3655	1290	4606	−2228
2000	−3474	893		
Mean	−3485	+980	+4638	−2188

Seasonal factors Q_1 −3485; Q_2 +980; Q_3 +4638; Q_4 −2188

12.5 (a) Graphs of data and trend
(b) Summary statistics for irregular components: mean = −0.053; st. dev. = 1.535
Mean nearly zero; standard deviation much reduced. Suitable model

12.6 (a) Graph of data
(b) First ratios:

Q_3 139.7/102.35 = 1.36492 = 136.492 as a percentage

Q_4 85.6/102.85 = 0.83228 = 83.228 as a percentage (3 dp in printout)

Tutorial 13   Forecasting

Note: Forecasts are only estimates, so the answers are here for guidance only.

13.1 (f)   forecast = extended trend value + seasonal factor
£550 000   £660 000   £630 000   £730 000
(g) £8150, ±£16 300

13.2 (c) Seasonal factors: −69.83   +22.69   +54.17   −7.63

	Forecasts:	
	1999 Q4	£3 490 000
	2000 Q1	£2 800 000
	2000 Q2	£3 700 000
	2000 Q3	£3 900 000

(d) ±£120 000

(e) £3 766 000   £3 808 000   £3 763 000   £3 678 000

(f) First residuals   mean = −2.23,   s.d. = 49.95
Second residuals   mean = −0.0001,   s.d. = 6.03
Zero mean, small standard deviation. Model reasonable.

13.3 (b) Forecasts   884   908   880   916 cars
(c) ±7 cars
(d) Deseasonalised values   847   856   872   874 cases
(e) First residuals   mean = 1.86   s.d. = 14.0
Second residuals   mean = 0.0002   s.d. = 3.63

Supplementary exercise 13

13.4 (e) Forecasts Q_1 6290 Q_2 10 800 Q_3 14 500 Q_4 7700 bookings

13.5 (c) Forecasts 2000 Q_3 £178 000 Q_4 £190 600
2001 Q_1 £174 800 Q_2 £192 700
(d) ±£3 070   (e) Deseasonalised values £154 400   £158 300   £160 900   £168 900

13.6 (c) Forecasts 2000 Q_3 £184 100 Q_4 £114 200
2001 Q_1 £93 500 Q_2 £157 800

A2 Numerical answers to exam type revision questions (16.11)

16.46 (a) 0.5   (b) 0.67
       (c) $CV = 9.49$, $TS = 61.83$ Opinion depends on user

16.47 (a) $r = 0.991$, significant   (c) $y = 4.77 + 0.483x$
       (d) 98.1%   (e) £10 564

16.48 (c) $CV = 3.68$, $TS = 5.66$ different stress levels
       (d) $LSD = 1.83$ so Package C different from A and B

16.49 (a) 20.1 to 42.7 w.p.m.
       (b) $CV = 1.89$, $TS = 2.56$ improvement < 10 w.p.m.
       (c) $CV = 1.76$, $TS = 0.614$ could be 10 w.p.m. improvement.

16.50 (a) $\bar{x} = 99.6$ g, $s = 1.04$ g
       (b) 99.4 g to 99.8 g. Machine underfilling as 100 g not included
       (c)(i) 6.68%   (ii) 77.5%   (iii) 102.5 g

16.51 (a)(i) 0.783   (ii) 0.070   (iii) 0.231
       (b) $CV = 13.28$, $TS = 23.5$. There is a difference in product preference

16.52 (a) Scatter diagram. Plot suggests linear relationship with sales decreasing as price increases
       (b) $r = -0.970$, $CV = 0.632$ Correlation significant.
       (c) Sales (000s) $= 818 - 157 \times$ price (£)
           On average sales decrease by 157 000 for every £1000 increase in price.
       (d) 94.1%
       (e) (i) 114 000 Should be reasonably accurate prediction.
            (ii) 4290 Outside range of given data, therefore not likely to be accurate.

16.53 (b) 103.56, -2.96, -0.177
       (d) Estimates: Q_1 £9 990 000; Q_2 £10 980 000, Q_3 £10 580 000, Q_4 £10 160 000
           Maximum likely error: £168 000 so rounding forecasts to nearest £100 000 better.
           (e) £10 200 000 £10 480 000

16.54 (b) 0.837 $CV = 0.514$, correlation significant
       (c) Sales $= 30.5 + 21.9$ experience   (d) 70.1%
       (e) Sales $= 44.8 + 0.638$ presales   (f) First model as R^2 higher

16.55 (a) 3.84%   (b) 26.2%   (c) £815 000
       (d) £57 300 to £65 000   Yes

16.56 (a) $CV = 16.81$, $TS = 32.21$ association present
       (b) 0.49, 0.074, 0.05   (c) 12.93 m

16.57 (a) 1997; 159, 166, 177; 109, 107, 105   (b) 120, 118, 109, 100, 102, 113, 125

16.58 (b) 211.750, -6.750 (d) In region of 225, 240, 224
       (e) ± 4.5

16.59 (b) $r = 0.871$, $CV = 0.811$ significant correlation
       (c) % profit $= -6.14 + 0.603$ % vehicles   (e) 12.0% and 48.2% but outside range

16.60 (a) 96.1%   (b) 53.9%   (c) 92.4%   (d) 73.8 to 78.2%

16.61 (a) CV = 11.07, TS = 27.2, cars sold not independent of month
      (b) 61.4% to 72.2%

16.62 (a) 1998   (b) 100. 107, 116, 126, 131
      (d) 9, 7.0%   (e) £1 368 000

16.63 (a) CV = 1.83, TS = 2.05, Mean mark could be less than 50%
      (b) From 37.2% to 53.4%
      (c) (i) From 33.2% to 50.9%, They could be the same as the intervals overlap.
          (ii) From 0.09% to 6.51% Positive change as zero excluded.

A3 Answers to multi-choice test revision (16.12)

1	a	14	b	27	b	40	a
2	c	15	a	28	b	41	d
3	b	16	a	29	d	42	b
4	d	17	a	30	d	43	a
5	d	18	b	31	a	44	d
6	d	19	c	32	c	45	c
7	a	20	a	33	d	46	c
8	c	21	a	34	b	47	d
9	a	22	d	35	a	48	b
10	c	23	b	36	d	49	b
11	d	24	c	37	b	50	d
12	a	25	d	38	a	51	b
13	b	26	a	39	c	52	c

Appendix B Glossary of Terms

Note: Intended for explanation rather than definition.

Accuracy	Ability to hit a target
A priori approach to probability	Probability from symmetry which therefore needs no experiment
Additive model	A model which assumes that any data is composed of a trend plus a seasonal effect plus some random variation
Adjusted R^2	R^2 (correlation coefficient squared) figure adjusted for the reduction in the degrees of freedom as additional independent variables are added to a regression equation
Aggregate price index	Composite price index for groups of items which may or may not be weighted by their relative importance
Alternative hypothesis	The hypothesis concluded to be true if the null hypothesis is rejected
Analysis of variance	A statistical procedure for determining whether the means of several different populations are equal
ANOVA table	A standard table used to summarise the analysis of variance calculations and results
Arithmetic mean	The mean calculated as the sum of the values divided by the number of the values
Assumptions about data	Conditions on which standard probability tables are based and which must be met by data if the result of its analysis is to be validly compared with those tables
Bar chart (graph)	A graphical method of presenting qualitative frequency data with the length of the bar being proportional to the frequency
Base period	The time at which the particular index had a value of 100
Binomial distribution	A probability distribution showing the probability of x successes in n trials of a binomial experiment
Blocking	The removal of a source of variation from the error term in the analysis of variance if it can be assigned to the levels of a second variable
Box plot	A graphical summary of data displaying the median, interquartile range, range and outliers
Categorical data	Data which can be categorised but not measured
Census	A complete enumeration of the whole population
Centrality	Any measure which identifies the 'centre' of the data. Usually a mean, mode or median
Central limit theorem	States that, whatever the distribution of the population, the distribution of the sample means will be approximately normal for large samples

Chi-squared test	A test for association between two categorical variables
Class interval	A range of values bounded by class limits
Cluster sampling	The population is first divided into a number of natural clusters and then the clusters are randomly sampled
Conditional probability	The probability associated with a second event which depends on the outcome of a preceding event
Confidence interval	The interval within which the population parameter is expected to lie
Confidence level	The probability that the true population parameter is included in a confidence interval
Confidence limits	The boundaries of a confidence interval
Contingency table	A cross-table for displaying the frequencies of all possible groupings on two variables
Continuous data	Data which can take values at any point within an interval
Correlation	The degree of association between two continuous variables
Critical value	A table value with which a test statistic is compared to determine whether H_0 should be rejected or not
Cross-tables	A table which includes the frequencies of all possible groupings counted on two variables
Cumulative frequency	The number or percentage of items below the end of the relevant interval
Cumulative frequency polygon (ogive)	A graphical display of the number, or percentage, of items up to and including the end of the relevant interval
Data	A collection of observations on one or more variables of interest
Decision analysis	The application of statistical concepts, such as expected values, in the making of decisions
Decomposition of time series	The splitting of any value in a time series into its component parts of trend and seasonal effect (and cycle)
Degrees of freedom	The number of free observations associated with the computation of a sample statistic
Dependent variable	The variable, usually denoted by y, which is being predicted or explained by the independent variable
Descriptive statistics	Tabular, graphical and numerical methods of classifying and presenting data
Discrete data	Data which can take values only at certain points within an interval
Empirical probability	A method of assigning probabilities based on past frequencies or experimentation
Estimation	The method of inferring the value of a population parameter from the value of the equivalent sample statistic
Event	A sub-collection of the outcomes of an experiment
Exclusive events	Any outcome is included in one and only one event
Exhaustive events	All possible outcomes have been included in the stated events

Expected frequencies	The frequencies which would be expected in the sample if a null hypothesis were true
Expected values	Mean of a random variable. Also value that would be expected if the null hypothesis were true
Experiment	The collection of data with control over the factors which may affect the variable of interest
Exponential distribution (negative)	A continuous probability distribution often used for describing the probability of time between occurrences of events
Exponential smoothing	A forecasting technique which uses a weighted average of past time series values to produce a smoothed time series
First smoothing constant, alpha (α)	The proportion of the error in the previous forecast value which is to be applied as a correction in the production of the next forecast value
Fisher index	$\sqrt{(\text{Laspeyre index value} \times \text{Paasche index value})}$
Fitted value	A 'predicted value' for past data used to judge the fit of a model
Forecasting	The method of using the forward projection from a time series for predictive purposes in the near future
Frequency density	Ratio of class frequency to width of class
Frequency distribution	A summary of data grouped into exclusive class intervals and frequencies
Frequency polygon	A graph produced from frequency data by joining the mid-intervals at the top of the histogram bars
F-test	A hypothesis test for comparing the variance of two independent populations using the variances of two small samples. Used in the analysis of variance
Geometric mean	The nth root of the product of n numbers
Goodness of Fit	A measure of how closely the observed values fit those predicted by a model. For regression, this is $r^2 \times 100\%$
Graphical description	Any diagrammatic representation of a set of data
Grouped data	Data organised into a frequency distribution
Growth model	The exponential smoothing model in which the trend does not remain fairly level
Histogram	A graphical method of presenting continuous data with the area of the bar being proportional to the relative frequency within the interval, the frequency density
Hypothesis testing	The process of testing a hypothesis about a population parameter by the use of information collected from a sample or samples
Independent probability	The probability associated with a second event which does not depend on the outcome of a preceding event
Independent samples t-test	A hypothesis test for comparing two independent population means using the means of two small samples

Independent variable	A variable, usually denoted by x, which can be decided independently and then used to predict or explain a dependent variable
Index numbers	A set of values, based on 100, used to measure changes in magnitude of single items or sets of items over time
Inferential statistics	Statistics gathered from a sample and used to infer some parameter of the population from which the sample was drawn
Interactions	The effect produced when the levels of one factor in an analysis of variance interact with the levels of another factor in influencing the response variable
Interquartile range	The spread of the middle half of ordered data
Interval data	Data which must be numeric and for which intervals between values must be measurable in terms of standard units
Interval estimate	The interval calculated from a sample expected to include the corresponding population parameter
Kolmogorov–Smirnov test	A test for the goodness of fit of sample data to some probability distribution such as the normal distribution
Kruscal-Wallis test	The non-parametric equivalent of analysis of variance
Laspeyre's price index	A weighted aggregate price index in which the weight of each item is its base period quantity
Least critical difference	The least difference between group means necessary for two of them to be judged significantly different
Least squares regression	The method of calculating the Pearson's correlation coefficient
Level of significance	The probability of rejecting a true null hypothesis due to sampling error
Linear regression	The straight line relationship between two continuous variables
log-linear regression	A form of regression which describes the relationship between variables which are other than continuous
Main effects	The differences between group means in analysis of variance assuming no interactions
Mann–Whitney U (Wilcoxon rank sum) test	A non-parametric equivalent of the two-sample t-test
Mean	The sum of all the data values divided by their number
Mean absolute deviation (MAD)	The mean of the absolute deviations from the mean used to judge the quality of a set of errors
Mean square error (MSE)	The mean of the squared errors used to judge the quality of a set of errors
Median	The location of the middle value of an ordered data set
Mode	The location of the most frequently occurring value of a set of data

Modelling	The representation of reality by a set of data or an equation from which predictions and explanations can be made
Moving average	A method of smoothing a time series by taking an average of each successive group of data points, the group being determined by any periodicity present
Multiple regression	The relationship between one dependent and more than one independent variables
Multiplicative model	A model which assumes that any data is composed of a trend multiplied by a seasonal effect multiplied by some random variation
Multistage sampling	A method of successively selecting smaller samples from within larger ones
Negatively skewed distribution	A distribution with a left hand tail
Nominal data	Data which can only be classified and not ordered or measured. It may be numeric or non-numeric
Non-linear regression	Any relationship between two continuous variables which is best described by a function other than a straight line
Non-parametric tests (Distribution free tests)	The tests which can be used validly when the assumptions needed for parametric testing cannot be met
Non-seasonal data	Data which exhibits no seasonal pattern
Normal probability distribution	A widely occurring symmetrical, continuous, bell-shaped asymptotic distribution
Null hypothesis	The hypothesis, which always includes equality, initially assumed to be true, although it may in fact be either true or false. The hypothesis challenged by the sample data
Observed frequencies	The frequencies actually counted in the sample
Odds	The ratio of the probability of an event occurring to the probability of it not occurring
Ogive	The shape of the graphical presentation of a cumulative frequency distribution
One sample t-test	A hypothesis test for a population mean using the analysis of data from a small sample
One tailed test	The test of a null hypothesis which can only be rejected when the sample statistic is in one extreme end of the distribution
One-way analysis of variance	Analysis of variance in which only one variable is being analysed for group mean differences
Operational research	The application of science to complex problems arising in the direction and management of large systems of men, machines, materials and money
Ordinal data	Data which may be numeric or non-numeric and which can be ordered but not measured
Outcome	A single result from an experiment
Paasche's price index	A weighted aggregate price index in which the weight of each item is its current period quantity

Paired data	Data describing two variables which can be sensibly related by change or difference
Paired samples *t*-test	A hypothesis test for comparing population means of paired data using a small paired sample
Pascal's triangle	A triangular array useful for calculating binomial coefficients
Pearson's correlation coefficient	A measure of the degree of the pairwise association between continuous variables
Percentage change	The difference between the two relevant index numbers as a percentage of the earlier of the two values
Percentage point change	The actual difference between the relevant index numbers
Percentile	The value below which a specified percentage of all the values in a distribution are to be found
Pie chart	A graphical method of presenting qualitative frequency data in sectors of a circle with the sector angle being proportional to the relative frequency
Point estimate	The single value estimate of a population parameter calculated from a corresponding sample
Poisson distribution	A probability distribution showing the probability of x occurrences of an event over a specified interval
Polygon	A many sided figure depicting, in statistics, an absolute or relative frequency distribution
Population	The collection of all elements of interest
Positively skewed distribution.	A distribution with a right hand tail
Power of a test	The ability of a test to reject H_0 when it is false
Precision	The width of an interval estimate
Predicted value	The value expected to be taken by the dependent variable for a given value of the independent variables
Price relative	The price in the current period relative to that in the base period (price index)
Probability	A numerical measure of the likelihood that an event will occur
Probability tables	A systematic list of all the values of a random variable with associated probabilities
Probability tree diagram	Graphical method of displaying the probabilities of multiple events
p-value	The probability of getting the sample statistic, or a more extreme value, when H_0 is true
Qualitative data	Data which may be numeric or non-numeric but is measured on the nominal or ordinal scales only
Quantitative data	Numerical data measured on the interval or ratio scales to describe 'how much' or 'how many'
Quartiles	The values which divide ordered data into four equal parts

Quota sampling	The population is first divided into homogeneous subgroups and then sampling takes place within each subgroup
Randomised block design	A two-way analysis of variance designed to eliminate any assignable extraneous variation from the analysis
Random sample	A sample whose members are selected at random so that every member of the sample has an equal probability of being selected
Range	The complete spread of ordered data
Ratio data	Data which must be numeric, have intervals measurable in standard units, and a meaningful zero
Raw data	The original data as collected
Regression	A description of the relationship between two continuous variables
Regression equation	The mathematical equation relating the dependent and independent continuous variables
Regression line	Usually the straight line describing the regression between two continuous variables
Regression model	The equation describing the relationship between two continuous variables
Relative frequency	Partial frequency as a proportion of total frequency
Residual analysis	The analysis of the differences between the observed and expected values in order to assess the model
Sample	A subset of a population usually intended for analysis
Sample space	All the possible outcomes from an experiment
Sampling	The selection of a subset of a population to represent that population
Sampling distribution of means	The distribution of the means of every possible sample combination from a population
Sampling error	Error arising from the incomplete enumeration of a population
Scale of measurement	Scale which classifies the data as being either nominal, ordinal, interval or ratio
Scatter diagram	A graph of bi-variate data used to identify any relationship which might be present
Seasonal data	Data which shows a periodic pattern related to a set of time periods such as months or quarters
Seasonal factor (effect)	The component of a time series model which is due to it being a particular season
Seasonally adjusted series	A time series from which the seasonal effects has been removed allowing comparison across seasons
Second smoothing constant beta (β) [gamma (γ)]	The proportion of the error in the previous forecast trend which is to be applied as a correction in the production of the next forecast trend
Semi-interquartile range	Half the interquartile range

Sign test	A simple non-parametric equivalent of a one-sample t-test
Significance level	The maximum probability of rejecting H_0 when it is true
(Simple) random sampling	Sampling such that every member of the population has an equal chance of being included in the sample
Skewness	Lack of symmetry in a distribution
Spearman's rank correlation coefficient, r_s (ρ)	A measure of the degree of the pairwise association between ordinal variables also known as Spearman's rho
Spread	Any measure which describes the closeness of data about its centre: usually, range, interquartile range, standard deviation or variance
Standard deviation	The square root of the variance
Standard deviation of the population	A measure of spread found by taking the square root of the average of all the squared deviations from the mean
Standard deviation of the sample	A measure of spread found by taking the square root of all the squared deviations from the mean divided by $(n-1)$
Standard error	The standard deviation of the distribution of sample estimators
Standardised (normalised) value	The number of standard deviations a data point is away from the mean
Steady model	The exponential smoothing model in which the trend is comparatively level
Stem-and-leaf plot	A data display which shows the shape of the data and also retains the numbers
Stratified random sampling	The population is first divided into strata and then a simple random sample is taken from each stratum
Subjective probability	A method of assigning probabilities based on judgement
Summary statistics	Numbers which give concise summaries of data distributions, usually in terms of centrality and spread
Sums of squares	The sum of the squared deviations from the mean used as a measure of variation, especially in the analysis of variance
Survey	A process designed to produce information about a population with evidence collected from a sample
Systematic sampling	A method of sampling by randomly selecting a first member and then selecting the others at regular intervals
Test statistic	A value calculated from the sample for comparing with the critical value from a standard table
Time series	A set of observations measured at successive points in time or over successive periods of time
Treatments	The traditional term for the levels of a variable of interest in the analysis of variance
Trend	The movement of a time series observable over many time periods often found from calculating moving averages
T-tests	Hypothesis tests for population means using data from small samples

Two tailed test	The test of a null hypothesis which can be rejected when the sample statistic is in either extreme end of the distribution
Two-way analysis of variance	Analysis of variance in which the interest may be in the difference between the group means of one or more variables but in which at least two are being analysed
Types of error	Type I: the rejection a true null hypothesis Type II: the failure to reject a false null hypothesis
Validity of test	The satisfying of the specified assumptions needed to be met for any particular test
Variance	A measure of dispersion based on the squared deviations of the data values from the mean
Wilcoxon matched pairs (signed rank) test	A non-parametric equivalent of a paired t-test
Wilcoxon rank sum test (Mann-Whitney U test)	A non-parametric equivalent of a two-sample t-test
Yate's correction	A continuity correction made when calculating the test statistic for a chi-squared test of a 2 x 2 contingency table

Appendix C Notation and Formulae

Greek alphabet

α	A	alpha	ι	I	iota	ρ	P	rho
β	B	beta	κ	K	kappa	σ	Σ	sigma
γ	Γ	gamma	λ	Λ	lambda	τ	T	tau
δ	Δ	delta	μ	M	mu	υ	U	upsilon
ε	E	epsilon	ν	N	nu	ϕ	Φ	phi
ζ	Z	zeta	ξ	Ξ	xi	χ	X	chi
η	H	eta	o	O	omicron	ψ	Ψ	psi
θ	Θ	theta	π	Π	pi	ω	Ω	omega

Notation

Parameter	Population	Sample
Mean	μ	$\bar{x}$
Standard deviation	σ	s
Variance	σ^2	s^2
Proportion	Π	p
Size	N	n
Correlation coefficient	ρ	r
Rank correlation coefficient	ρ_s	r_s
Regression coefficients	α, β for y-intercept and slope respectively	a, b for y-intercept and slope respectively

x is the independent variable and y the dependent variable in regression

O and E are the observed and expected frequencies, respectively in chi-squared testing

$\hat{\mu}$ and $\hat{\sigma}$ are estimates for μ and σ respectively

d represents differences between the paired values when working with paired data

Σ (Sigma) indicates 'the sum of'

f represents the number of items in a group of frequency data

z is shorthand for the standardised value

t is shorthand for the t value

Formulae

Summary statistics

Mean

$$\bar{x} = \frac{\sum x}{n} \text{ for single numbers} \qquad \bar{x} = \frac{\sum fx}{n} \text{ for frequency data}$$

Population standard deviation

$$s = \sqrt{\frac{\sum (x - \bar{x})^2}{n}} \quad \text{or} \quad \sqrt{\frac{\sum f(x - \bar{x})^2}{n}} \quad \text{for frequency data}$$

An equivalent formula which is often used is:

$$s = \sqrt{\frac{\sum x^2}{n} - \left(\frac{\sum x}{n}\right)^2} \quad \text{or} \quad s = \sqrt{\frac{\sum fx^2}{n} - \left(\frac{\sum fx}{n}\right)^2} \quad \text{for frequency data}$$

Sample standard deviation

$$s = \sqrt{\frac{\sum (x - \bar{x})^2}{n - 1}} \quad \text{or} \quad \sqrt{\frac{\sum f(x - \bar{x})^2}{n - 1}} \quad \text{for frequency data}$$

An equivalent formula which is often used is:

$$s = \sqrt{\frac{\sum x^2}{n - 1} - \left(\frac{\sum x}{n - 1}\right)^2} \quad \text{or} \quad s = \sqrt{\frac{\sum fx^2}{n - 1} - \left(\frac{\sum fx}{n - 1}\right)^2} \quad \text{for frequency data}$$

Probability

Binomial: For n trials with the probability of success in any one trial being p, the probability of getting r successes is:

$$\frac{n!}{r!(n - r)!} \times p^r (1 - p)^{(n - r)}$$

where $n!$ stands for factorial n, i.e. $n \times (n - 1) \times (n - 2) \ldots 2 \times 1$

Poisson: The probability of a particular number, x, occurring is given by

$$P(x) = \mu^x \frac{e^{-\mu}}{x!}$$

where μ is the mean and $e \cong 2.718$. ($\cong$ means 'approximately equal to')

Exponential: The probability of an event occurring x times is given by:

$$P(x) = \lambda e^{-\lambda x}$$

where λ (lambda) is the mean time between successive events.

Normal distribution

Standardised value

$$z = \frac{x - \mu}{\sigma}$$

Confidence intervals

Percentage or a proportion, π, is given by:

$$\pi = p \pm z \sqrt{\frac{p(100 - p)}{n}} \quad \text{for a percentage or } \pi = p \pm z \sqrt{\frac{p(1 - p)}{n}} \quad \text{for a proportion}$$

Mean from large sample and/or from sample with known standard deviation

$$\mu = \bar{x} \pm z \frac{\sigma}{\sqrt{n}}$$

Mean from small sample with unknown standard deviation

$$\mu = \bar{x} \pm t \frac{s}{\sqrt{n}}$$

Difference of means of paired data

$$\mu_d = \bar{x}_d \pm t \frac{s_d}{\sqrt{n_d}}$$

where $\bar{x}_d$, s_d and n_d refer to the calculated differences.

Hypothesis testing – test statistics

Proportion:

$$\frac{|p - \pi|}{\sqrt{\dfrac{\pi(1 - \pi)}{n}}}$$

Percentage:

$$\frac{|p - \pi|}{\sqrt{\dfrac{\pi(100 - \pi)}{n}}}$$

Mean:

$$\sigma \text{ known, } z = \frac{|\bar{x} - \mu|}{\sigma/\sqrt{n}} \quad \text{or} \quad \sigma \text{ unknown so } s \text{ needed} \quad t = \frac{|\bar{x} - \mu|}{s/\sqrt{n}}$$

Difference of two means with known population standard deviations

$$z = \frac{|\bar{x}_1 - \bar{x}_2|}{\sqrt{\dfrac{\sigma_1^2}{n_1} + \dfrac{\sigma_2^2}{n_2}}}$$

$\bar{x}_1$, $\bar{x}_2$ are the sample means, σ_1, σ_2 are the known standard deviations, n_1, n_2 are the sample sizes.

Difference of two means with unknown population standard deviations

F test:

$$F = \frac{s_1^2}{s_2^2}$$

where s_1 refers to the larger standard deviation so that F is always > 1
The formula used for 'pooling' the standard deviations is:

$$s_p = \sqrt{\frac{(n_1 - 1)s_1^2 + (n_2 - 1)s_2^2}{n_1 + n_2 - 2}}$$

where s_1 and s_2 are the standard deviations of samples 1 and 2 respectively.

Test statistic:

$$t = \frac{|\bar{x}_1 - \bar{x}_2|}{s_p\sqrt{\dfrac{1}{n_1} + \dfrac{1}{n_2}}} \quad \text{or} \quad t = \frac{||\bar{x}_1 - \bar{x}_2| - c|}{s_p\sqrt{\dfrac{1}{n_1} + \dfrac{1}{n_2}}} \quad \text{for a hypothesised value } c$$

Mann–Whitney non-parametric test:

$$U = R - \frac{n_1(n_1 + 1)}{2}$$

where R is the smaller sum of ranks and n_1 the size of the same sample.

Analysis of variance

The least critical difference

$$\text{CD} = t\sqrt{\text{MSE}\left(\frac{1}{n_1} + \frac{1}{n_2}\right)}$$

t has the MSE degrees of freedom and one tail.

Correlation and regression

The formula used to find the Pearson's product moment correlation, r, coefficient is (least squares method):

$$r = \frac{S_{xy}}{\sqrt{S_{xx}S_{yy}}} \qquad (-1 \le r \le +1)$$

where

$$S_{xx} = \sum x^2 - \frac{\sum x \sum x}{n}$$

$$S_{yy} = \sum y^2 - \frac{\sum y \sum y}{n}$$

$$S_{xy} = \sum xy - \frac{\sum x \sum y}{n}$$

The **regression line** is described, in general, as the straight line with the equation:

$$y = a + bx$$

The **gradient**, b, is calculated from:

$$b = \frac{S_{xy}}{S_{xx}} \quad \text{where } S_{xy} = \sum xy - \frac{\sum x \sum y}{n} \text{ and } S_{xx} = \sum x^2 - \frac{\sum x \sum x}{n}$$

Since the regression line passes through the centroid (both means) its equation can be used to find the *value of a*, the **intercept** on the y-axis:

$$a = \bar{y} - b\bar{x}$$

Spearman's rank correlation coefficient, r_s,

$$r_s = \frac{6 \sum d^2}{n(n^2 - 1)}$$

where d is the difference in rankings and n the sample size.

Chi-squared testing

For any cell the expected frequency is calculated by:

$$\frac{\text{Row total} \times \text{Column total}}{\text{Overall total}}$$

Test statistic for larger than 2×2 *table*:

$$\sum \frac{(O - E)^2}{E}$$

Test statistic for 2×2 *table (Yate's correction)*:

$$\sum \frac{(|O - E| - 0.5)^2}{E}$$

Index numbers

Index for any time period n: $\quad \dfrac{\text{value in period } n}{\text{value in base period}}$

Time series

Regression models:

Linear model: $y = a + bx,$

Quadratic model: $y = a + bx + cx^2$

Cubic model: $y = a + bx + cx^2 + dx^3$

Exponential smoothing models

Steady model:

New forecast = old forecast + alpha × error in previous forecast

where alpha (α) is the first smoothing constant.

Growth model:

New forecast = previous forecast + alpha × error in previous forecast

+ previous trend + beta × error in previous forecast trend

New trend = previous trend + beta × error in previous trend

where beta, β, is the second smoothing constant.

Seasonal decomposition – Additive model

Value = trend + seasonal factor

For further or more detailed tables see Henry R. Neave, *Elementary Statistics Tables for All Users of Statistical Techniques*.

Table D1 Areas under the standard normal curve

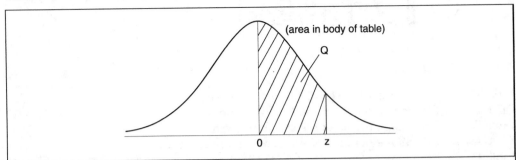

z	0.00	0.01	0.02	0.03	0.04	0.05	0.06	0.07	0.08	0.09
0.0	0.0000	0.0040	0.0080	0.0120	0.0160	0.0199	0.0239	0.0279	0.0319	0.0359
0.1	0.0398	0.0438	0.0478	0.0517	0.0557	0.0596	0.0636	0.0675	0.0714	0.0753
0.2	0.0793	0.0832	0.0871	0.0910	0.0948	0.0987	0.1026	0.1064	0.1103	0.1141
0.3	0.1179	0.1217	0.1255	0.1293	0.1331	0.1368	0.1406	0.1443	0.1480	0.1517
0.4	0.1554	0.1591	0.1628	0.1664	0.1700	0.1736	0.1772	0.1808	0.1844	0.1879
0.5	0.1915	0.1950	0.1985	0.2019	0.2054	0.2088	0.2123	0.2157	0.2190	0.2224
0.6	0.2257	0.2291	0.2324	0.2357	0.2389	0.2422	0.2454	0.2486	0.2517	0.2549
0.7	0.2580	0.2611	0.2642	0.2673	0.2704	0.2734	0.2764	0.2794	0.2823	0.2852
0.8	0.2881	0.2910	0.2939	0.2967	0.2995	0.3023	0.3051	0.3078	0.3106	0.3133
0.9	0.3159	0.3186	0.3212	0.3238	0.3264	0.3289	0.3315	0.3340	0.3365	0.3389
1.0	0.3413	0.3438	0.3461	0.3485	0.3508	0.3531	0.3554	0.3577	0.3599	0.3621
1.1	0.3643	0.3665	0.3686	0.3708	0.3729	0.3749	0.3770	0.3790	0.3810	0.3830
1.2	0.3849	0.3869	0.3888	0.3907	0.3925	0.3944	0.3962	0.3980	0.3997	0.4015
1.3	0.4032	0.4049	0.4066	0.4082	0.4099	0.4115	0.4131	0.4147	0.4162	0.4177
1.4	0.4192	0.4207	0.4222	0.4236	0.4251	0.4265	0.4279	0.4292	0.4306	0.4319
1.5	0.4332	0.4345	0.4357	0.4370	0.4382	0.4394	0.4406	0.4418	0.4429	0.4441
1.6	0.4452	0.4463	0.4474	0.4484	0.4495	0.4505	0.4515	0.4525	0.4535	0.4545
1.7	0.4554	0.4564	0.4573	0.4582	0.4591	0.4599	0.4608	0.4616	0.4625	0.4633
1.8	0.4641	0.4649	0.4656	0.4664	0.4671	0.4678	0.4686	0.4693	0.4699	0.4706
1.9	0.4713	0.4719	0.4726	0.4732	0.4738	0.4744	0.4750	0.4756	0.4761	0.4767
2.0	0.4772	0.4778	0.4783	0.4788	0.4793	0.4798	0.4803	0.4808	0.4812	0.4817
2.1	0.4821	0.4826	0.4830	0.4834	0.4838	0.4842	0.4846	0.4850	0.4854	0.4857
2.2	0.4861	0.4864	0.4868	0.4871	0.4875	0.4878	0.4881	0.4884	0.4887	0.4890
2.3	0.4893	0.4896	0.4898	0.4901	0.4904	0.4906	0.4909	0.4911	0.4913	0.4916
2.4	0.4918	0.4920	0.4922	0.4925	0.4927	0.4929	0.4931	0.4932	0.4934	0.4936
2.5	0.4938	0.4940	0.4941	0.4943	0.4945	0.4946	0.4948	0.4949	0.4951	0.4952
2.6	0.4953	0.4955	0.4956	0.4957	0.4959	0.4960	0.4961	0.4962	0.4963	0.4964
2.7	0.4965	0.4966	0.4967	0.4968	0.4969	0.4970	0.4971	0.4972	0.4973	0.4974
2.8	0.4974	0.4975	0.4976	0.4977	0.4977	0.4978	0.4979	0.4979	0.4980	0.4981
2.9	0.4981	0.4982	0.4982	0.4983	0.4984	0.4984	0.4985	0.4985	0.4986	0.4986
3.0	0.4987	0.4987	0.4987	0.4988	0.4988	0.4989	0.4989	0.4989	0.4990	0.4990
3.1	0.4990	0.4991	0.4991	0.4991	0.4992	0.4992	0.4992	0.4992	0.4993	0.4993
3.2	0.4993	0.4993	0.4994	0.4994	0.4994	0.4994	0.4994	0.4995	0.4995	0.4995
3.3	0.4995	0.4995	0.4995	0.4996	0.4996	0.4996	0.4996	0.4996	0.4996	0.4997
3.4	0.4997	0.4997	0.4997	0.4997	0.4997	0.4997	0.4997	0.4997	0.4997	0.4998

Table D2   Percentage points of the *t*-distribution

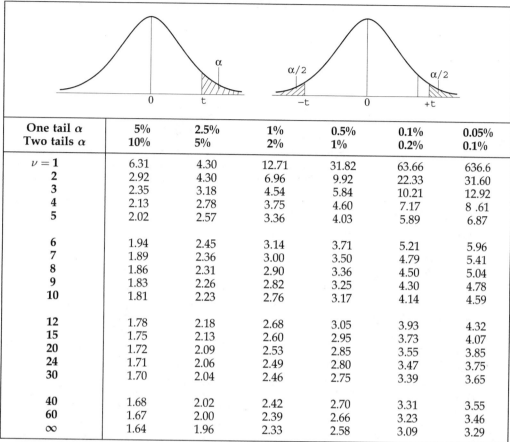

One tail α Two tails α	5% 10%	2.5% 5%	1% 2%	0.5% 1%	0.1% 0.2%	0.05% 0.1%
$\nu = 1$	6.31	4.30	12.71	31.82	63.66	636.6
2	2.92	4.30	6.96	9.92	22.33	31.60
3	2.35	3.18	4.54	5.84	10.21	12.92
4	2.13	2.78	3.75	4.60	7.17	8 .61
5	2.02	2.57	3.36	4.03	5.89	6.87
6	1.94	2.45	3.14	3.71	5.21	5.96
7	1.89	2.36	3.00	3.50	4.79	5.41
8	1.86	2.31	2.90	3.36	4.50	5.04
9	1.83	2.26	2.82	3.25	4.30	4.78
10	1.81	2.23	2.76	3.17	4.14	4.59
12	1.78	2.18	2.68	3.05	3.93	4.32
15	1.75	2.13	2.60	2.95	3.73	4.07
20	1.72	2.09	2.53	2.85	3.55	3.85
24	1.71	2.06	2.49	2.80	3.47	3.75
30	1.70	2.04	2.46	2.75	3.39	3.65
40	1.68	2.02	2.42	2.70	3.31	3.55
60	1.67	2.00	2.39	2.66	3.23	3.46
∞	1.64	1.96	2.33	2.58	3.09	3.29

ν = degrees of freedom α = total percentage in tails

Table D3   Percentage points of the standard normal curve

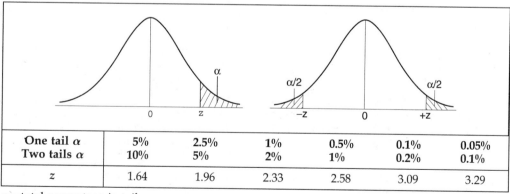

One tail α Two tails α	5% 10%	2.5% 5%	1% 2%	0.5% 1%	0.1% 0.2%	0.05% 0.1%
z	1.64	1.96	2.33	2.58	3.09	3.29

α = total percentage in tails

Table D4 Percentage points of the F distribution $\alpha = 5\%$

ν_1		Numerator degrees of freedom							
ν_2	1	2	3	4	5	6	7	8	9
1	161.40	199.50	215.70	224.60	230.20	234.00	236.80	238.90	240.50
2	18.51	19.00	19.16	19.25	19.30	19.33	19.35	19.37	19.38
3	10.13	9.55	9.28	9.12	9.01	8.94	8.89	8.85	8.81
4	7.71	6.94	6.56	6.39	6.26	6.16	6.09	6.04	6.00
5	6.61	5.79	5.41	5.19	5.05	4.95	4.88	4.82	4.77
6	5.99	5.14	4.76	4.53	4.39	4.28	4.21	4.15	4.10
7	5.59	4.74	4.35	4.12	3.97	3.87	3.79	3.73	3.68
8	5.32	4.46	4.07	3.84	3.69	3.58	3.50	3.44	3.39
9	5.12	4.26	3.86	3.63	3.48	3.37	3.29	3.23	3.18
10	4.96	4.10	3.71	3.48	3.33	3.22	3.14	3.07	3.02
11	4.84	3.98	3.59	3.36	3.20	3.09	3.01	2.95	2.90
12	4.75	3.89	3.49	3.26	3.11	3.00	2.91	2.85	2.80
13	4.67	3.81	3.41	3.18	3.03	2.92	2.83	2.77	2.71
14	4.60	3.74	3.34	3.11	2.96	2.85	2.76	2.70	2.65
15	4.54	3.68	3.29	3.06	2.90	2.79	2.71	2.64	2.59
16	4.49	3.63	3.24	3.01	2.85	2.74	2.66	2.59	2.54
17	4.45	3.59	3.20	2.96	2.81	2.70	2.61	2.55	2.49
18	4.41	3.55	3.16	2.93	2.77	2.66	2.58	2.51	2.46
19	4.38	3.52	3.13	2.90	2.74	2.63	2.54	2.48	2.42
20	4.35	3.49	3.10	2.87	2.71	2.60	2.51	2.45	2.39
21	4.32	3.47	3.07	2.84	2.68	2.57	2.49	2.42	2.37
22	4.30	3.44	3.05	2.82	2.66	2.55	2.46	2.40	2.34
23	4.28	3.42	3.03	2.80	2.64	2.53	2.44	2.37	2.32
24	4.26	3.40	3.01	2.78	2.62	2.51	2.42	2.36	2.30
25	4.24	3.39	2.99	2.76	2.60	2.49	2.40	2.34	2.28
26	4.23	3.37	2.98	2.74	2.59	2.47	2.39	2.32	2.27
27	4.21	3.35	2.96	2.73	2.57	2.46	2.37	2.31	2.25
28	4.20	3.34	2.95	2.71	2.56	2.45	2.36	2.29	2.24
29	4.18	3.33	2.93	2.70	2.55	2.43	2.35	2.28	2.22
30	4.17	3.32	2.92	2.69	2.53	2.42	2.33	2.27	2.21
40	4.08	3.23	2.84	2.61	2.45	2.34	2.25	2.18	2.12
60	4.00	3.15	2.76	2.53	2.37	2.25	2.17	2.10	2.04
120	3.92	3.07	2.68	2.45	2.29	2.17	2.09	2.02	1.96
∞	3.84	3.00	2.60	2.37	2.21	2.10	2.01	1.94	1.88

Denominator degrees of freedom

ν = degrees of freedom α = total percentage in tails

Table D4 Percentage points of the F distribution $\alpha = 5\%$ (continued)

ν_1	Numerator degrees of freedom									
ν_2	10	12	15	20	24	30	40	60	120	∞
1	241.90	243.90	245.90	248.00	249.10	250.10	251.10	252.20	253.30	254.30
2	19.40	19.41	19.43	19.45	19.45	19.46	19.47	19.48	19.49	19.50
3	8.79	8.74	8.70	8.66	8.64	8.62	8.59	8.57	8.55	8.53
4	5.96	5.91	5.86	5.80	5.77	5.75	5.72	5.69	5.66	5.63
5	4.74	4.68	4.62	4.56	4.53	4.50	4.46	4.43	4.40	4.36
6	4.06	4.00	3.94	3.87	3.84	3.81	3.77	3.74	3.70	3.67
7	3.64	3.57	3.51	3.44	3.41	3.38	3.34	3.30	3.27	3.23
8	3.35	3.28	3.22	3.15	3.12	3.08	3.04	3.01	2.97	2.93
9	3.14	3.07	3.01	2.94	2.90	2.86	2.83	2.79	2.75	2.71
10	2.98	2.91	2.85	2.77	2.74	2.70	2.66	2.62	2.58	2.54
11	2.85	2.79	2.72	2.65	2.61	2.57	2.53	2.49	2.45	2.40
12	2.75	2.69	2.62	2.54	2.51	2.47	2.43	2.38	2.34	2.30
13	2.67	2.60	2.53	2.46	2.42	2.38	2.34	2.30	2.25	2.21
14	2.60	2.53	2.46	2.39	2.35	2.31	2.27	2.22	2.18	2.13
15	2.54	2.48	2.40	2.33	2.29	2.25	2.20	2.16	2.11	2.07
16	2.49	2.42	2.35	2.28	2.24	2.19	2.15	2.11	2.06	2.01
17	2.45	2.38	2.31	2.23	2.19	2.15	2.10	2.06	2.01	1.96
18	2.41	2.34	2.27	2.19	2.15	2.11	2.06	2.02	1.97	1.92
19	2.38	2.31	2.23	2.16	2.11	2.07	2.03	1.98	1.93	1.88
20	2.35	2.28	2.20	2.12	2.08	2.04	1.99	1.95	1.90	1.84
21	2.32	2.25	2.18	2.10	2.05	2.01	1.96	1.92	1.87	1.81
22	2.30	2.23	2.15	2.07	2.03	1.98	1.94	1.89	1.84	1.78
23	2.27	2.20	2.13	2.05	2.01	1.96	1.91	1.86	1.81	1.76
24	2.25	2.18	2.11	2.03	1.98	1.94	1.89	1.84	1.79	1.73
25	2.24	2.16	2.09	2.01	1.96	1.92	1.87	1.82	1.77	1.71
26	2.22	2.15	2.07	1.99	1.95	1.90	1.85	1.80	1.75	1.69
27	2.20	2.13	2.06	1.97	1.93	1.88	1.84	1.79	1.73	1.67
28	2.19	2.12	2.04	1.96	1.91	1.87	1.82	1.77	1.71	1.65
29	2.18	2.10	2.03	1.94	1.90	1.85	1.81	1.75	1.70	1.64
30	2.16	2.09	2.01	1.93	1.89	1.84	1.79	1.74	1.68	1.62
40	2.08	2.00	1.92	1.84	1.79	1.74	1.69	1.64	1.58	1.51
60	1.99	1.92	1.84	1.75	1.70	1.65	1.59	1.53	1.47	1.39
120	1.91	1.83	1.75	1.66	1.61	1.55	1.50	1.43	1.35	1.25
∞	1.83	1.75	1.67	1.57	1.52	1.46	1.39	1.32	1.22	1.00

ν = degrees of freedom α = total percentage in tails

Denominator degrees of freedom

Table D5 Percentage points of the χ^2-distribution

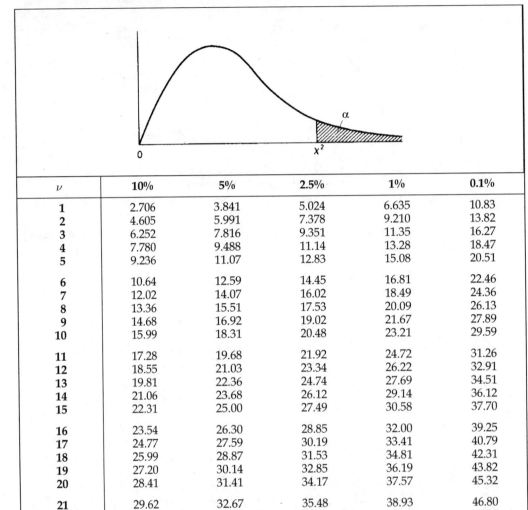

ν	10%	5%	2.5%	1%	0.1%
1	2.706	3.841	5.024	6.635	10.83
2	4.605	5.991	7.378	9.210	13.82
3	6.252	7.816	9.351	11.35	16.27
4	7.780	9.488	11.14	13.28	18.47
5	9.236	11.07	12.83	15.08	20.51
6	10.64	12.59	14.45	16.81	22.46
7	12.02	14.07	16.02	18.49	24.36
8	13.36	15.51	17.53	20.09	26.13
9	14.68	16.92	19.02	21.67	27.89
10	15.99	18.31	20.48	23.21	29.59
11	17.28	19.68	21.92	24.72	31.26
12	18.55	21.03	23.34	26.22	32.91
13	19.81	22.36	24.74	27.69	34.51
14	21.06	23.68	26.12	29.14	36.12
15	22.31	25.00	27.49	30.58	37.70
16	23.54	26.30	28.85	32.00	39.25
17	24.77	27.59	30.19	33.41	40.79
18	25.99	28.87	31.53	34.81	42.31
19	27.20	30.14	32.85	36.19	43.82
20	28.41	31.41	34.17	37.57	45.32
21	29.62	32.67	35.48	38.93	46.80
22	30.81	33.92	36.78	40.29	48.27
23	32.01	35.17	38.08	41.64	49.73
24	33.20	36.42	39.36	42.98	51.18
25	34.38	37.65	40.65	44.31	52.62
26	35.56	38.89	41.92	45.64	54.05
27	36.74	40.11	43.19	46.96	55.48
28	37.92	41.34	44.46	48.28	56.89
29	39.09	42.56	45.72	49.59	58.30
30	40.26	43.77	46.98	50.89	59.70
40	51.81	55.76	59.34	63.69	73.42
50	63.17	67.50	71.42	76.15	86.66
60	74.40	79.08	83.30	88.38	99.61
70	85.53	90.53	95.02	100.4	112.3
80	96.58	101.9	106.6	112.3	124.8
90	107.6	113.1	118.1	124.1	137.2
100	118.5	124.3	129.6	135.8	149.5

Table D6 Critical values for Pearson's correlation test

ν	α					
One tail α Two tails α	5% 10%	2.5% 5%	1% 2%	0.5% 1%	0.1% 0.2%	0.05% 0.1%
2	.900	.950	.980	.990	.998	.999
3	.805	.878	.934	.959	.986	.991
4	.729	.811	.882	.917	.963	.974
5	.669	.754	.833	.875	.935	.951
6	.621	.707	.789	.834	.905	.925
7	.582	.666	.750	.798	.875	.898
8	.549	.632	.715	.765	.847	.872
9	.521	.602	.685	.735	.820.	.847
10	.497	.576	.658	.708	.795	.823
11	.476	.553	.634	.684	.772	.801
12	.457	.532	.612	.661	.750	.780
13	.441	.514	.592	.641	.730	.760
14	.426	.497	.574	.623	.711	.742
15	.412	.482	.558	.606	.694	.725
16	.400	.468	.543	.590	.678	.708
17	.389	.456	.529	.575	.662	.693
18	.378	.444	.516	.561	.648	.679
19	.369	.433	.503	.549	.635	.665
20	.360	.423	.492	.537	.622	.652
25	.323	.381	.445	.487	.568	.597
30	.296	.349	.409	.449	.526	.554
40	.257	.304	.358	.393	.463	.490
60	.211	.250	.295	.325	.385	.408

ν = degrees of freedom α = total percentage in tails

Table D7 Critical values of Spearman's rank correlation test

$$r_s = 1 - \frac{6 \sum d^2}{n(n^2 - 1)}$$

n	5	6	7	8	9	10
Q%						
10	0.900	0.771	0.679	0.643	0.582	0.549
5		0.829	0.759	0.738	0.666	0.632

For $10 < n < 20$, $\dfrac{r_s}{\sqrt{1 - r_s^2}}$ is distributed as t with $(n - 2)$ degrees of freedom

For $n > 20$, $\rho_s \sqrt{n - 1}$ may be treated as normally distributed $(0, 1)$

Table D8 Critical values for the sign test (5% significance)

n	One tailed	Two tailed	n	One tailed	Two tailed
5	0		25	7	7
6	0	0	26	8	7
7	0	0	27	8	7
8	1	0	28	9	8
9	1	1	29	99	8
10	1	1	30	10	9
11	2	1	35	12	11
12	2	2	40	14	13
13	3	2	45	16	15
14	3	2	50	18	17
15	3	3	55	20	19
16	4	3	60	23	21
17	4	4	65	25	24
18	5	4	70	27	26
19	5	4	75	29	28
20	5	5	80	32	30
21	6	5	85	34	32
22	6	5	90	36	35
23	7	6	95	38	37
24	7	6	100	41	39

Mark all differences as '+' or '−' and find the total of each. S is the smaller of the two totals. If S ≤ critical value null hypothesis is rejected.

Table D9 Critical values for Wilcoxon matched pairs test (Wilcoxon signed rank test) (5% significance level)

n	One tail	Two tails	n	One tail	Two tails
5	0		25	100	89
6	2	0	26	110	98
7	3	2	27	119	107
8	5	3	28	130	116
9	8	5	29	140	126
10	10	8	30	151	137
11	13	10	35	213	195
12	17	13	40	286	264
13	21	17	45	371	343
14	25	21	50	466	434
15	30	25	55	573	536
16	35	29	60	690	648
17	41	34	65	820	772
18	47	40	70	960	907
19	53	46	75	1112	1053
20	60	52	80	1276	1211
21	67	58	85	1451	1380
22	75	65	90	1638	1560
23	83	73	95	1836	1752
24	91	81	100	2045	1855

Rank the non-zero differences, ignoring the sign of the difference. Find $T^+ =$ sum of ranks for positive difference and $T^- =$ sum of ranks for negative differences.

Test statistic: $W = \min(T^+, T^-)$.

Reject null hypothesis if $W \leq$ critical value.

Table D10   Critical values of the Mann–Whitney U test (Wilcoxon rank sum test)

5% one tail

n_1 n_2	4	5	6	7	8	9	10	12	15	20
4	1	2	3	4	5	6	7	9	12	18
5		4	5	6	8	9	11	13	18	25
6			7	8	10	12	14	17	23	32
7				11	13	15	17	21	28	39
8					15	18	20	26	33	47
9						21	24	30	39	54
10							27	34	44	62
12								42	55	77
15									72	100
20										138

5% two tails

n_1 n_2	4	5	6	7	8	9	10	12	15	20
4	0	1	2	3	4	4	5	7	10	14
5		2	3	5	6	7	8	11	14	20
6			5	6	8	10	11	14	19	27
7				8	10	12	14	18	24	34
8					13	15	17	22	29	41
9						17	20	26	34	48
10							23	29	39	55
12								37	49	69
15									64	90
20										138

Order the two samples together and indicate by A or B whether a mark comes from the first or second sample.

Form the sum R_A of the ranks of observations from sample A and similarly R_B from sample B. R is the smaller of the two rank sums.

Test statistic: $U = R - \dfrac{n(n-1)}{2}$

where n is the size of the sample which produced R.

Reject the null hypothesis if $U \leq$ critical value.

Appendix E Lecturer's materials

These materials are available on the Internet at www.palgrave.com and as hard copy from Palgrave.

Contents
Preface

Masters for lecture handouts

Introduction to this course and to statistics
Graphical representation of data
Numerical summary of data
Probability
Normal probability distributions
Estimation of population parameters
Hypothesis testing
Analysis of variance (ANOVA)
Correlation and regression
Contingency tables and chi-squared tests
Index numbers
Time series analysis 1 – Seasonal decomposition
Time series analysis 2 – Forecasting
Selected revision questions with answers
    Probability, contingency tables and chi-squared tests
    Normal distribution
    Confidence intervals
    Hypothesis testing
    Analysis of variance
    Correlation and regression
    Index numbers
    Time series analysis and forecasting

Masters for lecture overhead transparencies

Introduction to course and statistics
Graphical data preparation
Numerical summary of data
Probability
Normal probability distributions
Estimation of population prarmeters
Hypothesis testing
Analysis of variance
Correlation and regression
Contingency tables – chi-squared test
Index numbers

Time series analysis
Time series analysis 2 – Forecasting
Revision questions with worked solutions
  Probability, contingency tables and χ^2 tests
  Confidence intergals
  Hypothesis testing
  Analysis of variance
  Correlation and regression
  Index numbers
  Time series analysis and forecasting

Worked solutions to tutorial questions

Worked examples from Tutorial 2
Worked examples from Tutorial 3
Worked example from Tutorial 4
Worked example from Tutorial 5
Worked example from Tutorial 6
Worked example from Tutorial 7
Worked example from Tutorial 8
Worked example from Tutorial 9
Worked example from Tutorial 10
Worked example from Tutorial 11
Worked example from Tutorial 12
Worked example from Tutorial 13

SPSS worksheets with output

Graphical presentation with SPSS
  Output from SPSS graphics worksheet
Summary statistics with SPSS
  Output from SPSS summary statistics worksheet
Estimation and hypothesis testing with SPSS
  Output from SPSS estimation and hypothesis testing worksheet
Analysis of variance with SPSS
  Output from SPSS ANOVA worksheet
Correlation and regression analysis with SPSS
  Output from SPSS correlation and regression analysis worksheet
Time series analysis and forecasting with SPSS
  Output from SPSS time series and forecasting output worksheet

Minitab worksheets with output

Graphical presentation with Minitab
  Output from Minitab graphics tutorial
Summary statistics with Minitab
  Output from Minitab summary statistics worksheet
Estimation and hypothesis testing with Minitab
  Output from estimation and hypothesis testing worksheet

Analysis of variance with Minitab
Output from Minitab analysis of variance worksheet
Correlation and regression with Minitab
Output from Minitab correlation and regression worksheet
Time series analysis and forecasting with Minitab
Output from Minitab time series and forecasting worksheet

Excel worksheets with output

Graphical presentation with Excel
Output from Excel graphics tutorial
Summary statistics with Excel
Output from Excel summary statistics worksheet
Estimation and hypothesis testing with Excel
Output from Excel estimation and hypothesis testing worksheet
Analysis of variance with Excel
Output from Excel analysis of variance worksheet
Correlation and regression with SPSS
Output from Excel correlation and regression worksheet
Time series analysis and forecasting with Excel
Output from Excel time series worksheet

Additional revision material with answers

Descriptive statistics
Probability and chi-squared tests
Normal distribution
Confidence intervals and hypothesis tests
Analysis of variance
Index numbers
Time series and forecasting

Additional examination type questions

Additional multi-choice questions with answers

References

No extra books are really necessary for this course but more depth of information can be obtained from the following sources:

For all topics

Groebner, D. F. and Shannon, P. W. (1993) *Business Statistics: A Decision-Making Approach*, 4th edn (New York: Macmillan)

For more depth in statistics

Weimer, R. C. *Statistics*, 2nd edn (Dubuque, Iowa: Wm. C. Brown)

For operational research

Littlechild, S. C. and Shutler, M. F. (eds) (1991) *Operations Research in Management*, 2nd edn (Hemel Hempstead: Prentice Hall International UK)

Oakshott, L. (1997) *Business Modelling and Simulation* (London: Macmillan)

Daellenbach, H. (1994) *Systems and Decision Making, A Management Science Approach* (Chichester: Wiley)

For light relief

Huff, D. (1991) *How to Lie with Statistics* (Harmondsworth: Penguin)

Reichman, W. J. (1964) *The Use and Abuse of Statistics* (Harmondsworth: Penguin)

Comprehensive tables

Neave, H. R. (1992) *Elementary Statistical Tables for All Users of Statistical Techniques* (London: Routledge)

Index